LAWHEAD

MILITARY
SPACE FORCES

Other Volumes in Pergamon-Brassey's Future Warfare Series

MILITARY
SPACE FORCES

The Next 50 Years

John M. Collins

Commissioned by the
U.S. Congress

An Air Force Association Book
An Association of the U.S. Army Book

PERGAMON-BRASSEY'S
International Defense Publishers, Inc.

Washington • New York • London • Oxford
Beijing • Frankfurt • São Paulo • Sydney • Tokyo • Toronto

First edition 1989

Pergamon-Brassey's books are available at special discounts for bulk purchases for sales promotions, premiums, fund-raising, or educational use through the
    Special Sales Director,
    Macmillan Publishing Company,
    866 Third Avenue, New York, N.Y. 10022.

Editorial Offices
Pergamon-Brassey's International Defense Publishers, Inc.
8000 Westpark Drive, Fourth Floor
McLean, Virginia 22102

Library of Congress Cataloging-in-Publication Data
Collins, John M.
    Military space forces: the next 50 years / John M. Collins.—1st ed.
      p. cm.—(Future warfare series ; vol. 4) (An AUSA book)
    "An AFA book."
    Bibliography: p.
    Includes index.
    ISBN 0-08-037432-8
    1. Astronautics, Military.   2. Astronautics, Military—United
States.   3. Astronautics, Military—Soviet Union.   4. Space warfare.
I. Title. II. Series. III. Series: Future warfare series; v. 4.
UG1520.C65   1989
358.8'09'05—dc20

          89-34179
          CIP

British Library Cataloguing in Publication Data
Collins, John M.
    Military space forces : the next 50 years.—(Future
warfare series ; V. 4
    1. Space Warfare
    I. Title
    358'.8

    ISBN 0-08-037432-8

10 9 8 7 6 5 4 3 2 1

Printed in the United States of America

To

America's Military Space Forces

Whose purpose is to protect this
country's interests against
aggression from or in space.

FUTURE WARFARE
SERIES
Pergamon-
Brassey's

Pergamon-Brassey's has developed its Future Warfare Series for
everyone concerned about tomorrow's world. National policymakers, military and civilian teachers, defense industry executives, informed citizens, and professional military personnel will
all gain valuable insights through this series that will enhance
their ability to meet the challenges of future warfare. Each book,
written by an acknowledged expert, is intended to stimulate the
reader's thinking, to raise new issues, and to initiate debate by
peering into the future, boldly suggesting those factors that will
shape warfare well beyond the twentieth century. Though every
volume can and will stand on its own merit, our goal is to publish
a series that encourages mankind to address the full spectrum of
future warfare issues—now, before the future becomes the present and overwhelms the defenses of the past.

Maj. Gen. Perry M. Smith, USAF (Ret.)
General Editor

Contents

Maps

Figures

Tables

Congressional Introduction

John M. Collins, Senior Specialist in National Defense at the Congressional Research Service of the Library of Congress, is highly respected for his periodic comparative assessments of the U.S.–Soviet military balance. The issues raised in his first comprehensive and forward-looking assessment in 1976 acquired great significance during the presidential election of 1980. Many of the areas of U.S. military weakness that later dictated corrective attention in the 1980s had been identified by Collins in his 1976 study. The insights of his professional analysis were reasoned, deliberate, and careful in their identification of both strengths and weaknesses of the overall U.S. military position vis-à-vis that of the Soviet Union.

Since his latest volume on the balance, *U.S.–Soviet Military Balance 1980–1985*, Collins has written two other studies for the Congress: *United States and Soviet Special Operations*, for the Special Operations Panel of the Readiness Subcommittee of the House Armed Services Committee, and this present volume, *Military Space Forces: The Next 50 Years*, for our interested ad hoc group.

We asked John Collins in June 1987 to perpare "a frame of reference that could help Congress evaluate future, as well as present, military space policies, programs, and budgets." We knew that we could expect the same thorough, careful, and reasoned treatment of this important subject because of his past performance on other studies. We wanted it covered in a thorough fashion and on an unclassified basis.

This analysis will prove useful not only to interested parties on Capitol Hill, but also to those in the Pentagon, at the National Security Council, at NASA, in industry, in academia, and among the public at large. Many of the issues he addresses will require Congressional attention and scrutiny this year and in years to come. The fifth chapter, which identifies the comparative military space efforts of the United States and Soviet Union, will attract special attention.

As the United States attempts to tailor affordable military space capabilities with national security requirements, we believe that John Collins has once again provided a valuable service to the Congress. He has provided a frame of reference that can help us in our efforts.

IKE SKELTON
Member of Congress

JOHN SPRATT
Member of Congress

BILL NELSON
Member of Congress

JOHN GLENN
United States Senator

JOHN KASICH
Member of Congress

BEN BLAZ
Member of Congress

HAROLD VOLKMER
Member of Congress

Foreword

Among the most pressing and consequential defense issues facing this nation are whether or not the United States will redress critical deficiencies in our military space capabilities and the decision to proceed with the development of strategic defenses.

Future military space operations must be treated with the same "developed-for-war" approach that today is applied to operations on the land, sea, and in the air. Space systems must be developed with readiness, sustainability, modernization, and force structure in mind. The same basic principles applied to land, sea, and air operations today must be applied to tomorrow's space operations.

The United States must provide a measure of control over space before we can be assured of our use of space systems in conflict, just as we would first establish sufficient control of the seas for resupply operations and of the airspace over a battlefield in support of land operations. The United States does not currently possess the necessary capabilities to carry out the combat functions of space control. The Soviet Union does. Parity does not exist between the United States and Soviet Union in this combat area. The United States has no antisatellite capability.

Nor does parity exist in the ability to rapidly replace malfunctioning satellites or reconstitute combat losses in orbit which will surely occur in war. The Soviet Union has a demonstrated launch capability responsive to combat needs; the United States maintains a launch infrastructure designed for peacetime use.

The bottom line is clear: the evolution of space operations away from a solely peacetime orientation to one stressing warfighting requirements must continue—in order to deter aggression and, if deterrence fails, succeed on the battlefield.

In this study, John Collins assesses current military space operations and the requirements planning and programming process. He offers an in-depth examination of U.S. military space capabilities and those of our principal adversary, the Soviet Union. He gives a comprehensive analysis of this wide range of issues and an assessment of prospects and options for future debate and discussion.

I agree that the Soviets have developed, over time, a sounder foundation for military space power. This should cause the United States concern as we assess the military space balance today and for the future. Accordingly, I believe that the United States should pursue an antisatellite program, redundancy and reconstitution capabilities for essential military space systems, and a strategic defense system for ballistic missile defense. I also believe the current DOD organizational structure for space operations, which consists of a unified command with service component commands, is working well to further defense interests in space. As the future unfolds, we must ensure that our organization stays abreast of our missions and capabilities. John Collins' perspective is one of several alternatives.

Finally, John Collins offers a consistent vision for tomorrow's defense-related space operations—the imperative that we must use space effectively and efficiently to meet our national security objectives. We are doing that now, but there is much yet to be done.

General John L. Piotrowski, USAF
Commander in Chief
United States Space Command

Acknowledgments

Congressman Ike Skelton (D-Mo.), a member of the House Armed Services Committee, invited seven colleagues on Capitol Hill to cosponsor this project, because they collectively believe space "is a new military medium that may encompass much more than anticipated, sooner than expected." They therefore requested a comprehensive "frame of reference that could help Congress evaluate future, as well as present, military space policies, programs, and budgets." All eight patrons displayed great patience during the gestation period, which far exceeded their expectations (one departed Congress before I finished the first draft). Tommy Glakas, Skelton's lieutenant and previously my partner, arranged publication after 20 months.

The report depended on professional help every step of the way, because the author never heard of Kepler and Galileo before research began, or their influences on Newton's Universal Law of Gravitation and three Laws of Motion. My son Sean, an M.I.T. Ph.D. in aeronautical and astronautical engineering, on call at odd hours, days, nights, weekends, and holidays, provided unbeatable advice and assistance.

Contacts with the Office of the Secretary of Defense, Organization of the Joint Chiefs of Staff, Army, Navy, Air Force, Marine Corps, Defense Intelligence Agency, and U.S. Space Command coordinated comments chapter-by-chapter, with my understanding that their responses represented informal consultation, rather than official concurrence. Colonel Win Schmidt, JCS Strategic

Plans and Policy (Compliance, Testing, and Space Division),
Colonel Larry Flynn, Air Force Directorate of Plans (Space and
Strategic Defensive Forces Division), Lieutenant Colonel Dennis
Lenahan, an Air Force officer on loan to the Army, and Major
Scott Huddleson, U.S. Space Command (Plans), who got more
spot requests for information than most, helped me bypass men-
tal blocks that otherwise might have been insurmountable.

Mentors outside the U.S. defense community included G.
Harry Stine, whose *Confrontation in Space* inspired me at the
onset; Nicholas Johnson, a Soviet space specialist with Teledyne
Brown Engineering; Gregg Maryniak, Executive Vice President
of Space Studies Institute in Princeton, New Jersey; Rick Jurmain, with the National Aerospace Plane Joint Program Office,
McDonnell Douglas Corporation; and Major Pat Grieco, who
makes military space matters his avocation. All filled in blank
spots that no printed reports explore.

The Congressional Research Service (CRS) was a convenient
source of research materials and specialized advice. The list of
Science Policy Research Division members starts with Dick
Rowberg, the chief, and Jane Bortnick, his deputy. Marcia Smith,
an authority on U.S. and Soviet space activities, made a perfect
sounding board. Several specialists furnished firsthand information and opened their files: Bob Civiak (weapon effects); Cos
DiMaggio (directed energy weapons); Chris Dodge (life sciences);
John Justus (geosciences); Len Kruger (materials); and Jack
Moteff (materials; transatmospheric flight). Chris Hill, the Senior
Specialist in Science and Technology Policy, pointed me toward
articles about optics. Resident experts with the Foreign Affairs
and National Defense Division put a military spin on their technical input. Steve Hildreth specializes in strategic defense. Jon
Medalia, a purist, is his strategic offensive force counterpart. Al
Tinajero, a peerless compatriot who combines physics and engineering with technical intelligence and computer science, was
universally beneficial.

Reviewers with little knowledge of the subject were valuable,
precisely because they brought offbeat perspectives to bear. General Robert C. Kingston, a former unified command commander
with 37 years of active military service, made useful observations
while he quaffed my bourbon. Mike Lofgren, Legislative Assist-
ant to Congressman John Kasich, a cosponsor, labored through
successive drafts, above and beyond the call of duty. Stan Sloan,
the CRS Senior Specialist in Politico-Military Affairs, looked for
arms control angles. This category also included CRS colleagues
Steve Bowman, Bob Goldich, and Clyde Mark. One was a science
fiction buff, but their common contribution was bright, inquisitive minds, coupled with a rare capacity to make me think.

Administrative support was superlative. Carolyn Hatcher and Ida Eustis, as usual, furnished faultless library services. Bob Lane, the Air University Librarian, airmailed scarce source materials not available on local shelves. DOD press clippers, headed by Herb Coleman, flagged technical writings that otherwise would never have reached my desk. Jeannie Hamilton once again helped convert my hand-drawn sketches into professional maps and figures, working with Andy Hemstreet of Art Services, Inc. Joseph Olszar, who maintained his composure when pressures mounted, deciphered my scrawl, typed many drafts, and cranked in countless corrections without complaint. Jim Robinson, the chief CRS reviewer, then dotted every i and crossed every t before he approved the product for publication. Nancy Hoagland, his editorial equivalent for Pergamon-Brassey's, figuratively took me over Niagara Falls in a barrel several times, but we both emerged unbruised, with friendship intact. Vicki Chamlee, production manager at the head office, answered my endless questions with the patience of a saint.

No acknowledgments would be complete without special mention of Swift, my bride of almost 40 years. She bore the brunt for a lengthy unproductive period, when most observers believed I was brain dead. A less devoted woman would have left.

John M. Collins
Alexandria, Virginia

Background, Purpose, and Scope

Who rules circumterrestrial space commands Planet Earth;
Who rules the moon commands circumterrestrial space;
Who rules L4 and L5* commands the Earth-Moon System.
   Halford J. Mackinder's Heartland Theory Applied to Space**

Circumterrestrial space, the world's newest military medium, is unlike land, sea, and air. It encapsulates Earth to an altitude of 50,000 miles or so, but armed forces of major powers probably will reach much farther if civilian pioneers begin to colonize the moon and exploit its resources, then expand activities among distant planets, as predicted.[1]

Orbital operations to, from, within, and through space started with Sputnik I, a Soviet scientific satellite that flew in 1957. Military roles and missions since then have developed along lines like those air power took early in this century.[2] Intelligence and support operations came first, trailed by transportation; offensive and defensive space combat forces are following.

---

*See Chapter 1, Map 1 and subsection entitled "Key Terrain," for the location and significance of lunar libration points L4 and L5.

**Mackinder's so-called Heartland was largely East-Central Europe and Russia. The rest of Eurasia and Africa comprised his "World Island." He postulated that:

Who rules East Europe commands the Heartland.
Who rules the Heartland commands the World Island.
Who rules the World Island commands the World.[3]

International treaties and other expressions of peaceful intent eventually may obviate any reason for armed forces in space, even ban those now in place, but the odds are poor. Civilian communities and military establishments on Earth already depend heavily on satellite communications, meteorological information, navigation aids, and other services available only from space. More importantly, human nature imposes a huge impediment. Deep-seated traits create tremendous temptations for aggressors to take all, unless probable costs of such action exceed anticipated gains.

Mackinder's hypothesis has not proved correct, perhaps because he did not think big enough. Its adaption to space bears watching, however, because as President Kennedy postulated, space "may hold the key to our future on earth. No one," he continued, "can predict with certainty what the ultimate meaning will be of the mastery of space."[4] Prudent planners consequently should monitor trends closely to ascertain the imminence and intensity of perceived threats, then take timely steps to deter or deal with them successfully, in case legal, ethical, and moral constraints prove ineffective.

This foundation document, which is completely unclassified, serves a fourfold purpose:

- To describe space as a distinctive military medium;

- To describe military space planning and programming, with particular concern for problems and options;

- To compare present and projected U.S.–Soviet military space postures;

- To indicate courses of action that might improve U.S. military space posture at sensible costs.

Coverage concentrates on the Earth-Moon System, because interplanetary combat seems far in the future for many political, economic, and military reasons,[5] even if it becomes technologically feasible at some earlier date. Mars, for example, is the nearest planet able to augment resources on Earth. Trips out and back probably will take two or three years, depending on means of propulsion, turnaround times, and other variables. Two-way communications are measured in minutes. Marauders would find it less cost-effective to do battle in deep space than to intercept returning transports laden with rich raw materials and finished products.

All appraisals are predicated on present technologies and predicted improvements during the next 50 years, to separate apparent probabilities from possibilities. Area analyses and estimates of the situation follow traditional military formats, modified to meet new needs. Suitability, feasibility, and acceptability serve as assessment standards, along with time-proven principles of deterrence and war.

Chapters 1 through 4, which cover basic subjects, are nearly nonperishable. "Alphabet soup," such as GAPSAT, FLTSAT, and LEASAT, is virtually absent from chapter 5 (U.S.–Soviet military space postures), because assessments concentrate on big pictures, instead of details. End notes aid readers who want to pursue various topics in greater depth. Annex A is a glossary of military space terms unfamiliar to most laymen. Annex B is a companion list of acronyms and abbreviations.

The resultant compendium is intended as a tool to help Congress and the executive branch blend military space capabilities with land, sea, and air power in ways that best assure U.S. national security without avoidable destabilization or waste of time and resources.

1

Area Analysis of Earth-Moon System

National security policymakers, planners, programmers, and operators take geography into constant account, because it exerts strong influences on strategies, tactics, logistics, and force postures. *Geography*, however, excludes most of the Earth-Moon System, which comprises a vast environment loosely known as space.* This area analysis factually differentiates that largely unfamiliar medium from land, sea, and air, then summarizes salient aspects region by region before it assesses military significance.

UNIQUE CHARACTERISTICS

Air, water, weather, climate, and vegetation within the Earth-Moon System are exclusively indigenous to this planet. So are populations and industries at present. Land forms and natural resources are restricted to the Earth, moon, and asteroids. Cosmic radiation, solar winds, micrometeorites, and negligible or

---

*Webster defines geography as "a science that deals with the earth and its life; especially the description of land, sea, and air and the distribution of plant and animal life including man and his industries with reference to the mutual relations of these diverse elements."[1]

neutralized gravity (which induces weightlessness) are unique properties of free space. Near vacuum is present everywhere except on Earth and vicinity.

Space and oceans are superficially similar, but differences are more remarkable. Continents bound all seven seas, which are liquid and almost opaque. Topographic features configure ocean bottoms. The Earth's curvature limits visibility to line-of-sight; natural light never illuminates deeply. Water temperature, pressure, and salinity anomalies are common.

Transparent space is more homogenous. Day-night cycles are nonexistent. Space has no shape and little substance; affords almost limitless maneuvering room; admits electromagnetic radiation, whereas water is practically impervious to radio and radar signals; and smothers shock waves. Acoustics, an antisubmarine warfare staple, play no part in space, because sound cannot survive in a vacuum. Neither light nor focused energy rays refract.

Space has no north, east, south, or west. Right ascension and declination, calculated in different terms than latitude and longitude, designate location and directions. A nonrotating celestial sphere of infinite radius, with its center at Earth's core, is the reference frame. Declination, the astronomical analog of latitude, is the angular distance north or south of the celestial equator. Right ascension is the astronomical analog of longitude. The constellation Aries, against which spectators on Earth see the sun when it crosses Earth's equator in spring, defines the prime meridian. Angular positions in space are measured east from that celestial counterpart of Greenwich Observatory.[2]

Distances are meaningful mainly in terms of time. Merchant ships en route from our Pacific coast to the Persian Gulf, for example, take a month to travel 12,000 nautical miles. Apollo 11 made it to the moon—20 times as far—in slightly more than three days.[3] Real-time communications, transmitted at the speed of light (186,000 miles per second) are possible for most purposes; the delay between Earth and moon amounts to little more than a second. Serious problems even so could ensue when military actions and counteractions, such as those associated with ballistic missile defense, are separated by milliseconds.

REGIONS DEFINED AND DESCRIBED

The Earth-Moon System circumscribes four discrete regions: Earth and Atmosphere; Circumterrestrial Space; Moon and Environs; and Outer Envelope (Map 1). Boundaries are blurred and some attributes overlap, but each nevertheless is individualistic.

Map 1 MILITARY REGIONS
Earth, Moon, and Environs

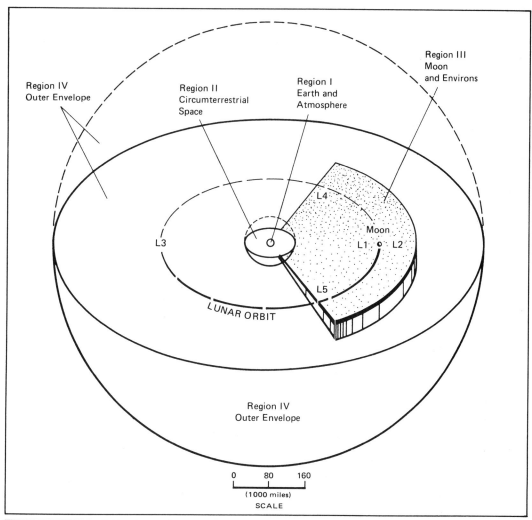

Distance in miles			
From Earth		**From Moon**	
Region I	Surface to 60	L1	45,000
II	60 to 50,000	L2	42,000
III	50,000 to 360,000	L3	480,000
IV	240,000 to 480,000	L4	60° ahead of moon
Lunar Orbit	240,000	L5	60° behind moon

NOTE: Regions I, II, and IV are globe-shaped. Region III is like a quarter slice of pie, with little depth in comparison. L1 through L5 are lunar libration points.

Region I: Earth And Atmosphere

Sophisticated installations on Earth presently provide requisite support for military space operations in regions addressed by this study. They facilitate strategic planning, programming and budgeting; research, development, test, and evaluation (RDT&E); production; supply; maintenance; training; command, control, and communications (C^3); launch and recovery. Tactical command posts, selected RDT&E, and some C^3 functions likely will be first to migrate from Region I to space stations and the moon. Large logistic installations likely will be last. Considerable infrastructure must remain on this planet.

Earth's atmosphere, gravity, and rotation strongly influence transit between that infrastructure and space. Most effects are adverse, but a few are advantageous.

Atmosphere

Rarefied atmosphere is found in the lower exosphere, several hundred miles above sea level. Ninety-nine percent, however, hovers within 20 miles of the surface. Half of that is below 15,000 feet, in the bottom of the troposphere (Map 2).[4] Most humans need supplemental oxygen to sustain efficient performance at elevations exceeding 10,000 feet. Pressurized suits or cabins become obligatory at about nine miles, because crew members, unable to expel carbon dioxide or water vapor from their lungs unassisted, otherwise would suffocate; blood literally would boil at 12 miles if they lacked such protection. Compressing thin outside air to pressurize space vehicles fails to satisfy at 15 miles. Heat transfer is excessive and ozone in the upper atmosphere is poisonous. Astronauts beyond that point must rely on pure air produced in a sealed environment independent of nature. Turbojet engines refuse to function much above 20 miles. Ramjets, gasping for air, sputter and stop at 28 miles. Rockets are required thereafter.[5]

Launch delays due to adverse weather are common, even for unmanned missiles. Recoveries also are sensitive. Restrictions surely would relax under combat conditions, but tolerance for high winds, extreme turbulence, lightning, and ice will always be limited. Our top-heavy piggyback space shuttle, for example, could capsize, if it tried to take off crosswind when anemometers register much more than the presently permissible 15 miles per hour (mph). Thunderbolts, such as the one that destroyed a U.S. Atlas-Centaur rocket with communications satellite in March 1987, pose equal dangers.[6]

Aerodynamic drag slows spacecraft near Earth's surface. It becomes progressively less important as vehicles rise through the

Map 2   ATMOSPHERE AND INNER SPACE
(Not to Scale)

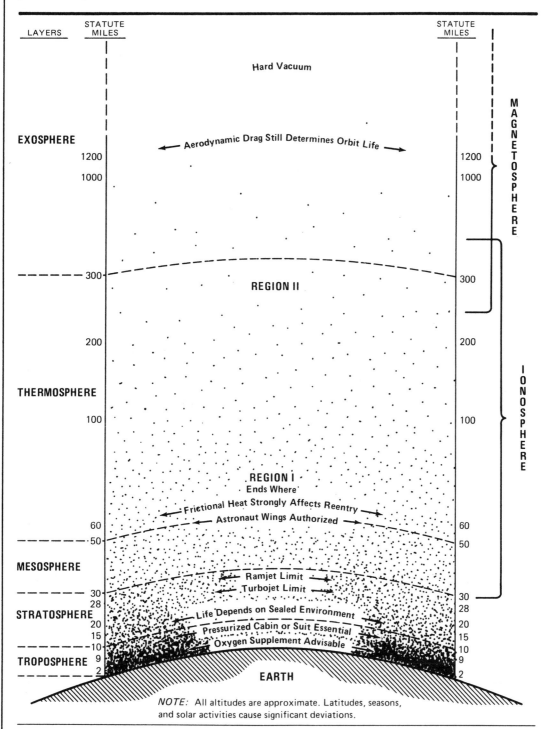

troposphere, because thinner air bears down with less pressure and expended fuel lightens the load they must lift. Prompt effects disappear for most practical purposes where the mesosphere and thermosphere merge at an altitude that approximates 60 miles.[7]

Frictional heat consumes space vehicles when they enter the atmosphere at high velocities, unless a shield protects the exterior and insulation keeps crews (if any) and other contents acceptably cool.* Apollo command modules returning from the moon, for example, briefly had to offset 5,000°F temperature, four times the heat of a blast furnace.[8]

There is, however, a bright side. Aerodynamic drag at the interface between atmosphere and space can act as a brake or alter orbit configuration without burning fuel. Computers, however, must calculate the reentry angle correctly. Vehicles will skip or bounce back erratically if the trajectory is too shallow; incineration results if it is too steep.[9] Safety margins vary. The reentry window, for example, opens wider for powered spacecraft than for those that glide.

Gravity

Gravity (g) keeps animate and inanimate objects on Earth without an anchor and pulls unsupported bodies from atmosphere or space toward the surface. Gravitational attraction decreases with altitude, but is still 95% of full strength (1g) at 100 miles, well beyond the boundary of Region I.[10]

Propulsion systems must be powerful enough to boost spacecraft into orbit, despite atmospheric drag and gravity.** Vertically launched vehicles, together with payloads, initially accelerate 1g (32.2 feet per second for each second of flight)***, provided thrust

---

*Submarine-launched ballistic missile (SLBM) and intercontinental ballistic missile (ICBM) warheads typically reenter Earth's atmosphere at about 10,000 mph and 16,000 mph, respectively. The U.S. space shuttle returns from low earth orbit at about 17,000 mph. Reusable space vehicles on higher orbits (that may encircle the moon) begin reentry when they reach perigee at speeds that approach 25,000 mph, unless they brake.[11]

**Issac Newton's three laws of motion, presented in his *Principia* (1687) all apply: *First Law*: Bodies at rest remain so, unless an unbalanced force intervenes; once in motion bodies move in a straight line until another unbalanced force intervenes. *Second Law*: Acceleration is directly proportional to the intervening force and inversely proportional to the body's mass (the quantity of matter it contains). *Third Law*: When one body exerts force on another, the second body exerts on the first body a force equal in magnitude and opposite in direction (to every action there is an equal and opposite reaction).[12]

***32.2 feet per second per second means velocity is 32.2 feet per second the first second, 64.4 feet per second during the next second, 96.6 feet during the third second, and so on. Stated in different terms, 1g acceleration causes velocity to increase 22 miles per hour every second.

applied is twice its weight at liftoff. Net force, acceleration, and velocity all increase rapidly thereafter, as engines expend propellant, which comprises about 90% of the original weight, and expel mass in the form of exhaust.[13] Stress on astronauts is extraordinary.[14]

Vehicles in orbit follow circular or elliptical paths around Earth at constant speeds that vary with altitude. Prompt drag effects are inconsequential, except for low earth orbits. Velocity counteracts gravity. Spacecraft in circular orbits fall the same distance every second that the Earth's curved surface seems to recede (Map 3), and thus stay in proper position, aided only by minor adjustments to prevent drifting. A lower orbit results, or the craft returns to Earth, if brakes are applied; additional energy propels them farther out.[15]

The term *weightlessness* is a misnomer, since relatively little reduction in weight takes place. Spacecraft and contents not battened down nevertheless float, unless slow rotation provides artifical gravity, because all free fall constantly at the same rate.[16]

Rotation and Inclination

The Earth-Moon System, with its center of mass 1,000 miles beneath Earth's surface, revolves around the sun in an elliptical orbit. One complete circuit takes 365.25 days at a mean linear velocity of 666,000 mph (Map 4). The Earth, tipped on its axis 23°27′ with respect to that orbit, also rotates (spins) west to east 1,040 mph at the equator, half that fast at the sixtieth parallels, and is stationary only at the poles. One turn is a day.[17]

Spacecraft launched due east get a flying start from the Earth's rotation, which makes it easier to attain orbital velocities. Benefits are greatest for vehicles launched near the equator, and progressively less toward the poles, where advantages are zero. Vehicles that head west conversely need much more power to achieve orbit, except near the poles. Rotation neither assists nor resists launches on north or south azimuths.[18]

Orbital inclination, measured in degrees above or below the equator (Map 4), determines what terrain any spacecraft will overfly as it travels around the world. Vehicles in polar orbits, with rare exceptions, eventually pass directly over every point on Earth; other inclinations cover less territory. Those launched on a 50° azimuth, for example, normally overfly everything between Newfoundland (50° north) and the Falkland Islands (50° south), but cannot look straight down on Greenland or Tierra del Fuego, which are at higher latitudes. Orbits at any given inclination may be circular or elliptical. The apogee (high point) of some ellipses may extend many thousands of miles from Earth, while

Map 3   GRAVITY VERSUS VEHICLE VELOCITY

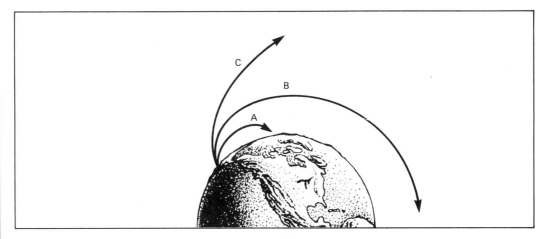

Path A. Suborbital; vehicle velocity too slow to overcome gravity.
Path B. Earth orbit; vehicle velocity and gravity equal.
Path C. Escape; vehicle velocity overcomes gravity pull.

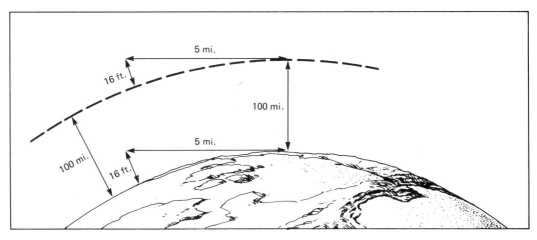

The Earth's curvature, on the average, dips 16 feet in a little less than 5 miles. Spacecraft circling the globe fall that same distance in the first second, wherever gravitational pull is 1g. A velocity of 5 miles per second (18,000 mph) therefore produces perpetual orbit, unless perturbations prohibit. The 100-mile altitude displayed is exemplary. It could be higher or lower, as long as gravity is about 1g.

Adapted from David Baker, *The Shape of Wars to Come*, pp. 33, 36.

the perigee (low point) may speed through the upper atmosphere.[19]

Orbital altitude determines the time it takes to circle the Earth. The period is 90 minutes for circular orbits at 125 miles, somewhat less at lower altitudes, and longer at higher altitudes, where paths are lengthy and less velocity is needed to counteract

Map 4   EARTH REVOLUTION AND ROTATION
Related to Orbital Paths and Planes

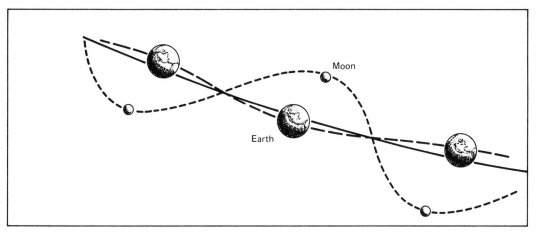

Orbital path of the Earth-Moon System as it revolves around the sun. Solid line tracks the center of mass.

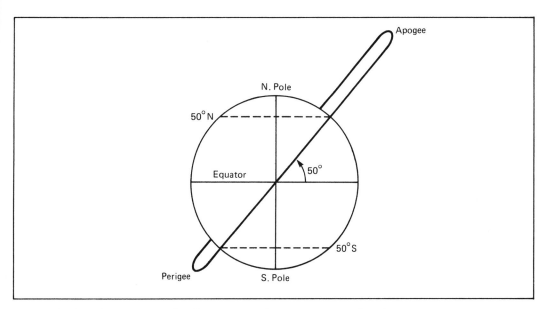

Typical orbit plane inclined to the equator as the Earth rotates on its axis.

Adapted from T. J. Wilson, "Earth," *Encyclopedia Americana*, and David Baker, *The Shape of Wars to Come*, p. 39.

gravity. The period of elliptical orbits averages nearest and farthest distances from Earth.[20]

Spacecraft orbiting at an average altitude of 22,300 miles are called geosynchronous, since their 24-hour period corresponds precisely with the time it takes the Earth to rotate once on its axis. Geosynchronous orbits that are circular and equatorial are called geostationary, because they seemingly hover above a single spot; the rest make figure eights from center lines over the equator. Sun-synchronous orbits pass prescribed spots at the same local time every day, winter, summer, spring, and fall.*[21]

Region II: Circumterrestrial Space

Circumterrestrial space, as defined in this book, begins about 60 miles above Earth, where aerodynamic drag and frictional heat lose most of their significance (Map 2). The arbitrary upper limit is 50,000 miles (Map 1). It is a harsh region for habitation.

Individualistic Environments

Asteroids and meteoroids of metal and stone, the only solid matter indigenous to free space, move through that vast void at speeds varying from 30,000 to 160,000 mph.** Most meteoroids are smaller than dust particles, but some weigh many tons. Catastrophic collisions with spacecraft, although possible, fortunately are improbable, but micrometeoroids that pepper poorly shielded capsules and space suits over long periods could pit optical lenses and chip temperature control surfaces.[22]

The latter are critical, since surface temperatures of objects in the thermosphere vary several hundred degrees daily from a maximum of 2,500°F at an altitude of about 300 miles. Sunlit sides of any object in circumterrestrial space figuratively fry, while shady sides freeze, unless reflective and insulative covers shield them. Systems additionally must be designed to expel excessive internal heat, including that generated on board.[23]

Space lies beyond "the wild blue yonder." The void between objects is absolutely black, because light cannot scatter in very thin air or hard vacuum. Total silence also prevails in that environment. There are no shock waves or sonic booms, regardless of vehicle velocities. Vacuum eliminates one form of metal fatigue found on Earth, where chemical reactions enlarge cracks, but "cold welding" can occur if metals touch accidentally, since no film of air separates exposed surfaces. Structures exposed to extreme heat and cold on opposite sides experience great stress.[24]

---

*Geosynchronous and sun-sychronous orbits lie far outside Region I, but relationships to Earth's rotation are important enough to mention in this section.

**Any meteoroid that enters the atmosphere and glows from frictional heat is a meteor. Those that strike the Earth are called meteorites.

Earth's gravity, which attenuates with altitude, never is negligible in Region II. Its pull is only 0.05g at 60,000 miles, one-twentieth of full strength, but in combination with other perturbations, such as solar winds, electromagnetic forces, and luni-solar gravitation above geosynchronous levels, causes spacecraft orbits to alter radically over time, unless corrected. Greater than anticipated drag due to sunspot activity, for example, slowed America's Skylab in June 1978; it incinerated on reentry the following year.[25]

X rays, ultraviolet light, infrared, and other forms of radiation flood the ionosphere and magnetosphere, which overlap regions I and II, as well as each other (Map 2). Some types are hazardous to health, hardware, and various activities in space.[26]

Two Van Allen radiation belts, separated by a low density slot, comprise electrons, protons, and perhaps other charged particles, trapped in a magnetic field that encircles the globe between latitudes 45° north and 45° south. The inner belt begins between 250 and 750 miles above the Earth, depending on latitude; it tapers off at about 6,200 miles. The outer belt expires at 37,000 to 52,000 miles, depending on solar activity. Intensities fluctuate daily with variations in the magnetosphere, but proton and electron flux respectively peak at approximately 2,200 and 9,900 miles. Prudent flight planning is required to reduce time in danger zones and, combined with shielding, avoid overdoses and electronic disruptions.[27]

Cosmic rays beyond the Van Allen belts pose serious problems for space travellers. Sporadic solar flares cause proton storms that project high-energy, high-charge, high-density, long-range flux a million times more powerful than particles in routine solar winds. Less potent doses can damage or destroy human cells, including components of the central nervous system. Temporary electronic malfunctions, including communication blackouts and discombobulated guidance systems, are common. Materials on the moon are ideally suited to shield lunar installations, but are too heavy to "harden" most space ships. Forecasts that defer flights or recall them in time to avoid solar flares meanwhile are crucial.[28]

Orbit Types and Inclinations

Objects in our universe orbit around Earth, its moon, other planets, the sun, or stars. Nothing stands still or flies a straight line to infinity.

Circumterrestrial orbits, as defined in this study, constitute four basic categories: low earth orbits (LEO) bracket 60–250 miles between sensible atmosphere and the bottom of Van Allen belts, with leeway in both directions; medium earth orbits (MEO) start where LEO leaves off, embrace both Van Allen belts, and terminate at an average altitude of 22,300 miles, which is the province of geosynchronous orbits (GEO). Geostationary orbits over Earth's equator are circular. Other GEOs provide planners assorted ellipses and planes from which to pick the most appropriate orbit for any given purpose* (Map 5). High earth orbits (HEO) theoretically extend as far beyond GEO as the Earth's gravitational field dominates, but the limit for practical purposes approximates 50,000–60,000 miles.[29]

Spacecraft orbiting entirely in lower LEO (under 100 miles) experience atmospheric drag that, although slight compared with suborbital altitudes, allows them to remain in position for more than a day only if they activate engines repeatedly. Those operating at 200 miles can linger almost a year without applying power. MEO is more stable, but radiation from Van Allen belts normally makes risks outweigh benefits, except perhaps for semisynchronous orbits at 12,860 miles, which permit users to circle the globe twice each day, repeatedly retracing two selected paths. High earth orbits avoid MEO's routinely intense radiation and the congestion that already typifies LEO and geostationary traffic. They also enjoy immense maneuver room.[30]

Space vehicles launched from Earth can reach LEO and lower MEO directly. Fuel expenditures, however, become prodigious for direct flights much above 600 miles. It therefore is common procedure to pick an initial "parking" orbit, then boost payloads (but not the launch vehicle) to a loftier altitude, after one or two laps around the globe** (Map 6). Engines "burn" first to reach the apogee of an elliptical transfer orbit. A second "burn" puts the spacecraft into a circular orbit at that altitude. Minimum energy transfers follow ellipses that ascend and merge gradually. High energy transfers are reserved mainly for high priority payloads and emergencies, because they expend far more propellant along shorter but steeper routes.[31]

Inclinational changes also are expensive in terms of propellant. Placing a spacecraft in equatorial LEO from Cape Canaveral, for example, demands nearly 50% more velocity than launches due east. Additional fuel to produce required velocity not only displaces payloads, but increases overall vehicle weight (more fuel is needed to lift more fuel).[32]

---

*Geostationary orbits circle at 22,300 miles above mean sea level on the Earth's surface. The average of perigee and apogee for other geosynchronous orbits is 22,300 miles.

**Expendable segments of spacecraft are potentially useful. Discarded shuttle tanks approximate 60,000 lbs., almost all aluminum. Frequently they contain 15,000–20,000 lbs. of fuel. Such assets would be worth a lot, if stored in stable orbits.

Map 5   CIRCUMTERRESTRIAL ORBITS
Types and Inclinations

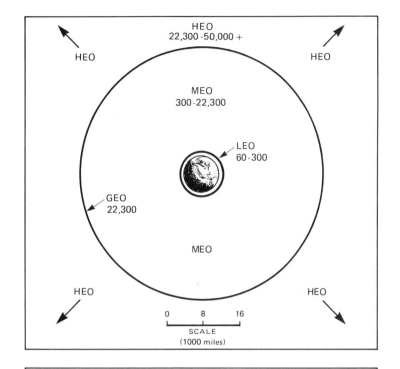

LEGENDS

LEO: Low earth orbit
MEO: Medium earth orbit
GEO: Geosynchronous orbit
HEO: High earth orbit

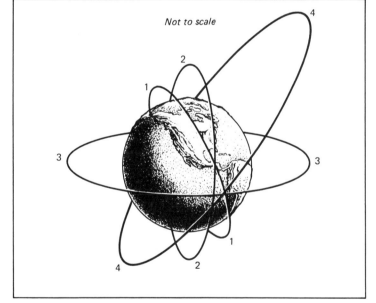

1. LEO, sun synchronous
2. MEO, polar orbit
3. GEO, equatorial
4. Eccentric orbit,
   overlaps LEO, MEO, HEO

Map 6   ALTERNATIVE ORBITAL TRANSFERS
From LEO to Higher Altitudes

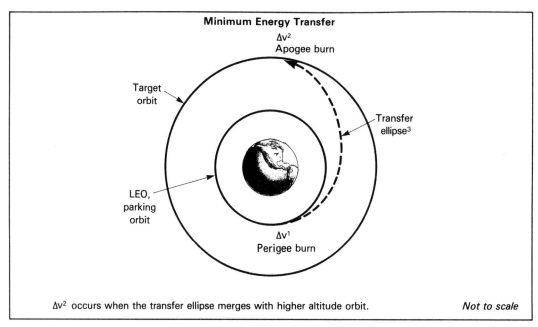

Minimum Energy Transfer

Δv^2
Apogee burn

Target
orbit

Transfer
ellipse[3]

LEO,
parking
orbit

Δv^1
Perigee burn

Δv^2 occurs when the transfer ellipse merges with higher altitude orbit.   *Not to scale*

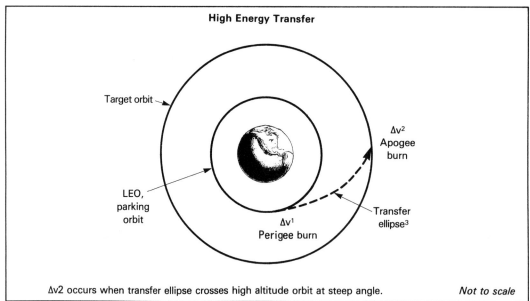

High Energy Transfer

Target orbit

LEO,
parking
orbit

Δv^2
Apogee
burn

Δv^1
Perigee burn

Transfer
ellipse[3]

$\Delta v2$ occurs when transfer ellipse crosses high altitude orbit at steep angle.   *Not to scale*

[1]Δv (Delta Vee) is velocity change.
[2]"Burn" is thrust to increase velocity at $\Delta v1$ and change velocity at $\Delta v2$.
[3]The transfer ellipse at perigee is the same altitude as the parking orbit; its apogee is the new orbit altitude.

Adapted from *Space Handbook*, pp. 2-38, 2-39.

Economies accrue when altitude and plane changes occur concurrently, especially in HEO, where the need for increased velocity is modest because gravity and orbital speeds are reduced. Even simple maneuvers nevertheless are time-consuming under ideal conditions, compared with operations in the atmosphere.[33]

Region III: Moon and Environs

The voyage from Earth to the moon averages 240,000 miles of cislunar space, most of it after leaving a LEO "parking" orbit, where ground controllers and/or astronauts verify performance and wait for an appropriate second phase "window" (Map 6). The intervening environment is much the same as circumterrestrial space above the Van Allen belts, with two prominent exceptions: Earth's gravitational and magnetic fields progressively diminish; perturbations caused by other planets, the sun, and moon (so-called three body problems) assume progressively greater importance. Lunar attributes and libration points, however, are distinctive enough to merit special mention.[34]

Lunar Attributes

Our moon is small, compared with the Earth. Equatorial diameters are one index (2,160 versus 7,910 miles). Total area is another. The moon's square mileage, for example, is essentially the same as that of Africa. Its smaller mass, slightly less than 1/80th that of this planet, allowed any lunar atmosphere to escape long ago, exposing the unprotected surface to all manner of meteoroids and radiation. Gravitational pull is one-sixth that on Earth. Human habitation thus demands an artificial biosphere and shield.[35]

That bleak orb rotates once on its axis in 27.3 days, the same time it takes to complete one revolution around our world. The moon therefore habitually presents the same face to observers on Earth. Lunar days and nights each last two weeks (Map 7). Temperatures at a depth of three feet or so consistently register about – 45°F, but the sunlit equatorial surface sizzles in readings that reach 260°F (water boils at 212°F) and freezes when they dip below – 245°F after dark. The poles, which receive no direct insolation, may never top – 190°F.[36]

Map 7   LUNAR LIGHTING AND LIBRATION POINTS
(Not to Scale)

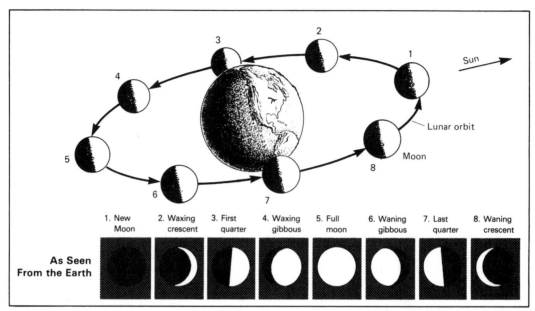

	1. New Moon	2. Waxing crescent	3. First quarter	4. Waxing gibbous	5. Full moon	6. Waning gibbous	7. Last quarter	8. Waning crescent
As Seen From the Earth								

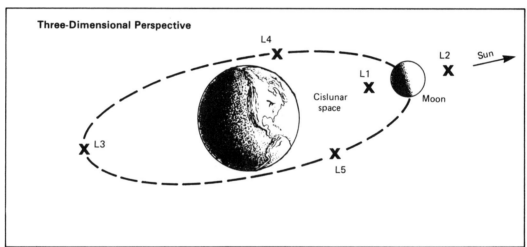

Three-Dimensional Perspective

DISTANCES IN MILES

From Earth	Lunar Orbit	240,000
From Moon	L-1	45,000
	L-2	42,000
	L-3	480,000
	L-4	60° ahead of moon
	L-5	60° behind moon

The moon, devoid of vegetation and water (except, perhaps, for ice at the poles), features five types of terrain. Rough highlands dominate the far side. Shallow, saucer-shaped formations, many of them more than 100 miles in diameter, predominate on the side facing Earth. Craters, some sharply defined, others with soft contours, are characteristic. Chains may extend as much as 600 miles. Echeloned ridges and canyons known as rilles, occasionally straight but often sinuous, crosshatch to form a lunar grid. Boulders, blocks, dimples, and hummocky debris from eons of pulverizing meteoroid impacts make smooth surfaces hard to find on the moon. Lunar dust, called fines, mantles most level land.[37]

Map makers and military men lack any criterion, such as sea level, from which to define elevations and depths. Each "molehill" and mountain therefore must be measured from base to crest, each canyon and crater from bottom to top. Spires of 12,000–15,000 feet are commonplace, even under those conditions. So are craters a mile or more deep; steep inner slopes may incline 50°.[38] Pike's Peak, the most imposing mountain in Colorado's Rockies, would loom slightly less than 9,000 feet, rather than 14,110, if measured in that fashion, because its base is more than a mile high.

The moon is rich in many natural resources. Volatile elements like sodium, potassium, carbon compounds, and perhaps hydrogen probably are very rare or missing, but iron, titanium, aluminum, manganese, and calcium are abundant. Oxygen, a primary constituent of water, air, and rocket propellant, is 40% by weight in lunar soils, which also contain an immense supply of silicon. Simple machines easily could strip top layers. Construction materials are abundant and readily available,[39] but there are no buildings, facilities, or fortifications at this time.

Libration Points

The five so-called lunar libration points are not points at all, but three-dimensional positions in space (Maps 1 and 7). Mathematical models and computer simulations indicate that free-floating objects within their respective spheres of influence tend to remain there, because gravitational fields of Earth and moon are in balance. Spacecraft theoretically could linger for long periods without expending significant fuel.[40]

L1 through L3, on a line with Earth and moon, are considered unstable. Objects at those locations, perturbed by the sun and other forces, will wander farther and farther away, if calculations are correct. L4 and L5, 60° ahead of and behind the moon in its orbit, assertedly are stable. Objects at those locations probably resist drift more vigorously and, if it begins, remain in that general region.[41]

The validity of those hypotheses, however, has not yet been verified empirically. There are no observable counterparts of the Trojan asteroids that inhabit areas analogous to L4 and L5 along Jupiter's orbit. No probe from Earth has ever confirmed or denied the presence of particle clouds that some scientists believe must be held captive. The size, shape, and importance of each lunar libration area thus remain subjects for speculation. L4 and L5, for example, may be larger or smaller than the 10,000-mile "kidney beans" alleged. L1, L2, and L3 may encompass comparable areas, more, or less.[42]

Region IV: Outer Envelope

The globe-shaped outer envelope that comprises Region IV radiates from the Earth in all directions. It terminates arbitrarily at twice the distance to the moon* (Map 1). Beyond that range, Earth-Moon System influences dissipate; solar and other planetary influences dominate.[43]

Region IV shares most characteristics of cislunar space. Its immense volume, which affords valuable maneuvering room, is void of sizable matter, except for large meteoroids and small asteroids that cross Earth's orbit. Some of the latter are potentially rich, easily accessible sources of raw materials.[44]

MILITARY IMPLICATIONS

The four regions just described influence military plans and operations differently at every organizational level. This appraisal, which modifies traditional U.S. intelligence formats to accommodate topics peculiar to space, views strategic, tactical, and logistical implications from present and prospective national security perspectives.[45]

Key Terrain

Strategically significant key terrain, the environmental foundation for national security objectives and targeting policies, con-

---

*The outer limit of Region IV is elastic. G. Harry Stine, for example, extends it to 1 million kilometers (600,000 miles).

stitutes physical features, natural and artificial, the seizure, retention, destruction, or indirect control of which would confer distinctive (sometimes decisive) advantages on a country or coalition.[46] The Earth-Moon System contains six categories:

- Critical space installations on Earth;
- Critical economic and military enterprises on the moon;
- Critical military bases and civilian colonies in orbit;
- Geostationary and other equatorial Earth orbits;
- Polar Earth orbits;
- Lunar libration points.

The first three, all manmade, have intrinsic value. The remainder are important only because of position.

Installed Features

No nation now can mount and sustain large-scale military operations in space without earthbound infrastructures to provide for command, control, launch, recovery, and essential support. That dependence will persist indefinitely. Each focal complex consequently qualifies as key terrain in every sense.

Installations worth defending inevitably will accompany economic exploitation of lunar resources and, perhaps eventually, the colonization of space. Military space forces at the bottom of Earth's so-called gravity well (Map 8) are poorly positioned to accomplish offensive/defensive/deterrent missions, because great energy is needed to overcome gravity during launch. Forces at the top, on a space counterpart of "high ground," could initiate action and detect, identify, track, intercept, or otherwise respond more rapidly to attacks. Put simply, it takes less energy to drop objects down a well than to cast them out. Forces at the top also enjoy more maneuvering room and greater reaction time. Gravitational pull helps, rather than hinders, space-to-Earth flights, with one exception: high-speed vehicles must expend great energy if required to enter any Earth orbit on return. Aerobraking reduces such demands.[47]

Natural Features

Few orbital paths can even loosely be called "discrete features," an essential element of key terrain, because variations are virtually limitless.

Map 8 EARTH AND MOON GRAVITY WELLS
(Not to Scale)

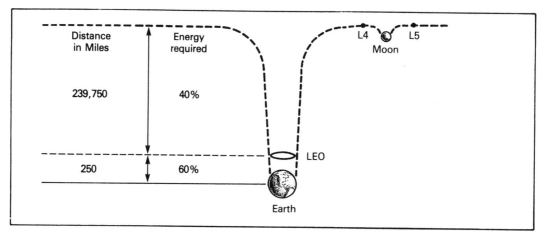

Low earth orbits, near the bottom of Earth's gravity well in terms of distance (60-250 miles), are more than half way up in terms of energy required to reach that altitude. Spacecraft velocity must be about 4.5 miles per second (mps) to attain LEO. A mere 2.4 mps more is enough to reach the top, nearly 240,000 miles higher.

One prominent exception is the circular track 22,300 miles above the Earth's equator. Three geostationary communications satellites, interspersed equidistantly around that ring, can receive signals from any location and relay them anywhere in our world, except the poles. Orbits that overfly the North and South Poles on each revolution are another exception, because reconnaissance and surveillance missions inclined 90° sooner or later loop directly over every place on Earth (those that finish several circuits daily finish first).

Circumlunar flights lack similar advantages. The moon's slow rotation (one turn every 27.3 days) makes polar orbits militarily impractical. It would take interminable time to pass over every spot below. Selenostationary (the lunar equivalent of geostationary) orbits are impossible. Flights at 53,000 miles above the surface, well beyond the controlling influence of lunar gravity (about 36,000 miles) would have to orbit Earth. Compensatory observation and communications benefits, however, might accrue from L1, which always views the near side of the moon, and L2, which always views the far side. L4 always views one "flank," L5 the other.[48]

Additional reasons make all five lunar libration points candidates for key terrain (Maps 1 and 7). L1, the lowest energy transfer site for 230-million-mile trips between Earth and Mars, could be fitted with military facilities, as well as the "motel/gas station/warehouse/restaurant/garage" the U.S. National Commission on Space currently envisions.[49] Armed forces might lie in wait at that location to hijack rival shipments on return. L2, currently considered an ideal place to collect raw materials catapulted from the moon, also is a potentially important clandestine military assembly area, since cislunar and Earth-based sentinels cannot see it.[50] L3 is the only semi-stable area outside cislunar/translunar space from which to stage or conduct assorted military operations against HEO, GEO, LEO, or Earth. Nature reserves decisive advantage for L4 and L5, two allegedly stable libration points that theoretically could dominate Earth and moon, because they look down both gravity wells. No other location is equally commanding.[51]

Avenues and Obstacles

The location, length, multiplicity, reliability, and capacity of available avenues determine the accessibility of critical terrain features to friend and foe. Those factors also influence operational flexibility and vulnerability. Great diversity is evident.

Terrestrial and Lunar Arteries

Road, rail, and air routes lead to and from all space support installations on Earth, supplemented by sea lanes in some cases. Corridors that connect with friendly countries are more secure than those across or along hostile frontiers. Space-related facilities deep in defensible territory are less susceptible to saboteurs, aerial attacks, and land invasions than sites on exposed peripheries, including coasts.

Surface movement on the moon, entirely cross-country until roads are constructed, will pose special problems, because maps for land navigation do not yet exist and magnetic compasses cannot assist dead reckoning. Rough topography will always restrict surface traffic.[52]

Space Approaches

Avenues to, from, and within space connect all key terrain in the Earth-Moon System. Opportunities to pick the most appropriate approach for any military purpose seem almost endless, but flexibility in fact is limited.

The disadvantage of launching Earth-to-space missions west and wartime need for trajectories that avoid enemy terrestrial defenses en route to orbit confine initial lines of flight. Orbital patterns and periods thereafter are relatively easy for rivals to predict. Parking orbits, a frequent requirement given current technology, reduce responsiveness in emergencies. Sharp altitude and inclination changes are very costly in terms of fuel and time. Even minor deviations demand fine-tuned activation of auxiliary thrusters with a limited fuel supply. Loop-the-loops, barrel-rolls, violent evasive actions, and other flamboyant tactics popularized in movies like *Star Wars* will remain science fiction until technologists develop new ways to maneuver in a vacuum.[53]

Aerodynamic drag and gravitational pull rule out high-speed movement of craft from Earth to space with presently deployed vehicles. Reentry angles that avoid excessive frictional heat when spacecraft hit the atmosphere canalize offensive approaches and reduce prospects for surprise. Those restrictions even affect forces designed expressly to function well in air and space, much like amphibious formations adapt to land and water. One source, in fact, asserts that the atmospheric interface and gravity wells "totally govern . . . strategic and tactical military operation doctrines in space warfare" and dictate feasible weapons.[54]

That statement, however, seems too strong, because radiation, a third major obstruction, also restricts launch/recovery times and channels movement. Intermittent nuclear detonations, for example, probably could make the Van Allen belts impassable to poorly shielded manned flights for prolonged periods. Polar avenues between Earth and GEO or beyond bypass the Van Allen belts, but currently are unattractive for at least two reasons: maneuvers to attain essential orbits beyond the Van Allen belts would expend immense amounts of fuel, and polar parts of the magnetosphere serve as funnels for sporadic solar flares that could cripple military operations in or through HEO, until better lightweight shielding becomes available.[55]

Observation and Concealment

Traditional relationships between observation, direct fields of fire, concealment (shelter against visual detection), and cover (shelter against rival weapons) pertain on the moon, with minor modifications. New techniques for attaining security and preventing surprise in the vastness of space are obligatory.

Hide and Seek on the Moon

Topographic features and surface curvature limit line-of-sight for viewing and shooting on Earth and moon, but no form of humidity or precipitation restricts lunar visibility. Neither do vegetation, urban barriers, or ocean depths. There are, however, dark sides. Subjects in lunar shadow become jet black and very hard to see, because light does not diffuse in a vacuum. Two-week-long lunar nights, preceded and followed by lengthy periods of morning and evening twilight, will obscure optical observation unless technological devices amplify available light.

Camouflage could assist concealment on the moon much the same as on Earth. Lunar foxholes would provide better cover than terrestrial counterparts, because the absence of air confines blast effects to much smaller areas. Materials for other field expedient and sophisticated fortifications are plentiful on the lunar surface.

Neither offensive nor defensive forces will be able to take full advantage of clear views and fine fields of fire until cartographers develop large-scale contour maps suitable for military operations. Meanwhile, they must devise a common base other than sea level from which to measure elevations and a grid with eight-digit coordinates from which to measure ranges and pinpoint positions.

Hide and Seek in Transparent Space

There is no natural cover in transparent space. Concealment depends mainly on distance, random maneuvers, shadowing, stealthy technology, decoys, and other deception.

Equatorial GEO, a slim belt that girdles the globe at a constant altitude, is the hardest place to hide. Radiation rules out protracted operations in most of MEO; areas outside the Van Allen belts are relatively easy to scan. Odds against detection are a bit better in LEO, which covers 52 billion cubic miles of void 60–300 miles above Earth. Military space vehicles nevertheless are vulnerable. Few can accomplish assigned missions unless they follow predictable orbits, high velocities prevent swift evasive actions, and perigees lie within easy reach of surface-to-space interceptors. Low earth-orbiting craft that overfly hostile territory thus would run serious risks in wartime.[56]

HEO and above are many orders of magnitude more difficult to search systematically. Surveillance systems with broad detector beams are best able to observe immense areas in great depth. Narrow beams have better resolution, but search times can be protracted. One telescope at Lick Observatory, California, another at McDonald Observatory, Texas, took 12 and 30 days, respectively, to locate laser signals from a reflector at a preselected spot on the moon during an Apollo 11 experiment. Proficiency has improved since 1969, but finding nonreflective targets stashed in uncharted space well outside GEO remains a monumental problem for detection systems on Earth or the moon.[57]

Radar, which bounces impulses off targets, then records returns, requires tremendous power. One plausible estimate, for example, indicates that each installation would need 100–200,000 megawatts to probe HEO (wattage at Grand Coulee Dam approximates 10,000). Radar, as a result, seems prohibitively expensive with present or projected technology, whether systems are Earth- or space-based. Sensors on shorter wavelengths use less power, because outside sources (especially targets) generate the signs they look for across an electromagnetic spectrum that includes infrared, visible, and ultraviolet light. The huge size and fine tolerances needed to find faint objects in Region IV, however, likely will keep system costs high.[58] Clouds, haze, fog, and air pollutants limit optical instruments that scan the skies from Earth.

Forces able to elude detection enjoy a sanctuary in free space from which to attack or retaliate at times and places of their choosing. The ceaseless technological contest between offense and defense nevertheless limits such abilities.[59]

Weapon Performance

Physical influences on nuclear, directed energy, chemical warfare, and conventional weapon effects in space are far-reaching and fundamental. The following examples show a few ways that vacuum, its interaction with atmosphere, and little or no gravity alter performance.

Nuclear Effects

Vacuum severely restricts the range of blast and heat from nuclear explosions in space. Initial nuclear radiation ranges far and wide. Residual radiation from surface bursts could occur locally on the moon, but fallout cannot form in the absence of atmosphere.

Blast and Heat

Nuclear weapons detonated in atmosphere create shock waves, violent winds, and intense heat that can inflict severe damage and casualties well beyond the hypocenter.* A one-megaton ex-

---

*Ground zero and surface zero are meaningless terms in space, except near the moon or planets. Hypocenter, a synonym, is universally appropriate.

plosion at 10,000 feet, for example, produces peak overpressures of 5 pounds per square inch and 160-mile-an-hour winds 2 miles away from the burst—more than enough to disable spacecraft on launch pads or in flight. Flash burns and fire storms supplement blast.[60]

Such peculiarities are absent from space, because winds never blow in a vacuum, shock waves cannot develop where no medium (air, water, earth) resists compression, and neither fireballs nor superheated surrounding air develop above about 65 miles.[61] Consequently, it would take direct hits or near misses to achieve required results with nuclear blast and thermal radiation. Collateral damage and casualties from those effects would be fairly easy to confine, even if military installations and space colonies collocate.

Initial Radiation

Initial radiation from nuclear explosions in space reacts uniquely, particularly when it contacts the boundary between vacuum and atmosphere. Some phenomena disrupt signal propagation. Others destroy equipment.

Beta particles and gamma rays respectively cause intensive and extensive alterations in the ionosphere. Both warp or weaken radio and radar waves. The dearth of practical testing makes it difficult to predict repercussions, but planners anticipate lengthy high frequency (HF) blackouts over broad areas, followed by periods of impaired radio/radar performance.[62] The megaton-range TEAK test shot, detonated on August 1, 1958 at an altitude of 252,000 feet (almost 48 miles) over Johnson Island, degraded HF radio traffic throughout a region several thousand miles in diameter from shortly after midnight until sunrise.[63]

X rays, which radiate only a few feet from low-level nuclear explosions before atmosphere absorbs them, travel thousands of miles at the speed of light where air is thin or absent. All man-made objects in space are sensitive. Strong doses that strike poorly protected targets can peel metal skins and destroy delicate mechanisms through intense heat or hypervelocity shock waves induced internally.[64]

Electromagnetic pulse (EMP), widespread and potentially paralyzing to electronics on land, sea, or in the air, occurs when a cascade of gamma rays from any nuclear explosion in space collides with the upper atmosphere (Map 9). Negatively charged electrons, knocked spinning en masse along the Earth's magnetic field (so-called Compton recoil), leave positively charged parent atoms in place. Resultant charge imbalances in the deposition region produce a prodigious electronic surge that peaks 100 times faster than lightning, then bolts toward ground. Every

Map 9   ELECTROMAGNETIC PULSE PROPAGATION
Gamma Rays Related to EMP

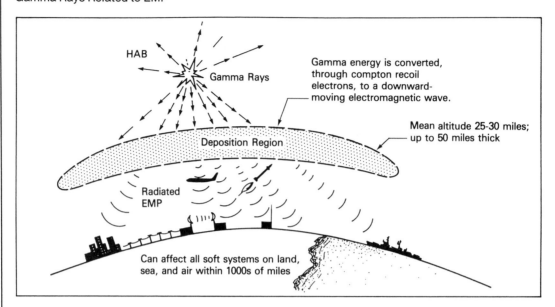

HAB

Gamma Rays

Gamma energy is converted, through compton recoil electrons, to a downward-moving electromagnetic wave.

Mean altitude 25-30 miles; up to 50 miles thick

Deposition Region

Radiated EMP

Can affect all soft systems on land, sea, and air within 1000s of miles

Radii Related to HOB

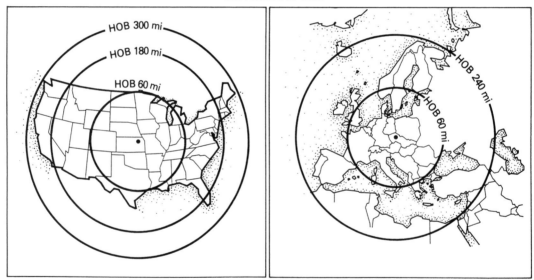

HOB 300 mi
HOB 180 mi
HOB 60 mi

HOB 240 mi
HOB 60 mi

1. HAB is high altitude burst.
2. HOB is height of burst in miles.
3. EMP is electromagnetic pulse.
4. Average EMP within each circle is 25,000 volts per meter. Peaks are twice that high.

Anthony P. Trippe, "The Threat of Electromagnetic Pulse," *National Defense*, December 1984, p. 24; Jörg Lippert, "The Hidden Destroyer: EMP—Disturbance from Space," *NATO's Sixteen Nations*, May 1983, p. 39; Daniel L. Stern, "Electromagnetic Pulse—The uncertain Certainty," *Bulletin of The Atomic Scientists*, March 1983, p. 52.

unshielded conductor acts as an EMP antenna. Most lightning arresters, power shunting switches, and other protective devices respond too slowly to cope. Areas afflicted and degrees of danger are almost independent of weapon yield above a few hundred kilotons, but expand remarkably in response to increased heights of burst (see Map 9 for comparisons).[65]

Solid state circuitry packed in the smallest feasible space may be a million times more vulnerable to EMP than vacuum tubes are, because miniature components cannot tolerate high currents. Immense overvoltages sufficient to melt semiconductor materials can turn sophisticated electronics instantaneously into irreparable trash. Results could be ruinous for civilian communities as well as military establishments. Erasing computer memories, for example, could cripple communications, power transmission facilities, public utilities, and banking systems; misdirect missiles; make avionics malfunction; and detonate time-fused munitions prematurely.[66]

System-generated EMP (SGEMP) originates in much the same manner when highly energetic gamma rays strike solids instead of atmosphere. Pulse effects similar to those just described, however, are confined inside intercepted systems. Poorly protected satellites and solar power systems in orbit are particularly vulnerable, because risk radii extend hundreds (sometimes thousands) of miles farther in space than in absorbent air.[67]

Initial nuclear radiation, regardless of type, is indiscriminate. Collateral damage and casualties would be difficult to predict and expensive to control. Nuclear warriors therefore should consider consequences carefully and proceed cautiously, lest they wound themselves worse than foes.

Directed Energy Effects

Directed energy weapons (DEW), in various stages of research, development, test, and evaluation, occupy two basic categories. Electromagnetic beams embrace high energy lasers (HEL) and high powered microwaves (HPM). Particle beams subdivide into charged particle beams (CPB) and neutral particle beams (NPB).

All project energy at or near the speed of light. All are designed to engage small, discrete targets without causing unwelcome side effects (HPM are an occasional exception). All have a huge effective range. All possess "soft kill" capabilities that could blind sensors and disrupt electronics well beyond "hard kill" range, within which personnel casualties and permanent damage to hardware occur. None, however, perform equally well in atmosphere and space.[68]

Electromagnetic Beams

Laser weapons, regardless of type (gas, chemical, excimer, free electron, solid state, X ray), concentrate a tightly focused shaft or pulse of radiant energy photons on the target surface. Thermal kills are most common. The beam burns through if it dwells on one spot long enough, then destroys critical components, ignites fuel, and/or detonates munitions. Efforts fail when the beam wobbles too much or otherwise wanders. Impulse kills occur when a brief but intense beam vaporizes the target skin, creating a shock wave that causes structural collapse or destroys sensitive internal mechanisms.[69]

Space is a nearly perfect laser environment. Power output is the main range limitation, because light propagates unimpeded in a vacuum. Diffraction is significant over long distances, but can be controlled. Free-floating laser platforms, designed to minimize beam vibration, may help prevent excessive spread.[70]

Atmosphere, on the contrary, imposes at least five forms of interference: scattering, two kinds of absorption, thermal blooming, and turbulence (Figure 1). Clouds, fog, invisible vapors, dust, smoke, and other matter buoyed by air break up or block part of each laser beam. A plasma of charged particles absorbs more energy when electromagnetic radiation from laser light ionizes the atmosphere. Air in the path of that light heats and expands, making the beam splay or "bloom." Finally, up/down drafts, cross currents, heat waves, and other atmospheric phenomena (such as those that make stars seem to twinkle) further impair efficiency which, in total, may fall by a factor of 100 to 300 in a few miles.[71]

Weapon-quality HELs require so much power to offset refraction, diffusion, and absorption that size and cost become critical limitations for Earth-based systems aimed at hard targets in space, and even more so for space-to-Earth missions. Ways to mitigate such problems are under study. Steps to pick optimum wavelengths for particular weapon systems seem promising. Other experiments emphasize adaptive optics, which refocus laser beams to compensate for turbulence. There may be no way, however, to retrieve energy lost from scatter. Meanwhile, atmospheric interference remains a serious drawback, especially for defensive lasers that must perform well at times and places the user does not control.[72]

Unclassified literature contains little about experimental high powered microwave weapons, which also attack heat intolerant targets. HPMs reportedly work well in the vacuum of space, but their main attraction apparently is a better ability than lasers have to penetrate clouds. HPM beams, however, break down dielectrically in atmosphere at relatively low energy den-

Figure 1   ATMOSPHERIC INTERFERENCE WITH LASER WEAPONS
Five Common Problems

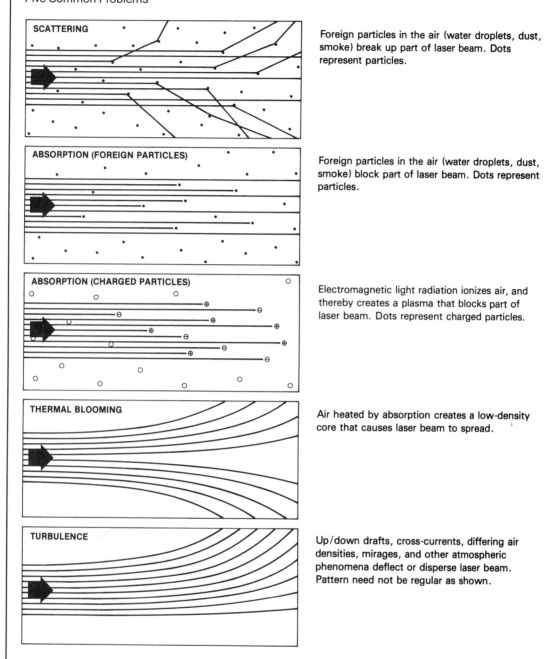

SCATTERING
Foreign particles in the air (water droplets, dust, smoke) break up part of laser beam. Dots represent particles.

ABSORPTION (FOREIGN PARTICLES)
Foreign particles in the air (water droplets, dust, smoke) block part of laser beam. Dots represent particles.

ABSORPTION (CHARGED PARTICLES)
Electromagnetic light radiation ionizes air, and thereby creates a plasma that blocks part of laser beam. Dots represent charged particles.

THERMAL BLOOMING
Air heated by absorption creates a low-density core that causes laser beam to spread.

TURBULENCE
Up/down drafts, cross-currents, differing air densities, mirages, and other atmospheric phenomena deflect or disperse laser beam. Pattern need not be regular as shown.

NOTE: Lines on each diagram indicate Laser beams.

Adapted from Kosta Tsipis, "Laser Weapons," *Scientific American*, December 1981, p. 56.

sity levels. Space-to-Earth and Earth-to-space lethality thus will be poor compared with lasers, until technologies correct that tendency.[73]

Particle Beams

Particle beams differ from thermal kill lasers in two basic respects: they project a stream of highly energetic electrons, protons, neutrons, hydrogen atoms, or ions, rather than radiant energy photons; and they instantaneously penetrate target interiors, where they attack components, propellants, and explosives without first burning a hole in the surface. Space vehicles "hardened" to survive reentry heat are just as vulnerable as soft-skinned craft, unless specifically protected.[74]

Neither charged nor neutral particle beams are potentially important Earth-to-space or space-to-Earth weapons, because CPBs propagate well only in atmosphere, NPBs only in vacuum. The "boundary" between is a barrier to both. All-weather CPBs, which presently are limited by short range, may someday be able to reach targets in thin atmosphere, if laser-produced plasma channels, now in experimental stages, facilitate conduction.[75]

Chemical/Biological Warfare Effects

Chemical warfare (CW) munitions, dispensed as aerosols, vapors, liquids, and viscous compounds, incapacitate or kill when inhaled, ingested, or absorbed. Toxicity, concentration densities, dosage times, and other variables determine how quickly and to what extent each type agent takes effect.[76] Biological warfare (BW) munitions, which are living microorganisms that reproduce themselves under favorable conditions (viruses, rickettsias, bacteria, protozoa, fungi, and derivative infectious materials), cause diseases in people, livestock, and/or plants.[77] Such weapons are cheap to produce and employ, but costly to counter.

Self-contained biospheres in space afford a superlative environment for chemical and biological warfare compared with Earth, where weather and terrain virtually dictate delivery times, places, and techniques. All but the smallest spacecraft flying short sorties rely on closed-circuit life support systems that continuously circulate air and recycle water. Clandestine operatives thus could dispense lethal or incapacitating CW/BW agents rapidly and uniformly throughout enemy facilities without damaging hardware or directly endangering friends (occupants and visitors who vector contagious diseases elsewhere are the only possible source of collateral casualties).* Time available to detect colorless, odorless chemicals and then react would be very short. BW agents are almost impossible to spot before symptoms appear.**[78]

The equivalent of space suits would protect individuals, provided warning/response times permitted, but price tags would be high and performance levels much lower than normal. Sanctuaries similar to the toxic-free "citadel" that eats up precious space aboard some ships could preserve selected personnel, but not everyone. Any vehicle or structure victimized by persistent chemicals probably would become permanently uninhabitable (even tear gas would linger a long time in closed biospheres). CW decontamination would demand techniques different than those now used on Earth, where vast quantities of wash water and solvents are essential.[79] BW agents might die, if exposed to hard vacuum, but spacecraft and crews would experience other problems in the process.

Conventional Weapon Effects

Conventional weapons also function differently in space than on Earth. Tanks, cruise missiles, and other systems with "air breathing" engines would be inoperative in a vacuum. Battery-powered motors and rocket-propelled engines that oxidize fuel on board are present alternatives. Newton's Third Law of Motion (to every action there is an equal and opposite reaction) establishes requirements for recoilless artillery in the vacuum of space, except on the moon, where heavy vehicles could anchor each self-propelled tube and trails could lock each towed piece in place. Elsewhere, blast would propel cannons backward for great distances with momentum equal to that of the shells. Newton's First Law of Motion (bodies in motion move in a straight line until another force intervenes) basically regulates projectile trajectories, unopposed by atmospheric drag. Predictable paths, shaped exclusively by velocity and low lunar gravity, make "fire-and-forget" an attractive mode, provided that orbital fragments could be confined or controlled.[80]

Conventional explosives and nuclear weapons must hit targets directly or detonate nearby, because no shock waves form in

---

*Epidemics emanating from space were a NASA nightmare during the first lunar landings in 1969–71. Decontamination and extensive quarantine followed Apollo 11, 12, and 14 missions to reduce risks that microorganisms from the moon might wipe out life on Earth. Later flights dispensed with such precautions.

**BW operations commonly are considered strategic, rather than tactical, because pathogens normally take days or weeks to incubate, but surreptitious preemptive strikes could be timed to take effect on or about a particular date.

a vacuum. Fragmentation from warheads normally is more destructive than concussion for that reason, and is more effective than on Earth, where atmosphere interferes. Pressurized space facilities are peculiarly vulnerable to shaped charges like naval limpet mines that special operation forces could stick on outside walls or set off inside. Flimsy bulkheads built to withstand twice the design load or less would rupture easily, with ruinous results.[81]

Kinetic energy weapons (KEW) can kill as effectively as explosives when they collide at tremendous speed with spacecraft and installations, most of which perforce must be fragile until cheaper ways are found to launch much larger loads up Earth's gravity well or manufacture in space. Impact converts KEW energy to pulverizing shock waves that wrack each structure they strike. Range and rates of fire vary with delivery systems. Destructive power depends on projectile size and speed (damage potential quadruples when velocity doubles). High-speed birdshot, for example, could seriously damage or destroy most space facilities, which are strong enough to maintain structural integrity and repel micrometeoroids, but not much more. Half-ounce pellets propelled at 15,000 mph penetrate four inches of aluminum. Mass drivers, which are immense electromagnetic railguns that armed services some day might mount on the moon as heavy artillery, could accurately hurl huge lunar rocks at city-sized targets on Earth, according to one contentious source. A ton-sized stone would hit with force equivalent to 500 tons of TNT. Megaton impacts reportedly are possible.[82]

Personnel Performance

Humans cannot survive in space without support systems that provide a life-sustaining environment. Breathable air, food, and water, plus tolerable temperatures, humidity, pressure, light, noise, vibration, radiation, and other variables are bedrock requirements. Individual and group proficiency also depends on personal attributes, both physical and psychological, together with compatible partners. Associated problems influence crew selection, mission duration and frequency, force size, the design of manned military spacecraft and, eventually, of lunar installations.[83]

Individual Proficiency

Four environmental problems that affect individual proficiency merit special mention: subsistence, which is inseparable from sanitation; safeguards against radiation; motion sickness; and weightlessness. Psychological stresses may prove extreme during uninterrupted interplanetary flights measured in months (even years), but are easily manageable within the Earth-Moon System.[84]

Subsistence and Sanitation

Every average adult daily demands almost 30 pounds of oxygen, food, and drinking water. Supplies for a crew of three on a one-month space mission would amount to more than a ton, stored at the expense of precious propellant and military payloads, if recycling were impossible. Every adult deposits an equal amount of waste in the form of feces, urine, perspiration, intestinal gases, carbon dioxide, and other exhalation vapors that could quickly reach toxic proportions in sealed capsules, unless quelled, expelled, or sterilized for use in non-hydroponic gardening.[85]

Life-support systems currently dump or stow organic waste on short missions, but such practices do nothing to reduce long-term resupply problems. High priority research projects consequently include alternative techniques to recycle consumables. Scientists have devised expedient ways to recover oxygen and convert impure fluids into potable water, but continue the search for improvements and means to salvage solid human waste.[86]

Potentially pathogenic microorganisms, which proliferate in sealed spacecraft and communes where water for personal hygiene is strictly rationed, cause further concerns. Concentrations may be ten times greater than normal and exposure times extended. Effects on respiratory tracts under low-gravity conditions are difficult to predict. Inorganic contaminants introduced in amounts greater than safe thresholds also are harmful if inhaled. Countermeasures under development are comparatively simple since recycling is unnecessary.[87]

Radiation Risks

Military personnel in space enter a perilous realm of radiant energy when they leave Earth's protective atmosphere. Risks are least in low earth orbit, but rise rapidly in the Van Allen belts and beyond, where high-energy, high-charge cosmic flux poses persistent hazards. Sporadic dangers emanate mainly from surface eruptions on the sun, which reach peak intensities every 11 years. Solar flares are most prominent.[88]

Human central nervous, blood, digestive, and reproductive systems are particularly vulnerable to such radiation, which attacks non-dividing cells. Dosages and tissue types determine whether damage will be immediate or deferred, reversible or irreversible, survivable or fatal. Cumulative effects make total exposure time a critical factor. There is, however, no consensus concerning safe levels. Even means of measuring dosages are under review. Better understanding is obligatory, because early disablement could cause mission failures. Delayed results that could include leukemia, solid tumors, cataracts, and infertility would retard recruitment and retention of military personnel.[89]

Technologists and tacticians presently pursue several approaches to improve protection—some simple, others complex. Lunar installations, for example, could be well sheltered from cosmic radiation by soil cover, but spacecraft demand much lighter materials in various stages of research and development. One alternative, in its infancy, would replace solid shields with an electronic field to deflect radiant and micrometeoroid particles before they strike the capsule. Flight profiles currently limit time in Van Allen belts; accurate forecasts could reduce radiation dangers during periods of acute solar activity. Both methods, however, limit mission flexibility. Finally, planners may be able to plot permissible exposure on a sliding scale, because personnel under age 35 apparently can tolerate very high radiation levels and recuperate more quickly than older persons, who seem better able to withstand moderate overloads for long periods.[90]

Motion Sickness

Motion sickness, which afflicts about half of each spaceship crew, may undermine mission proficiency enough during the first few days of each flight to mark the difference between military success and failure. Symptoms vary from drowsiness and indifference to severe vomiting. It is difficult to predetermine which individuals are most susceptible, because study samples are small, causes are in dispute, and responses to medical suppressants under evaluation are unpredictable.[91]

Weightlessness

Earth's gravity exerts great force. Humans need strong bones and muscles merely to sit or stand. Heart and lungs must work hard to distribute blood and oxygen. Weightlessness, manifest when gravity's force is neutral, produces opposite effects. Physical dexterity, bone density, muscle tone, blood circulation, and bodily fluids all decrease.[92]

Weightlessness impairs response times, precision movements, and work capacities of the best trained and conditioned space crews. Dehydration, a contributor, occurs when the brain tells bodily organs to discharge fluids that pool in the chest.

Blood, which thereafter thickens and flows less freely, supplies needy tissues with smaller than usual amounts of fresh nutrients and oxygen. Reduced abilities to exercise in turn cause muscles to lose mass and tone. Odds favoring fractures and kidney stones increase, because weightlessness transfers calcium from bones to bloodstream.[93]

Evidence so far suggests that human bodies adapt reasonably well to weightlessness and recover completely after return to any environment with 1g gravity. Bone demineralization, which seems irreversible, is the most prominent exception. Artificial gravity may someday alleviate or eliminate the most debilitating aspects of weightlessness in large, slowly rotating space stations that serve as military bases. Scientists, however, first must conquer Coriolis force.* Weightlessness may forever be unavoidable in tactical vehicles, such as interceptors, but short duration missions make it bearable.[94]

Group Proficiency

Psychological strains imposed by space flight are more easily controlled than most physiological malfunctions, although "cabin fever" may affect group performance adversely during very long missions. Biorhythms nevertheless can make or break military organizations in the Earth-Moon System, depending on how well they promote team play.[95]

The absence of identifiable day and night, which disrupts human habit patterns, causes psychophysical problems. Crews in low earth orbit repeat the light-dark-light cycle several times every 24 hours; clock hands seem to stand still in HEO. Effects derange work-rest routines like jet lag magnified many times. Results range from emotional instability, fatigue, and poor attention span to impaired vital functions, such as pulse, heart beat, brain activity, body temperature, endocrine activity, and metabolism. Low resistance to infection may even be manifest.[96]

Some individuals perform best before breakfast, others after supper. Optimum unit efficiency consequently is possible only if crews contain the proper mix of biorhythms, and schedules have each member performing duties during his/her period of peak proficiency. Many military tasks make it impossible for all to work and relax simultaneously. Most astronauts with less than optimum assignments, however, adapt adequately, just as shift workers do on Earth.[97]

---

*In oversimplified terms, Coriolis is the apparent force you feel if you try to walk from the edge of a merry-go-round toward the center.[98]

CUMULATIVE CONSEQUENCES

Space, the fourth military medium, contrasts so starkly with land, sea, and air that it invalidates a good deal of conventional wisdom concerning control structures, strategies, tactics, force postures, administration, and logistics. National defense specialists accordingly must modify many (perhaps replace some) time-tested principles, policies, and concepts that serve well on this planet, but appear inappropriate elsewhere in the Earth-Moon System.

Chapter 2 explores a wide variety of related problems and options. The intent is to provide a few fresh insights of possible value for planning, programming, budgeting, and oversight purposes.

CHAPTER

2

Strategic Problems and Options

Space, the newest military medium, needs a distinctive school of strategic thought to complement land, sea, and air counterparts in ways that assist the development of cohesive plans and programs.[1] Elements, as a minimum, should include politico-military purposes, principles, and threat indicators, together with theories and concepts that address deterrence, offensive/defensive operations, and arms control. The product could help planners create sound strategies that match ends with means (a measure of effectiveness) while minimizing waste (a measure of efficiency), despite enemy countermeasures and inescapable limitations (such as resources and expertise).

POLITICO-MILITARY PURPOSES

A clear sense of purpose at the highest levels must underpin space strategies. National security interests, coupled with implementing objectives, indicate what must be done to achieve desired ends.

Security Interests In Space

Every country and coalition on Earth has political, economic, military, social, and scientific interests in space. Survival, by definition, is the only vital interest. Physical security, prosperity, power, progress, and freedom of action are universally important. Additional interests of similar magnitude, such as peace and stability, appeal to some, while others spurn them or assign them low priorities.[2]

Nearly every interest in space has potential security implications. Economic competition on the moon or Mars, for instance, could cause war.[3] Scientific probes to advance understanding of our universe could have serendipitous consequences comparable to Einstein's Special Theory of Relativity, which unexpectedly paved the way for nuclear weapons.[4]

This chapter singles out three competitive, perhaps incompatible, interests with sweeping significance: political cooperation; economic exploitation; military power.

Political Cooperation

Political cooperation, the most widely professed interest in space, conforms with the Charter of the United Nations (UN), which seeks to create "conditions of stability and well-being" that must accompany "peaceful and friendly" international relations. Ninety-six nations subscribe to the Outer Space Treaty of 1967 (Annex C). Article I specifies that exploration and other endeavors "shall be carried out for the benefit . . . of all mankind." Article II disapproves of sovereignty anywhere in space. The Moon Treaty of 1979 has attracted only seven parties,* none of whom now have space capabilities, but its explicit restrictions seem to reflect prevailing UN views: "Neither the surface nor the subsurface of the moon [or other celestial bodies within the solar system] . . . shall become property" of any person, state, or other organization.[5]

National leaders generally live in a less altruistic world, but openly proclaim that collaboration serves the common good better than zero-sum games with only one winner. They also agree that community efforts are preferable to hegemony by any power in space, if public statements reflect true sentiments. Responsible authorities rarely release opinions that oppose equal opportunities to share rewards and risks. The strength of such convic-

*Australia, Austria, Chile, the Netherlands, Pakistan, the Philippines, and Uruguay were parties to the Moon Treaty in 1989, when this report was published.

tions will be tested when economic competition quickens in space.[6]

Economic Exploitation

Economic interests in space center on vast and diversified raw materials, inexpensive solar power, and industrial techniques made possible by near vacuum and low gravity. Prospects for extraordinary productivity and growth are within relatively easy reach of planet Earth.[7]

The lunar mantle contains all essential elements for the full range of manufacturing and construction on a grand scale, plus so much oxygen that some call the moon "a tank farm in space." Smelters could rely less on costly chemical treatments, because heat alone would remove most impurities from many ores in that environment. Waterless cement, specialty alloys, exotic composites (such as glass/metal mixtures stronger than steel, yet as transparent as crystal), powder metallurgy, cold welding, free-fall casting, and superconductors represent a few among many processes and products that plants in space could facilitate. "Sanitation engineers" could dispatch inconvertible waste on trajectories that collide with the sun or disappear into deep space.[8]

Interests in economic exploitation of space are intrinsically neither virtuous nor evil. Efforts that benefit the world community could foster strategic stability. Peaceful competition, such as that in Antarctica (where seven countries have staked out territorial claims), is theoretically possible.* Efforts by any superpower or collection of states to monopolize the bounties of space and couple them with earthbound assets, however, might trigger international strife, because success in some circumstances could sensationally upset the global balance of power.

Military Power

Space, the ultimate "high ground," overarches planet Earth, its occupants, and all activities thereon. Effective use of that medium for military purposes therefore may be needed to safeguard

---

*Disputes in Antarctica, another forbidding frontier, thus far have been peaceful, perhaps because occupation remains sparse and exploitation minimal. Rich strikes that intensify economic interests could sour relations rapidly. Claimants include Argentina, Australia, Chile, France, New Zealand, Norway, and the United Kingdom. The United States and Soviet Union recognize no claims, but reserve rights to make future claims of their own.[9]

national interests in survival, security, peace, power, stability, and freedom of action.

Every technologically advanced land, sea, and air service already depends on space satellites to such a degree that traditional command, control, communications, and intelligence (C³I) skills may languish, much like pocket calculators made slide rule proficiency rare. Reliance continues to increase, because systems in space offer strategic and tactical advantages that are otherwise unavailable: national technical means of verification for treaty compliance and crisis monitoring; geodetic surveys to assist military map makers and target planners; weather prediction; early warning and post-attack assessment; nuclear detonation detection; global positioning/navigation data; and observable order of battle information. Satellites relay most military intercontinental telecommunications and an increasing share of tactical traffic.[10]

Military interests in space almost surely will intensify and spread during the next decade. How smoothly they will mesh with aforementioned interests in political cooperation and economic exploitation is problematic. Reconciliation and collision are divergent possibilities. Plans that address both extremes and contingencies between seem advisable, pending clarification.

Security Objectives In Space

Politico-military objectives in space, as elsewhere, specify what any country or coalition must do to support or dispute security interests during peacetime and war (see Figure 2 for sample options). Force goals that feature parity and nonprovocation, for example, might promote political cooperation. Quests for supremacy, which mesh well with interests in military power, probably would not. Parties that hope to satisfy economic interests in space must maintain ready access to resources on the moon and beyond, despite opposition if necessary, and perhaps deny access to competitors who seek monopolies.

Goals on Earth and in space should be complementary, otherwise gaps and incompatibilities occur. Determination to preserve land, sea, and air links in the C³I chain, but not satellites on which they depend, would weaken the whole apparatus. Major powers that seek to deter and, if necessary, deal decisively with coercive acts and armed aggression on this planet may find those tasks increasingly formidable, perhaps unachievable, if they cannot fulfill supportive aims in space. Such interconnections are almost endless.

Short-, mid-, and long-term objectives vary in value. Most are complex. Strategists therefore must break them into component

Figure 2 MILITARY OBJECTIVES MATRIX

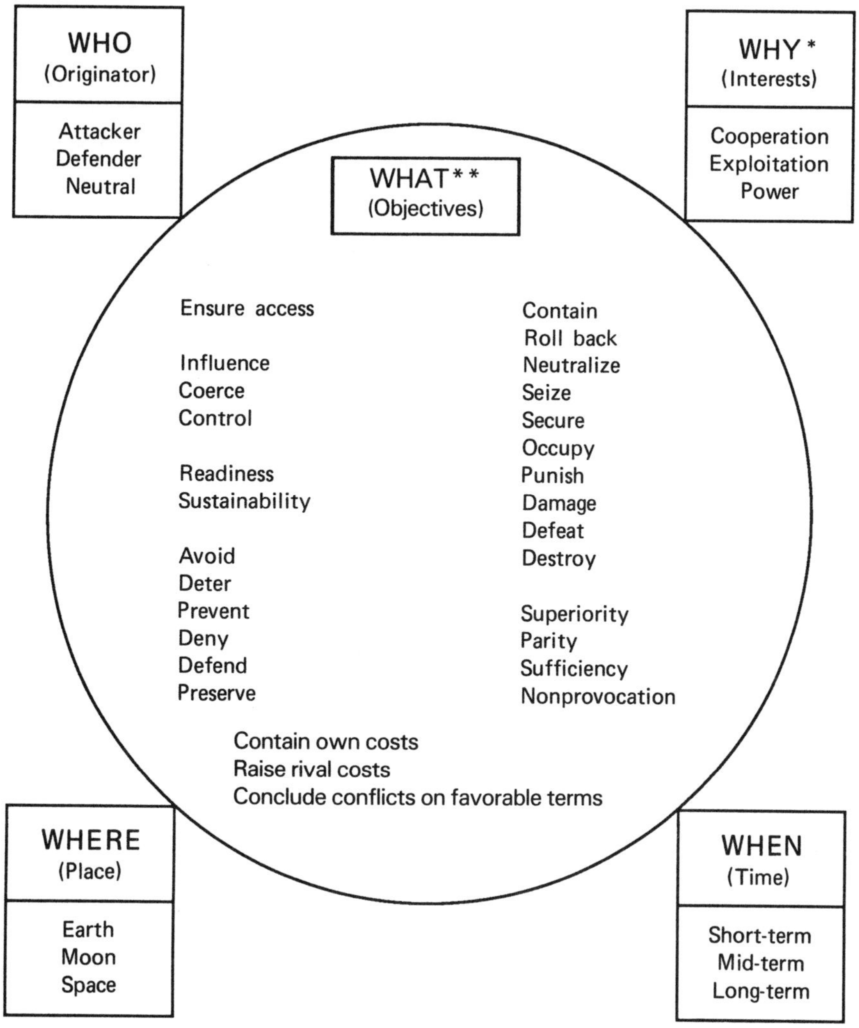

WHO (Originator)
Attacker Defender Neutral

WHY * (Interests)
Cooperation Exploitation Power

WHAT** (Objectives)

Ensure access

Influence
Coerce
Control

Readiness
Sustainability

Avoid
Deter
Prevent
Deny
Defend
Preserve

Contain
Roll back
Neutralize
Seize
Secure
Occupy
Punish
Damage
Defeat
Destroy

Superiority
Parity
Sufficiency
Nonprovocation

Contain own costs
Raise rival costs
Conclude conflicts on favorable terms

WHERE (Place)
Earth Moon Space

WHEN (Time)
Short-term Mid-term Long-term

*Sample Interests
**Sample Objectives

parts before assigning priorities. The remainder of this section, which illustrates that process, describes three subdivisions of the basic objective called "control": arms control, terrain control, and attitude control.

Control Arms

Arms control agreements should leave signatories more secure than unrestrained force postures. Mutually acceptable accords could relax international tensions; reduce risks of war; limit conflict types and intensities if war should erupt; decrease own vulnerabilities and costs; increase those of rivals; impede, preserve, or open doctrinal/technological options; or convey a particular impression for psychological purposes.[11]

It may be too late to reverse the militarization of space, which is well under way.[12] Arms control objectives, however, could still influence developments and deployments in at least five significant ways:

- Limit/ban military installations

- Limit/reduce armed forces

- Limit force characteristics

- Limit force modernization

- Limit military activities/functions.

The Outer Space Treaty, signed by 96 nations, formally proscribes military bases, installations, fortifications, maneuvers, and weapon testing of any type on the moon or other celestial bodies. It further prohibits "nuclear weapons or . . . other weapons of mass destruction" in Earth orbit or anywhere else in space (which is not legally defined).[13] Every strategic nuclear arms control accord since the SALT I ABM Treaty (Annex D) and Interim Agreement of 1972 frowns on interference with "national technical means of verification," which mainly comprise reconnaissance and surveillance satellites.[14] Future agreements might forbid various kinds of launch vehicles and/or facilities, space-to-earth offensive weaponry, and space-based homeland defense. Arms controllers alternatively could try to confine the range, power, speed, and deployment areas of certain space systems.

Representative applications, which could shape or prevent antisatellite (ASAT) development and deployment, are under active consideration. International law, for example, might proscribe mines that maneuver or possess standoff capabilities, and prescribe minimum distances between satellites. Trespass into resultant sanctuaries would be a hostile act. It would be impossible to perfect ASATs for use against maneuverable targets, while allegedly practicing space station linkups, if allowable rendezvous speeds were slow. Limitations on power output might make lasers useless for ASAT. Moratoriums that tolerate existing systems, but freeze ASAT technology (a practice often called "grandfathering"), would impede modernization. Suspension of ASAT tests would further impede future capabilities. Arms controllers, however, admit that freezing an inequitable balance could be destablizing and ambiguities might make some restrictions hard to monitor. Ballistic missile defense weapons designed to intercept small, high-speed targets, for example, could easily double as ASATs.[15]

The face value of arms control objectives, including those identified with ASAT, is seldom obvious. Verification is critical. Space strategists therefore should look for underlying reasons before they become euphoric about apparent rival concessions. "If you don't pay attention to the periphery, the periphery changes, and the first thing you know, the periphery is the center," is the way former Secretary of State Dean Rusk once put it.

Control Terrain

Major military and civilian installations on the moon and in free space, associated facilities on Earth, selected orbits, and lunar libration points constitute critical terrain (see chapter 1 for discussion). Control of features in those categories may sometimes seem preferable to arms control during periods of peace, if political, economic, and/or military power are predominant interests. Terrain control objectives almost invariably take precedence over arms control during combat.

Not all critical terrain in the Earth-Moon System, however, is equally advantageous. Present and potential values reflect many variables, including costs, risks, and time. Short- and long-term objectives may be dissimilar. Only one goal qualifies as the strategic center of gravity: "the hub of all power and movement, on which everything depends."[16]

Lunar libration points L4 and L5 eventually may evolve as the strategic center of gravity if, as alleged, they prove to be the ultimate high ground. Meanwhile, C^3 and launch sites on this planet will clearly qualify well into the twenty-first century, because all military and civilian activities in space would cease without their support. Serious threats to such installations would more likely elicit sharp responses than *any* endeavors to control *any* critical terrain in space.

Control Attitudes

Lenin once wrote that "The soundest strategy is to postpone [military] operations until the moral disintegration of the enemy renders . . . a . . . mortal blow both possible and easy."[17] Many great minds before and after agreed.* National will to compete in space thus may comprise the strategic center of gravity during peacetime, and might retain that pinnacle position during any protracted war.

Control over elitist and popular opinion, using inexpensive psychological operations (psyop) as a nonlethal weapon system, could convince rivals that it would be useless to start or continue military space programs. The basic objective would be to deprive opponents of freedom of action, while preserving it for oneself.[18] Senior national executives, legislators, members of the mass media and, through them, the body politic, would be typical targets. Representative psyop themes might include the futility of efforts to achieve military superiority in space, concomitant perils to world peace, and a waste of resources better spent on living standards than on a fruitless arms race.

THREAT INDICATIONS

Intelligence estimates that deal with the nature, imminence, and intensity of threats to security interests and objectives in space are particularly complicated, because many traditional indications are inapplicable. Present capabilities, projected capabilities, and intentions pose special problems, in ascending order of difficulty. So do conclusions concerning resultant risks and opportunities. Space may prove to be a particularly fruitful environment for deception, because it is virgin territory.

Enemy Capabilities In Space

Capacities to execute specific courses of action in space (deter, attack, defend) at specific times and places rest in large part on quantities, qualities, characteristics, and locations of forward deployed forces, plus components in reserve.

---

*Sun Tzu, in the first treatise on the art of war, circa 500 B.C., affirmed that "to subdue the enemy without fighting is the acme of skill." B.H. Liddell Hart, one of Britain's most famous strategists, paraphrased that thought this way 25 centuries later: "The true aim is . . . to seek a strategic situation so advantageous that if it does not of itself produce the decision, its continuation by a battle is sure to achieve this."[19]

Present Capabilities

Ascertaining current capabilities is the simplest part of any threat appraisal. Attempts to assess existing strengths and weaknesses of enemy space forces nevertheless must lean extensively on subjective intelligence at this moment, because so little is objectively knowable.

The attributes of formations on land, at sea, or in the air are comparatively familiar. Weapons and equipment, with rare exceptions, are well observed during predeployment tests, training, and occasionally in combat. No layman is likely to confuse tanks with trucks or bombers with light observation aircraft. Command ships that bristle with antennae bear little resemblance to amphibious landing craft. Space systems, however, presently display fewer distinctive external features. Civilian vehicles can be used surreptitiously for military activities. Components as diverse as lasers, sensors, and telecommunication devices commonly are developed and tested separately, then marry inside covers that conceal composite purposes. Weapons, for example, may piggyback on satellites that are advertised as, or appear to be, purely for reconnaissance and surveillance.

Hard intelligence about enemy space capabilities thus is hard to acquire. Launch times and places, orbital paths, maneuver patterns, and flight durations frequently offer better clues to enemy capabilities than can be inferred from satellite configurations. Soviet communication satellites, for example, commonly occupy highly elliptical orbits that allow long loitering times over the northern hemisphere. American equivalents prefer GEO. Telemetry, even encoded, may help rivals unravel secret purposes of the emanating source.[20]

The finest intelligence analysts in this arcane field, like detectives forced to fall back on circumstantial evidence, must possess inquisitive minds, intellectual acuity, intuition, and tenacity. Geoffrey E. Perry, senior science master at Kettering Grammar School in England, exemplifies those traits. That amateur satellite tracker and his students have produced invaluable insights into Soviet space reconnaissance programs since 1962.[21]

Projected Capabilities

Superiority in space could culminate in bloodless total victory, if lagging powers could neither cope nor catch up technologically. Lesser unilateral breakthroughs could reduce rival abilities to agress or resist aggression on Earth and beyond in many significant ways.[22]

Science and technology are twin keys to future space capabilities, but forecasters in those fields find it troublesome to predict the progress of friends, much less that of opponents whose exploratory programs are well concealed. Pundits who insist that any technological problem is insolvable have repeatedly been proven wrong. Cracked crystal balls invariably overlook impending developments of great magnitude. *Technological Trends and National Policy*, a 1937 U.S. study, failed to foresee radar, jet engines, and nuclear weapons, which were operational within eight years or less. Dr. Vannevar Bush, Director of Scientific Research & Development, and the Von Karmann report entitled *New Horizons* both discounted ICBMs in 1945; Soviet tests took place in 1957. Skeptics in 1961 doubted men would soon land on the moon and return safely during that decade.[23]

Since surefire predictions perhaps are impossible, given the dearth of hard data, it is important to press states of art wherever technological surprise in or from space conceivably could alter the military balance decisively. Failure to do so would deprive decisionmakers of sufficient vision to determine what enemy capabilities are possible in any given time frame, separate possibilities from probabilities, and take appropriate action

Enemy Intentions In Space

The most dangerous capabilities become dangerous threats only if opponents intend to employ them at specific times and places. Interests, objectives, policies, principles, commitments, and national will are determinants.

Some elemental intentions in space are easily discernible. The appearance of large military bases and mobile stations clearly would signify determination to establish a permanent manned presence and open options. Beyond basics, however, intelligence analysts find that space operations magnify uncertainties in the estimative process.

Some signs of impending enemy attack, such as political crises, intensified reconnaissance/surveillance, sudden cessation of communications, and increased message traffic from control centers to potential assault forces, apply equally well to land, sea, air, and space. Occupation of standby bases and forward movement of reserve forces, transportation, and supplies may be among them. Many traditional intelligence indications, however, seem immaterial, even irrelevant (NATO's watchlist exceeds 700, according to the last public count). Mobilization, large-scale leave cancellations, operations suspended to permit maintenance, and arrival of personnel fillers that bring combat forces to full strength, for example, may never be important omens of impending space combat.[24]

Distinctive indicators that foretell enemy Earth-to-space, space-to-Earth, and space-to-space offensives therefore are in demand. Tip-offs could include such disparate factors as the inexplicable deployment of additional spacecraft peculiarly adapted for offensive armed conflict; the assembly near launch sites of spare enemy payloads and boosters perhaps intended to replenish combat losses in space; and orbital alterations that might embellish enemy abilities to strike particular targets. Directed energy weapons (lasers, particle beams), which propagate at the speed of light, put a premium on strategic warning,* since tactical warning after they attack may be measured in milliseconds. Eternal vigilance might not ensure survival, if DEWs proliferate. Arms control thus seems advisable.

Military Strategies, Doctrines, And Tactics In Space

High commands design military strategies to attain national and regional security objectives, despite perceived threats. Major combatant commands, which specialize in operational art, prepare supporting plans that put strategic concepts into practice. They conduct military campaigns, if armed conflict occurs. Subordinate forces employ techniques called tactics to implement strategies and operational plans in detail during battles and lesser engagements.[25]

Military space planners, whose province is unlike land, sea, and air, need to develop new theories, concepts, assumptions, and options in three categories: attack, deterrence, and defense. Full discussion is beyond the scope of this book. The following briefs simply illustrate the breadth, depth, and complexity of short-, mid-, and long-range problems that await sound solutions.

Planning Assumptions

The time, place, type, scope, intensity, and duration of threats that endanger national security interests and objectives are hard to predict. Other developments are equally unforeseeable. Assumptions, presumed correct in the absence of contrary proof, replace facts concerning the present and future. Military space

---

*Strategic warning may be received minutes, hours, days, or longer before opponents attack. Tactical warning may be received any time from the moment attack commences until first effects are felt.

planners must rely more on assumptions than earthbound counterparts, who deal with familiar mediums.

Many assumptions apply equally to Earth and space. War, for example, is probable or implausible; warning times will be short or long; armed conflict will be high-, mid-, or low-intensity, nuclear or conventional, volitionally limited or boundless, brief or prolonged.[26] Space-specific assumptions with profound implications might include:

- Superpowers will (not) pose the only serious threats in space for the next 25–50 years.

- Space colonies and competition for lunar resources will (not) cause armed conflict.

- Space warfare can (not) exist in isolation from conflicts on this planet.

- Military superiority in space would (not) confer decisive advantage.

- Lunar libration points L4 and L5 do (not) militarily dominate the Earth-Moon System.

- Deterrence in space does (not) depend on survivable space-based systems.

- Offense will (not) dominate space combat operations for the foreseeable future.

- Special operations will (not) become significant factors in space.

- A mix of manned and unmanned military spacecraft is (not) imperative.

- Technological breakthroughs will (not) revolutionize space warfare within 25–50 years. By the year 2025, for example: (a) orbital mechanics will (not) severely impede operations between space and Earth; (b) atmosphere will (not) severely impede operations between Earth and space; (c) radically new forms of power and propulsion will (not) be commonplace in space.

- Resources, and the will to employ them, are (not) and will (not) remain sufficient to satisfy national security interests in space during the next 25–50 years.

Space planners and overseers on Capitol Hill could double or triple the foregoing political, economic, military, technological, and geographic assumptions in a few minutes, without padding the list.

Attack Options

Sun Tzu probably overstated his case when he wrote, "Invincibility lies in defense; the possibility of victory in attack,"[27] because victory can be variously defined. Defenders who deny foes success, protect themselves at acceptable cost, and accomplish other negative aims "win" as much as they want. They must attack, however, to seize hostile territory, control most enemy activities, or achieve other positive objectives.

Perhaps more important, present trends indicate that offensive forces soon may dominate space much like nuclear weapons outclass countermeasures on this planet, and retain marked advantage until much better defenses emerge.[28] If so, countries and coalitions that lack strong offensive or counteroffensive capabilities in space could forfeit freedom of action and find it difficult to deter armed aggression against their interests anywhere.

Strategies, operational art, and tactics emphasize options. Uniservice, joint, and collective security doctrines prescribe standard procedures under specified conditions. Military space planners, who must blend those seemingly irreconcilable qualities in their quest for sufficient offensive capabilities, make dominant decisions concerning mission priorities, target preference, and weapons.

Mission Priorities

The Principle of War called Mass sends an important message: concentrate strength on vital objectives, economize elsewhere. Air power proponents, who grasped the full significance of that notion, long ago assigned top priority to air superiority, because strategic bombing, battlefield interdiction, close air support, reconnaissance, transportation, and command/control missions are difficult or infeasible if rivals rule the air.[29] Strategists now should ascertain whether analogous needs exist in space, where reconnaissance/surveillance and homeland defense currently compete for first place. Forces deployed for those purposes, however, could not survive long in hostile environments in which opponents have the upper hand. Mission priorities thus may be imprudent.

Target Preference

The desirability of attacking any given target depends on variables that include objectives, perceived threats to their accomplishment, degrees of difficulty, escalatory limitations, unwelcome side effects, and costs to attack. Troublesome trade-offs arise when key considerations conflict.

Criticality and Constraints

Elaborate facilities to launch and control space vehicles from Earth will be strategically attractive targets far into the future. They are scarce, vulnerable, indispensable, and cannot be replaced expeditiously. Complementary installations eventually may appear on the moon, and perhaps in free space. Destruction or protracted disruption might immediately and decisively alter military balances on a grand scale. Enemy space-based interceptors and active defenses in position to interfere constitute high priority tactical targets. Naval surface ships comprise a third inviting target category that may be strategic or tactical. Former astronaut Michael Collins, who has been there and back twice, believes space is an ideal place from which to attack aircraft carriers and other major surface combatants, which are expensive and slow; even 100-knot hydrofoils would be easy for satellites to track, because ships "stand out as clearly as billiard balls on green felt."[30]

Latitude for striking such targets would be greatest during high intensity conflicts with few holds barred, but hard choices nevertheless will crop up in situations short of total war. Unwanted escalation, for example, could follow attacks on space facilities in the enemy homeland, even if collateral damage were strictly confined.[31] Leaders who strive to provide space support for their own land, sea, and air forces, deny space support to opponents, and simultaneously avoid adverse effects during low- and mid-intensity conflicts likely will declare many lucrative targets off limits. Representative targets in the left-hand column of the short list below as a general rule risk greater escalation than those on the right:[32]

L4 and L5	Space mines
Lunar garrisons	Spares stored in space
Manned space stations	Unmanned satellites
Battle management satellites	Antisatellites

Inconstancies and Costs

Photoreconnaissance satellites illustrate how target values may vary with situations. Those positioned to collect strategically important basic intelligence in peacetime pose no immediate threat, but identical satellites positioned to provide pictures that help direct wartime operations on Earth or in space could be quite dangerous. Satellites able to accomplish both missions without altering orbits are comparatively benign before war begins, but become lethal weapon systems thereafter.[33]

There rarely is any requirement to damage, destroy, or otherwise interdict every component in high priority target complexes. Surgical strikes against communications switching centers and relay satellites, for example, would be quicker and more cost-effective than saturation attacks on an entire ballistic missile defense constellation, unless its components operate autonomously. Life-support systems will always be weak spots in space colonies and major military installations on the moon.[34]

Costs to attack some targets on Earth with space-based weapons probably will be prohibitive until far in the future (perhaps forever). High-resolution satellite sensors currently can see inside foxholes on cloud-free days. They can spot individual armored vehicles and aircraft. Not many commanders, however, would expend high-priced orbital ordnance on such low value targets. Airborne Warning and Control System (AWACS) aircraft and nuclear strike forces might be prominent exceptions.[35]

Weapon Preference

Planners must pick the most appropriate arms from a diversified arsenal. Mass destruction and precision instruments compete for attention. Directed energy weapons (DEW) and some types of radiation attack at the speed of light. Space mines move sluggishly in comparison. Spoofing, a form of electronic deception, normally is a nonlethal option, but might misdirect space weapons against friendly forces.[36] Target accessibility and survivability, concerns for escalation, and damage desired strongly influence decisions to engage any point or area target with particular weapons (see chapter 1 for selected nuclear, directed energy, chemical, and conventional weapon effects in space).

Hard Kill Weapons

"Hard kill" weapons forcibly break the surface of targets, then damage or destroy their contents. Violence is evident to observers. Explosives and kinetic projectiles are representative instruments.

Nuclear warheads are the most escalatory of all area weapons. Space-to-surface and surface-to-surface shots that detonate on Earth or in its atmosphere would be equally lethal, but space-to-surface delivery currently is (may always be) more costly, less accurate, and tougher to control. Nuclear hard kill capabilities would seldom be cost-effective against targets in space, because vacuum restricts blast and heat radii so severely that conventional explosives and kinetic energy weapons can accomplish most missions equally well at less expense.

Conventional explosives and kinetic energy weapons (KEWs) are designed exclusively for hard kills. Proper employment in space depends extensively on precise targeting intelligence, plus "smart" (even "brilliant") munitions. Direct hits are almost obligatory for conventional explosives, because vacuum cancels the concussive effects that make many near misses deadly on Earth. The tolerable margin of delivery error also is small for KEWs, even "shotgun" styles that scatter pellets in the orbital paths of speeding targets. Offensive KEWs plummeting from space to Earth at Mach 12 or more with terrific penetration power have a marked advantage over defensive Earth-to-space counterparts that accelerate slowly while they fight to overcome gravity. Simple weapons associated with sabotage and other special operations open low key, hard kill offensive options for use against space installations anywhere in the Earth-Moon System.[37]

Speed-of-light directed energy weapons likely will be preferred whenever space-to-space attackers try to take point targets by surprise. Weapon quality lasers and particle beams await substantial technological breakthroughs, however, before they can operate successfully across the boundary between atmosphere and space. Space-*toward*-Earth capabilities against targets in rarefied atmosphere are simplest to perfect. Space-*to*-Earth DEW operations are much further in the future, because dense air is more difficult to penetrate and targets ashore or afloat on the surface are easier to shield. R&D specialists anticipate Earth-to-space DEWs at an earlier date, since large power supplies are more readily attainable on terra firma than on spacecraft, and most targets in space will always be relatively soft. One additional attribute merits mention: the source of super fast laser attacks that bounce off space-based reflectors may be untraceable. Catalytic conflicts* and retaliation against wrong parties could result. Space strategists concerned with unplanned escalation and other unwanted contingencies should consider such possibilities, and employ DEWs cautiously.[38]

*Catalytic conflicts are instances of armed combat between two countries or coalitions that a third party instigates deliberately. Suspicion, for example, almost spontaneously would point toward an innocent Soviet Union, if a third nation bombarded the United States with SLBMs during a U.S.–Soviet crisis. Opportunities for mischief will multiply after several countries deploy DEWs in space.

Soft Kill Weapons

"Soft kill" weapons penetrate target surfaces without impairing them, then selectively disorient, damage, or destroy humans and/or sensitive mechanisms inside. Electronic countermeasures and nuclear radiation are representative instruments.

Soft kills generally cost less and escalate conflict less than hard kills. Jamming, which reduces communication data rates or renders signals unintelligible, requires complex techniques and sophisticated equipment. Other potential methods are simple. Spray paint on satellite camera lenses, blinding light on laser reflectors, and surreptitious introduction of foreign objects into booster fuel are typical possibilities. False commands and other forms of spoofing may cause enemy satellites to malfunction. Victims who suspect foul play would be hard pressed to prove it, if opponents were clever.[39]

Nuclear radiation, unimpeded by atmosphere, could cover orders of magnitude more volume than near Earth's surface. It would work especially well against suspected targets in low earth orbit but less consistently in deep space, unless targets were located more accurately, since the lethal range of radiation is limited, even in a vacuum. Nuclear radiation in any event suffers one great disadvantage: it cannot distinguish friend from foe. Electromagnetic pulse, for example, might "wound" users as grievously or worse than intended victims.[40]

Attack Techniques

Armed forces in space, as on Earth, must concentrate physical presence or firepower to defeat enemies. Simultaneous assaults to decrease warning times and/or increase shock effects on widely separated targets, however, are tricky propositions, particularly when weapons have dissimilar characteristics and firing points are far apart. Directed energy weapons promise to simplify, but cannot solve, such problems. Opportune maneuvers, coupled with surprise and deception, always will be important.

Offensive Maneuvers

Strike forces on the moon could choose from the full range of offensive maneuvers in vogue on Earth. Broad-based frontal assaults and narrow penetrations, both of which meet the enemy head on, would be least imaginative, and useful mainly against clearly inferior opposition. Envelopments from above or against flanks and turning movements that bypass forward defenses to attack the rear would need fewer assets to achieve superior results. Clandestine infiltration of hostile positions completes the list of potential lunar maneuvers.[41]

Free space is different: Front, flanks, top, bottom, and rear depend more on the direction orbiting sensors and weapons face than on directions of flight. Peacetime infiltration, which could put attacking forces in decisive positions before or during crises, need not be clandestine, since space, like international waters, is no single nation's preserve. Complex enemy space formations called constellations may make axes of attack immaterial, because widely separated satellites point sensors and weapons omnidirectionally. Strategic and tactical maneuvers moreover may be dissimilar. Flank attacks on individual targets, for example, might be a frontal assault on an enemy constellation.

Orbital mechanics and human ingenuity are the main limitations on maneuvers in space (see Map 10 for three imaginative possibilities). Offensive armaments that engage high velocity orbital targets at sharp angles must solve formidable problems. Counterrotation ASATs that attack almost head-on (Map 10a) must follow tracks slightly different than those of their targets or collide. Long leads and superlative homing devices are essential at extended ranges for all but speed-of-light weapons.* Accuracy is easily attained by systems that coorbit with targets at close range, but they forfeit any possibility of strategic surprise.[42]

Surprise and Deception

Speed (typified by directed energy weapons that strike without warning) and audacity (you can get away with almost anything once) can contribute to surprise. Earth-to-GEO (and much of MEO) ASATs probably always will forfeit surprise, because they would be easily observable during flights that take hours, given any technology now foreseen. Space mines, conversely, would be in constant position to pounce. Bombardment anywhere in the Earth-Moon System from bases floating far beyond GEO might well avoid early detection, particularly if missile burn times were brief.[43]

Prototypical strategist Sun Tzu professed that all warfare is based on deception,[44] which might abet surprise in space, even

---

*Even DEWs must lead distant targets, which they identify by infrared or reflected light. Spacecraft 1,800 miles away, for example, would move 50–100 yards or more in the 0.01 second it would take for reflections to reach the weapon, and another 50–100 yards before a laser beam could return.

Map 10 SELECTED ANTISATELLITE ORBITS
(Not to scale)

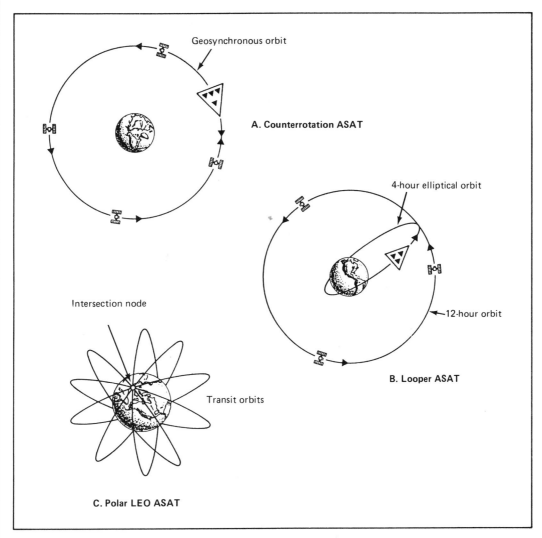

A. Counterrotation ASAT traverses GEO in "wrong" direction. Attacks all enemy satellites there in 12 hours.

B. Three enemy satellites are in semisynchronous orbit 4 hours apart. Looper ASAT picks off each one as it passes the intercept point.

C. Battery of ASATs at North Pole take less than 2 hours to destroy all enemy satellites in polar LEO.

NOTE: Adapted from Carter, Ashton B., "Satellites and Anti-Satellites," International Security, Spring 1986, p. 83.

though sensors can spot potential enemies at great distances in every direction. Vacuum makes it hard to discriminate between heavy missile warheads and lightweight decoys, which flutter in telltale fashion when they enter the atmosphere. Spoofers in space, like those on this planet, would find it easy to flood rival receivers with deceitful messages; recipients would find it hard to separate bogus from bona fide traffic. Civilian "fronts" for military space activities likely will become more common. Prewar proof of fraudulence will be elusive. Camouflage specialists face formidable problems. Offensive satellites that simulate meteoroids or space debris, for example, would scarcely fool sentinels that watched them arrive from the Earth or moon; surreptitious insertions from HEO to GEO or LEO, however, would be more difficult to detect. Fakers, however, might choose a different tack when camouflage is infeasible. One possibility: deploy falsely advertised, widely dispersed space weapon components, then assemble them unexpectedly.

Deception is risky business in any case, because failures can backfire disastrously. Planners who pioneer techniques in space must be even more imaginative than their earthbound counterparts.

Deterrent Options

Attacks never take place if deterrent powers are sufficient.[45] "Sufficiency" nevertheless is hard to define, partly because planners never can prove what worked, partly because they must counter many possible causes of war that include (but are not confined to) uncontrollable crises; justifiable confidence in favorable outcomes; overconfidence; other miscalculations, such as fallible brinkmanship; unacceptable provocations; accidents; and catalytic conflicts. Deterrent postures that alleviate one cause may aggravate others.[46]

Preparedness and Nonprovocation are Principles of Deterrence.[47] Those yardsticks give some feeling for the scope and perplexity of problems that military space policymakers face, as they seek the best balance between desirable and undesirable features.

Preparedness

Nothing encourages aggressors more than opponents with their guards down. Preparedness consequently is one price of peace. Deterrence architects, however, cannot even get started until they answer the question: Prepare to do what?

Preparation to surge space deployments on short notice in response to severe provocation purportedly could strengthen deterrence, by demonstrating readiness and resolve. Some committed forces already in space might move swiftly to more favorable stations. Standby elements on the moon and/or in orbits also could augment "forward deployments" rapidly. Reinforcements from Earth would take a little longer, but lags would be acceptable, unless strategic warning times were short.[48] Decisions to surge nevertheless are dicey unless enemy response is reasonably predictable. A sudden military buildup in space might precipitate the attack it sought to discourage if deterees believed the deterrer was about to preempt.

Readiness to reciprocate in kind is another deterrent notion, an eye for an eye, a tooth for a tooth: assault my spacecraft, I assault yours. Antisatellite capabilities pose a powerful disincentive, according to that concept, provided adversaries are vulnerable, cannot replenish losses quickly at acceptable cost, and want to preserve their own vehicles more than they want to repress rivals. Some critics, however, question the need for ASAT-induced deterrence, because aggression against space systems could have adverse unanticipated consequences. Others insist that threats to retaliate against maritime or terrestrial targets could discourage attacks on spacecraft as well or better than ASAT, despite countercontentions that doing so might elicit unwelcome escalation, and thus degrade deterrence. Careful thought consequently should precede any decision to accept or reject ASAT for deterrent purposes.[49]

Catch-22 conundrums, however, do not justify protracted indecision. Space policymakers who delay preparedness despite evident peril may jeopardize deterrence, if enemy leaders interpret inactivity as lack of will and act accordingly.[50]

Nonprovocation

Preventive and preemptive wars erupt when real or imagined provocations convince aggrieved parties that a shootout is inevitable sooner or later.* They have little to lose and maybe something to gain by striking first. Successful deterrent strategies must dampen such proclivities, which is no mean task, since "provocations" are subjective matters.

Space-based defenses designed to deter ballistic missile attacks, for example, may seem innocuous to installers, but per-

---

*Degrees of premeditation differentiate preventive and preemptive wars. Deliberate preparation precedes the former. Threatened parties preempt on short notice to attenuate the effects of imminent enemy attack.

nicious to opponents, because any nation unilaterally able to neutralize most enemy nuclear-tipped missiles in flight could secretly harbor first strike ambitions. Armed with a few offensive weapons, it might in fact win without fighting (the ultimate achievement), then direct losers to disarm. Poorly shielded foes would face two unattractive alternatives: surrender or suicide.[51] Dividing lines between deterrence and destabilization thus are indistinct. Planners who try to draw them sharply could trigger the trouble they hope to avoid.

Risk reduction measures, much like those now designed to forestall nuclear conflict on Earth, might promote deterrence equally well in space. Routine discussions between suspicious protagonists; crisis consultations, including high-level "hot line" conversations; advance explanation of potentially disturbing operations (large maneuvers, major relocations); and on-site inspections of launch sites, satellites, space stations, and lunar installations typify potentially helpful confidence-building techniques. Prudence, however, is imperative, because revelations could devitalize deterrence predicated on uncertainty. Planners also must guard against false impressions derived from enemy deception and disinformation.[52]

Defense Options

Defense may bolster deterrence by denying aggressors a free ride.* It also reduces dangers if deterrence fails. What, where, and how to defend are fundamental policy decisions.[53]

Five factors help planners determine which assets on Earth, its moon, and in orbit would benefit most from defense:

- Relative target value

- Relative target vulnerability

- Relative likelihood each target will be attacked

- Relative time each target must survive

- Reconstitution times.

Many factors that include missions and financial costs determine target values. Enemy capabilities determine the relative

*Some deterrent concepts, such as Assured Destruction, scorn defense. Assured Survival advocates find defense indispensable (insecure forces, they contend, tempt rivals to preempt). Compromise positions separate those polarized positions.

vulnerability of each target. Intelligence estimates indicate which ones most likely will be attacked in what sequence. The time each target must survive depends on its purpose. Trained manpower and materiel reserves, standby delivery systems, production schedules, and construction capacities determine reconstitution times.

Space strategists and tacticians use those five factors to put defense problems in priority, then devise schemes to reduce detection by enemy sensors, defeat attacks by enemy units, and reduce damage to targets that are hit.

Active and passive defenses listed in the left-hand column of Table 1 are complementary. A few options are applicable only on Earth and moon or in free space, but several serve well in all environments. Some have limited utility, others are universally convenient. Proper mixes are complicated matters. Many trade-offs, for example, not only increase costs but decrease spacecraft capabilities, because they add weight, exclude preferred deployment patterns, and complicate control.

Elude Detection

The world's best offensive space weapons would be worthless if wielders were unable to locate targets accurately and identify their functions. The first line of defense, in peacetime as well as war, therefore is to frustrate enemy reconnaissance and surveillance efforts.

Targets on Earth and Moon

Large space support installations and other high value static targets on the Earth and moon may be impossible to veil very long. Defenders, however, can make it difficult for opponents to pinpoint key components and catalog activities. Cover and concealment help hide targets from electronic, infrared and other optical sensors. Geographic isolation, restricted areas, and local security forces do little to foil airborne and space-based finders, but reduce surface observation (such measures, for example, effectively screened facilities at Los Alamos and Alamogordo, New Mexico, where final development of the first atom bomb and its open air test took place in complete secrecy). It currently is possible to move some targets temporarily out of view when surveillance satellites pass overhead, but that option will disappear when hostile spies crowd the skies. Defenders could reduce rival detection capabilities most decisively by disabling snoopers. Such action during peacetime crises, however, would risk retaliation.

Table 1   DEFENSE AND DAMAGE LIMITING OPTIONS

	Elude Detection by Enemy Sensors			Defeat Attacks if Detected — Direct Attack		Defeat Attacks if Detected — Standoff Attack		Reduce Damage from Enemy Weapons — Hard Kill Weapons			Reduce Damage from Enemy Weapons — Soft Kill Weapons		
	Optical	Electronic	Infrared	Assault	Sabotage	Close Range	Long Range	DEW	KEW	Explosives	EMP	ECM	Spoof
Unique Options, Earth & Moon													
Concealment	X		X										
Isolation[1]	X	X	X										
Mobility	X	X	X				X						
Natural Cover	X		X	X		X		X	X	X	X	X	
Restricted Areas[1]	X	X	X	X	X	X	X						
Security Forces[1]	X	X	X	X	X	X							
Unique Options, Orbiting Spacecraft													
Autonomy[2]								X	X	X	X	X	
Elusive Orbits	X	X	X				X						
Isolation[1]	X	X											
Maneuver				X				X					
Restricted Areas[1]				X	X	X							
Security Forces[1]				X	X	X							
Short-lived Craft[2]								X	X	X	X	X	
Single Mission Craft[2]								X	X	X	X	X	
Space Mines				X		X		X	X	X			
Unmanned Craft[2]								X	X	X			
Ubiquitous Options													
Deception	X	X		X	X	X	X	X					X
ECM, ECCM		X										X	X
EHF Frequencies											X		X
Encryption													X
Hardening	X	X	X	X	X		X	X	X	X	X	X	
Interceptors	X	X	X	X		X	X	X	X				
Reconstitution[2]								X	X	X	X	X	
Redundancy[2]								X	X	X	X	X	
Stealth	X	X	X										

[1] Not entirely unique to Earth and moon or to spacecraft; one or more attributes are dual purpose.
[2] Option does not reduce damage from enemy weapons, but reduces adverse results.
NOTE: See Annex A (Glossary) for precise definitions.

Targets in Space

Procedures to prevent detection of targets in transparent space are different. Natural cover and concealment (other than isolation) are nonexistent, with one exception: orbital objects on any given side of the moon are safe from line-of-sight sensors and weapons on the other side. Restricted areas and security forces are irrelevant. Defensive deception has serious drawbacks, like those described in the section on attack techniques.

Nevertheless, some targets are hard to detect. Systems orbiting in deep space are like needles in haystacks. Elusive orbits help defenders escape detection. GEO, for example, is beyond the range of most Earth-based radars. Weather and lighting conditions restrict optical tracking.[54]

Stealth technology, which honors the adage, "lose sight, lose the fight," seeks to obscure spacecraft in flight by combining sleek contours with nonmetallic materials, absorptive coatings, heat shields, emission controls, passive guidance, and countermeasures that muffle or falsify enemy sensor returns. Several advanced composites blot radar beams better than any alloy. Optically transparent compounds blend with natural light in ways that render reflecting surfaces virtually invisible. The cycle of innovation, neutralization, and renovation has just started.[55]

Stealthy spacecraft in some respects will be easier to create than will-o-the-wisp aircraft and cruise missiles.[56] Hard-to-conceal external stabilizers are unnecessary in the vacuum of space. Hi-lo-hi flight profiles never subject external materials to great stress unless orbits dip deeply into the atmosphere. Engine emissions are momentary and intermittent. Pluses and minuses nevertheless mix. Space vehicles that launch under enemy surveillance are easier to track than aircraft, because most must fly predictable paths at predictable speeds. Attempts to conceal locations thus might be impossible, unless accompanied by stratagems like those that let submarines slip out of port undetected. Solar power panels, which will be popular until a better replacement appears, are difficult to camouflage. Large space stations may someday enjoy closed ecologies, but other spacecraft must dump easily detected waste and heat to avoid intolerably high temperatures and insanitation.

Defeat Attacks

Offensive forces certainly will detect and identify many high value targets, despite clever countermeasures. The second line of defense therefore is to deflect or defeat attacks.

Passive defense includes all protective measures short of armed force in any form. Active defense features weapon systems. Defensive maneuvers on the moon will be much different than those in free space.

Passive Defense

Many passive defenses that perform well on Earth would also work well in free space. Deception, hardening, mobility, restricted areas, electronic countermeasures (ECM), and counter-countermeasures (ECCM) are typical (Table 1). All would apply on the moon, where shelters could include topographic features and manmade fortifications, for which lunar construction materials are abundant and readily available. Subterranean installations, impervious to all but burrowing nuclear weapons, seem feasible.

Launch/recovery sites, C³ installations, production bases, support facilities, and other earthbound infrastructures for space operations may be vulnerable to attacks from land, sea, and air, as well as space. Assets positioned far from hostile frontiers and ocean shores are least accessible to conventional armed forces. Isolation, however, does less to reduce dangers from saboteurs. Local security precautions could include strict counterintelligence checks, bare perimeters around hard-to-breach buildings, obstacles, guard posts, roving patrols, anti-intrusion devices, other sensors, and convoy "shotguns.[57]

Defensive Maneuvers

Positional defenders on the moon, much like those on Earth, could employ small elements well beyond the main body to distract and disrupt enemy thrusts from front, flanks, top, and rear, then counterattack. Mobile defenses, conversely, could rely on light forces to hold selected strong points. Large, agile reserves deployed in great depth could strike back when invaders become most vulnerable. Retrograde maneuvers would be feasible if those forms of defense fail. Units could leapfrog from one delaying position to another in the rear, break contact and withdraw, or retire before they make contact.[58]

Defensive maneuvers in free space allow decisionmakers less discretion. Incentives to opt for positional defense will be few compared with those on Earth and the moon, because little territory is intrinsically valuable enough to retain (lunar libration points, large space stations, and irreplaceable C³ locations along GEO may be prominent exceptions). Delaying actions likely will be uncommon, since the scarcity of geographic obstacles makes most sites equally hard to defend. Forces well-shielded against radiation might fall back on the Van Allen belts, if opponents were poorly protected against radiation, but would remain vulnerable to standoff weapons and might be unable to accomplish assigned missions from that location. The term *contact*, in context with withdrawals and retirements, must be redefined and concepts redescribed to address interactions between defensive space forces many miles apart. One military space specialist suggests the following definitions:[59]

- *Contact*: within sensor range

- *Engagement*: within weapon range

- *Withdrawal*: movement beyond enemy weapon range

- *Retirement*: movement beyond enemy sensor range.

The cost of maneuvering spaceships to escape interception varies from cheap to expensive. No significant penalties, for example, would accompany slight phasing irregularities that frustrate "looper" attacks (see Map 10). Automated frequency hopping, another frugal form of maneuver, could give enemy jammers fits. Evasive actions that substantially alter spacecraft orbits, however, exact a price in propellant, reduce payloads, and perhaps interrupt important missions at inopportune times.[60]

Active Defense

Active defenses identified in Table 1 fit two broad categories: surface-to-space and space-to-space interceptors; close-in and on-site security forces.

Nuclear-tipped missiles that transit space currently threaten targets on Earth. Voluminous studies, especially those associated with U.S. strategic defense initiatives (SDI), address various means of active defense, which center on KEW, DEW, and nuclear interceptors.[61] Policymakers must make elemental decisions, of which the following are representative: proportional contributions of land, sea, air, and space components; proportional contributions of point and area defenses; relative roles of active and passive security, including civil defense; how far forward to defend; how much to deploy in what time frame; the proper role of arms control.

Unclassified literature contains few references to defensive satellites (DSATs) or anti-ASATs. Almost all concern orbital interceptors of some sort, perhaps equipped with long-range weapons. Other modes, however, may prove more cost-effective under certain conditions. Shipboard DSATs might be among them, since any satellite killer launched in any direction from any location on Earth must pass over a predictable point on the opposite side of the globe halfway through its first orbit. Those points, it so happens, almost all are over some ocean, and will remain so as long as most ASATs launch from land.[62]

Active defense against direct assaults and special operations in space demands different techniques. Space mine fields might delay, disorganize, and channelize final approaches to targets in ways that make offensive spacecraft more vulnerable to other defensive weapons. Local security forces and booby traps could repel boarding parties.[63]

Rules of engagement should specify limitations that pertain when defenders initiate, conduct, and terminate military operations to, from, and through space under given circumstances during peacetime, transition periods, and war. Commanders, to cite one typical case, need to know how far they should let unidentified or suspicious space vehicles penetrate restricted areas at what speeds before particular responses are permissible. Tailormade guidelines are required, because many variables influence minimum allowable distances and maximum closure rates. Violators, target values, the range and reliability of defensive weapon systems, reaction times, and environmental factors (such as atmosphere and gravity) are cogent considerations. Rules of engagement designed to protect reconnaissance satellites in LEO, for example, will bear little resemblance to those that affect scientific research stations in translunar space.[64]

Reduce Damage

Deterrence and defense rarely safeguard targets completely. Damage limiting endeavors accordingly are advisable. Table 1 displays two complementary types: one reduces the destructive power of enemy weapons; the other reduces disruption after successful enemy attacks.

Limit Destruction

Large space support facilities on the Earth and moon will always be costly to protect against hard kill weapons, and coverage likely will be incomplete. Segments buried in bedrock would be safest from high yield nuclear bursts. Critical components on the surface, however, remain exposed to sabotage and standoff attacks. Thin-skinned space vehicles, like aircraft and cruise missiles, are vulnerable to destruction by DEWs, KEWs, and explosives, whether parked or in flight. Exotic materials eventually may shield craft and occupants better than the best composites do today. Even slight wiggling motions could diffuse particle beams which, unlike laser burns, easily penetrate the hardest shells.[65] Survivability nevertheless will be poor, until technologists and tacticians devise hard kill damage limitation measures much better than those now known.

The outlook for soft kill damage reduction is more favorable, but costs of security for space-related C[3] and other electronic systems vary considerably. Encryption and deception, which could virtually nullify enemy attempts to spoof, are least expensive. Extremely high frequencies (EHF) could reduce nuclear scintillation and absorption from minutes to seconds. EHF also narrows transmission beams, so that enemy jammers must almost be in the line of sight between transmitter and receiver. Outlays for hi-tech hardware, however, would be large. Higher price tags would accompany programs to cope with electromagnetic pulse induced by large nuclear detonations in space. The acquisition, installation, operation, and maintenance of Faraday cages, filters, surge arresters, waveguide cutoffs, fiber optic links, and other sophisticated new devices would simply be step one. Retrofits for existing civilian and military sites would also be required.[66]

Limit Debilitation

Steps to limit debilitation are desirable, because enemy weapons are sure to damage or destroy some intended targets, despite defensive efforts, unless the offense is very weak.

One way is to reduce relative target values. Many simple, single-mission, unmanned spacecraft designed to fly for short periods could do so. Individual losses would undercut the owner's overall capabilities significantly less than casualties among a few expensive, multipurpose counterparts with long-duration tasks. Largely autonomous space vehicles, able to perform most functions well without external instructions or support, would make C[3] centers on Earth and moon less lucrative aiming points, especially if cross-link communications let satellites bypass them easily.[67]

Redundant deployments and reconstitution capabilities could also make damage more bearable. The former furnishes immediately available backup. The latter facilitates short-notice surges, permits tit-for-tat tactics that otherwise would be unattractive, and simplifies replacement. Proliferation and replenishment costs for space installations and systems, however, are literally astronomical. Large control centers, launch facilities, and space stations may always be impractical to duplicate and impossible to restore rapidly. Active and passive defenses able to keep damage within tolerable limits therefore are imperative.[68]

Comparative Versatility and Value

Some defensive options described above are much more versatile than others, as Table 2 indicates. Versatility and value, however,

Table 2   DEFENSE AND DAMAGE LIMITING OPTIONS: RELATIVE VERSATILITY

	Multipurpose	Dual purpose	Unipurpose
Elude Detection, Defeat Attacks, Reduce Damage			
Hardening	X		
Natural Cover	X		
Deception	X		
Elude Detection, Defeat Attacks			
ECM, ECCM	X	X	
Interceptors	X	X	
Security Forces[1]	X	X	
Isolation[1]	X	X	
Elusive Orbits	X	X	
Mobility	X	X	
Restricted Areas[1]	X	X	
Defeat Attacks, Reduce Damage			
Maneuver	X	X	
Elude Detection			
Stealth	X	X	X
Concealment	X	X	X
Defeat Attacks[2]			
Restricted Areas	X	X	X
Security Forces	X	X	X
Mines	X	X	X
Reduce Damage			
Autonomy	X	X	X
Short-lived Craft	X	X	X
Single-mission Craft	X	X	X
EHF Frequencies	X	X	X
Encryption	X	X	X
Reconstitution	X	X	X
Redundancy	X	X	X

[1] Earth and moon only

[2] Space only

NOTE: Options with the greatest versatility in each category along the left-hand margin are listed first. The least versatile are last.

do not always correlate closely. Hardening is most versatile, but high costs and unhappy tradeoffs between survivability and capabilities confine its usefulness in many important respects. Encryption, the least versatile entry in any category, conversely is valuable, because it is the best way to defend against spoofing and denies enemy forces free access to classified transmissions. Stealth technology, which serves a single basic purpose (elude detection), makes all other defensive options irrelevant if it succeeds.

Military space budgets may never be big enough to buy the optimum defense package. Planners and programmers who must compromise might bear the following principles in mind: identify a sensible balance between defensive measures and missions; pick options that blend best; concentrate on centers of gravity and key components of high value targets.[69]

Organizational Problems and Options

Space forces must be quantitatively and qualitatively sufficient to implement strategies, doctrines, and tactics successfully for offensive, defensive, and deterrent purposes. The best laid plans would be worthless without sound implementation programs, both present and projected. Optional solutions to associated postural problems should address the following subjects: force composition, organization, locations, dispositions, weapons, equipment, training, readiness, sustainability, control, and logistics.

COMMAND ARRANGEMENTS

Roles, missions, territorial responsibilities, perceived threats, technological developments, and service politics shape command/control arrangements of every military organization. This chapter deals exclusively with high-echelon alternatives that include coalitions.

Apparatus at the Apex

One writer recently opined that the "the future of the Army is not in space but in the mud."[1] He might also have mentioned that future air forces will still function in atmosphere, and navies afloat. Military activities in space nevertheless strongly influence all armed forces on Earth.

Military space policymaking, planning, and programming at the apex consequently should transcend partisan interests. Sound organizational decisions based on objective reviews of realistic options seem especially desirable during early stages of the Space Age, because far-reaching decisions made in the near future will have long-term ramifications. Four topics listed below, then discussed in the same order, are of special importance:

- The composition and responsibilities of national space commands

- Similar arrangements for coalition space commands

- The advisability of a separate armed service for space

- Space-peculiar staff functions.

National Space Commands

National space commands may be organized regionally, functionally, or both. They may be joint structures, like U.S. unified commands, or uniservice. The latter commands may be under joint control, like U.S. specified commands, or respond to the parent service (Army, Navy, Air Force, for example).* Pluses and minuses accompany every option. The trick is to select the optimum compromise.

Functionally Structured Space Commands

The world's first and only military space commands belong to the United States. Unclassified literature contains no reference to similar arrangements in the Soviet Union, where Strategic Rocket Forces apparently exercise overall responsibility, except for cosmonaut training, which is vested in the Soviet Air Force.[2]

All U.S. space commands follow functional lines. All typify space structures formed primarily to support armed services on Earth. All were activated to centralize control and consolidate space-related responsibilities previously scattered among many loosely affiliated organizations at various levels.[4]

*Ten major U.S. combatant commands have broad, continuing missions. Eight are unified commands that contain armed forces from two or more military departments. The chain of command in each case runs from the President to the Secretary of Defense to the commander of the combatant command. Communications and some oversight may be through the Chairman of the Joint Chiefs of Staff, if the President so directs.[3]

The evolutionary process started on September 1, 1982 with U.S. Air Force Space Command. Naval Space Command emerged about a year later (October 1, 1983). Those two organizations originally lacked formal connecting links. Respective services still administer and support assigned forces, but "authoritative direction over all aspects of military operations, joint training, and logistics" soon passed to United States Space Command (USSPACECOM), a unified command activated on September 23, 1985.[5] USSPACECOM's initial Army component, a four-officer Space Planning Group, became a full-fledged Army Space Command on April 7, 1988. Table 3 and Figure 3 summarize relationships before and after USSPACECOM appeared.[6]

USSPACECOM operational control and administrative support procedures parallel those for all other geographically oriented U.S. unified commands. Further evolution, however, need not follow that path indefinitely. Performance, for example, might improve, if offense-defense, or strategic-tactical, or combat-support replaced Army–Navy–Air Force as the major components of any unified space command (Figure 4). Joint rather than uniservice elements, organized functionally at every subordinate echelon, might reduce (even eliminate) undesirable dominance by any military department, and facilitate better balanced capabilities. Figure 4, which displays heavy-medium-light, high-intensity, low-intensity, dual-purpose, and long-, medium-, short-range options, omits many other combinations, such as static-mobile, which might reflect parent roles and missions more effectively. Free competition for key command and staff assignments, rather than routine rotation among participating services or consistent allocations to one of them, could help solidify unification, put the best qualified candidate in each post, and retain required expertise.[7]

Table 3   U.S. SPACE CHAINS OF COMMAND

| | | Operational Control | | |
	Commander	Before 23 Sep 85	After 23 Sep 85	Admin., Logistics
U.S. SPACECOM	General		SECDEF	
Army SPACECOM	Colonel		CINCSPACE	Sec. Army
Naval SPACECOM	Radm (lh)	CNO	CINCSPACE	Sec. Navy
Air Force SPACECOM	Lt. Gen.	C/S AF	CINCSPACE	Sec. AF

Abbreviations:

Admin.	Administration	Lt. Gen.	Lieutenant General
AF	Air Force	Radm (lh)	Rear Admiral (lower half)
CINCSPACE	Commander in Chief, US	Sec.	Secretary
	Space Command	SECDEF	Secretary of Defense
CNO	Chief of Naval Operations	SPACECOM	Space Command
C/S	Chief of Staff		

Figure 3   EVOLUTION OF U.S. MILITARY SPACE COMMANDS

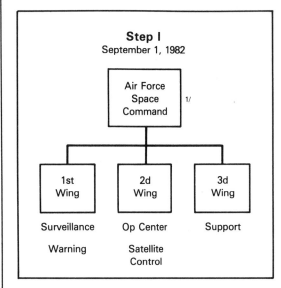

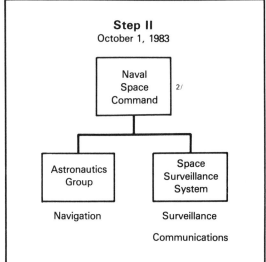

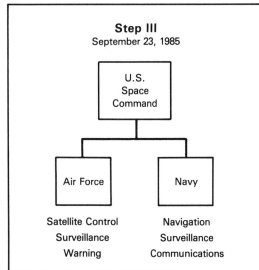

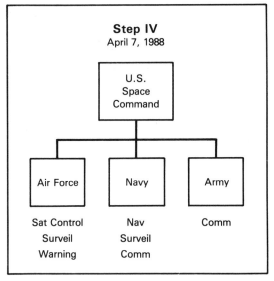

1/ Air Force Space Command, a major command of the U.S. Air Force, became a USSPACECOM component as well on September 23, 1985.

2/ Naval Space Command, an Echelon 2 Command of the U.S. Navy, became a USSPACECOM component as well on September 23, 1985.

Abbreviations: Communications (Comm); Navigation (Nav); Operations (Op); Satellite (Sat); Surveillance (Surveil).

Figure 4   MILITARY SPACE COMMANDS
Representative Functional Components

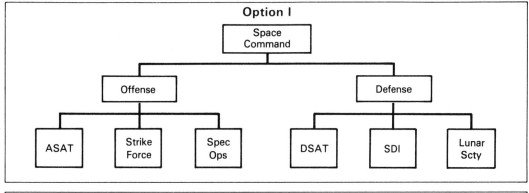

Option I
- Space Command
  - Offense
    - ASAT
    - Strike Force
    - Spec Ops
  - Defense
    - DSAT
    - SDI
    - Lunar Scty

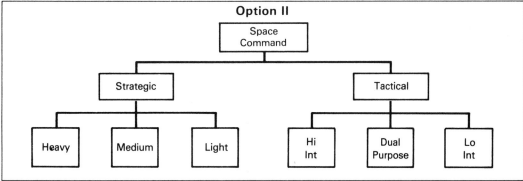

Option II
- Space Command
  - Strategic
    - Heavy
    - Medium
    - Light
  - Tactical
    - Hi Int
    - Dual Purpose
    - Lo Int

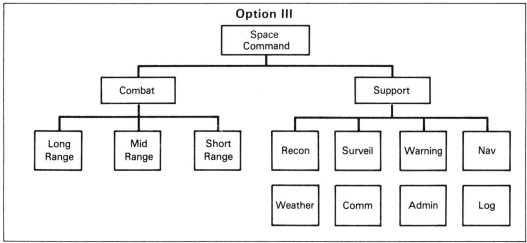

Option III
- Space Command
  - Combat
    - Long Range
    - Mid Range
    - Short Range
  - Support
    - Recon
    - Surveil
    - Warning
    - Nav
    - Weather
    - Comm
    - Admin
    - Log

Abbreviations:

Admin	Administration	Hi Int	High Intensity War	Scty	Security
ASAT	Antisatellite	Log	Logistics	SDI	Strategic Defense Initiative
Comm	Communications	Lo Int	Low Intensity War	Spec Ops	Special Operations
DSAT	Defensive Satellites	Nav	Navigation		

Note: All components contain support elements in some combination.

Figure 5   MILITARY SPACE COMMANDS
Representative Regional Components

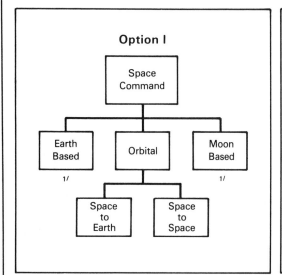

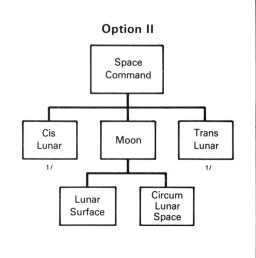

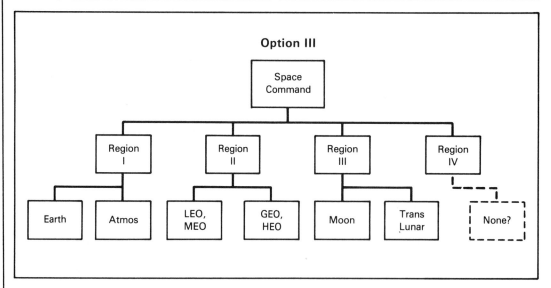

Abbreviations:

Atmos	Atmosphere
GEO	Geosynchronous Orbit
HEO	High Earth Orbit
LEO	Low Earth Orbit
MEO	Medium Earth Orbit

1/ Diagrams are too small to show typical subordinate elements.

Regionally Structured Space Commands

Regional structures might suit some space commands better than functional arrangements. Two major components probably would suffice, as long as circumterrestrial space remains the

Figure 6   MILITARY SPACE COMMANDS
Representative Regional-Functional Combinations

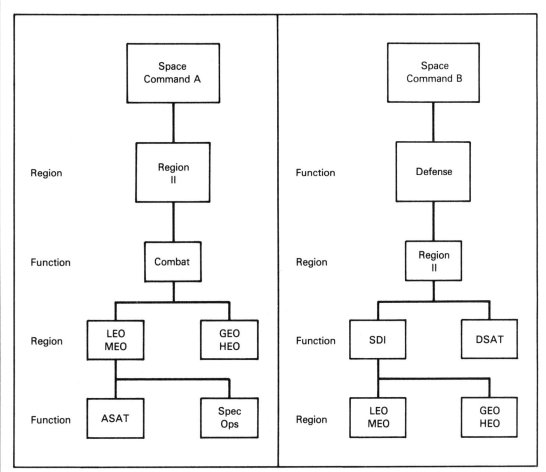

Note: Each component command has several subordinate elements at each echelon. All include various types of support. Only a few examples show on diagrams above.

Abbreviations:

ASAT	Antisatellite	LEO	Low Earth Orbit
DSAT	Defensive Satellites	MEO	Medium Earth Orbit
GEO	Geosynchronous Orbit	SDI	Strategic Defense Initiative
HEO	High Earth Orbit	Spec Ops	Special Operations

center of attention.[8] Candidates include Regions I and II, as previously defined. Earth-based and orbital components bounded by LEO and HEO are two other options. Policymakers could build on either couplet, as shown in Figure 5, if military responsibilities on the moon and beyond cause space command areas of responsibility to spread.

Regional-Functional Combinations

Space commands organized along purely regional or functional lines seem least desirable, because they sacrifice efficiency. Figure 6 portrays two representative combinations. Space Command A alternates region-function-region-function from top to bottom; Space Command B inverts that sequence.

Mixtures also may make it easier to match structures with missions at any given echelon. Space command architects who seek the best regional-functional blend consequently should test horizontal as well as vertical variations on trial blueprints, before they affix a seal of approval.

Coalition Space Commands

The primary purpose of any collective security system is to multiply the power of participants who find it too costly and risky to bear related burdens alone. Serious difficulties develop under ideal conditions.[9] Coalition space commands, immensely more complex than national counterparts, promise to introduce new alliance problems and exacerbate old ones.

No coalition now has a component command for space. All must rely on individual members or outsiders* for intelligence support (reconnaissance, surveillance, weather data, early warning), navigation aids, and satellite communications. Closer collaboration will become obligatory when land, sea, air, and space combat become inseparable and commonplace.

Planners soon should redefine theaters of operation in three-dimensional terms that transcend Earth's atmosphere, then draw regional boundaries through transparent space, where there are no visible benchmarks, to demark area responsibilities for major commanders and subordinates. Rhetorical questions, such as "How high is up?," "How far is out?," and "Where does territorial sovereignty stop?" will call for carefully calculated answers. "Front" and "rear" will need new delineations, especially when selected combat forces and supporting infrastructures displace permanently into space.

Coalition leaders eventually may find it advisable to designate a Supreme Allied Commander for Space (SACSPACE), analogous to NATO's Supreme Allied Commanders for Europe and Atlantic (SACEUR, SACLANT).[11] United Nations peacekeeping and combatant commands for space also are plausible.

---

*The United States, a nonbelligerent and nominal neutral, provided invaluable satellite intelligence information to British forces during their brief war with Argentina over the Falkland Islands in 1982.[10]

Separate Service Versus Service Specialty

Armies, navies, and air forces currently share responsibilities for space, an increasingly important military medium. Whether senior officials should transfer some or all space missions to a new armed service created solely for such purposes, and the timing of such action if the answer is affirmative, probably will become contentious issues before the next decade ends. Possible precedents and probable prerequisites thus merit mention.[12]

Possible Precedents

Possible precedents are scare. Strategic Rocket Forces, the only new Soviet armed service since World War II, were activated in 1959 to control all land-based missiles that reach 1000 km (600 statute miles) or more.[13] Technologically innovative components are geographically removed from ground force commanders, but most remain a form of long-range artillery. Only intercontinental ballistic missile (ICBM) missions are distinctively different.

Policymakers who ponder the suitability of a separate military service for space might learn more from events that preceded and followed the first formation of a U.S. armed service since the late eighteenth century. The U.S. Army Signal Corps activated an aeronautical division with three men and one reconnaissance aircraft in 1907, soon after the first flight at Kitty Hawk, North Carolina. Five redesignations, many mission adjustments, and two world wars preceded decisions to form a separate U.S. Air Force four decades later. Personnel at that point approximated 305,800 (down from a wartime peak of more than 2 million) and 26,590 aircraft of all types (210 squadrons), active and reserve.[14] Major milestones were:

	From	To	Years
U.S. Army			
Signal Corps			
Aeronautical Division	Aug. 1, 1907	July 18, 1914	7
Aviation Section	July 18, 1914	May 24, 1918	4
Army Air Service	May 24, 1918	July 2, 1926	8
Army Air Corps	July 2, 1926	June 20, 1941	15
Army Air Force	June 20, 1941	Sep. 18, 1947	6
U.S. Air Force	Sep. 18, 1947		40

Dissimilar environments led the Army and Air Force to split in 1947. So did divergent missions. Land forces, for example, contribute little to strategic bombardment, homeland air defense, air superiority, deep air interdiction, intertheater airlift, and many aerial intelligence activities. Senior flag officers in the Army Air Force also exercised political suasion to ensure a separate service. Their endeavors were decisive.[15]

The U.S. Navy and Marine Corps retained tactical air arms after the National Security Act of 1947 created a separate Air Force. Congress accepted their contentions that only tightly knit land-sea-air teams could satisfy specialized missions, such as fleet air defense, air power projection along littorals from platforms afloat, and aerial support for amphibious operations.[16]

Statutes that transferred some, but not all, close air support and battlefield interdiction functions to the Air Force created persistent areas of contention that center on a Principle of War called Unity of Command. Air Force doctrine in those regards differs so drastically from those of Navy and Marine Corps that controversy over central control continues, despite JCS policy decrees.[17] Many senior Army troopleaders express discontent, because the Air Force often assigns lower priorities to air-ground missions than they prefer.[18]

Probable Prognosis

The United States and Soviet Union both may install a separate armed service for space before the next decade ends, if the 40-year gestation period and other precedents described above are valid (U.S. military satellites began to orbit in 1959, Soviet competitors a bit later).[19]

Space, a unique environment, is at least as different from Earth and its atmospheric envelope as land is from air and water. That fact alone, however, seems insufficient justification to activate a new service. Military space operations, much like U.S. tactical air combat power, probably will remain a specialty within several military services that squabble over respective budgets/prerogatives, until important space missions involve more than support for armed forces on Earth and powerful spokesmen present decisionmakers a persuasive case.[20]

Existing armed services then might logically battle to retain selected space capabilities that influence earthbound operations, but multiservice competition to control the moon and lunar libration points would be senseless. Neither navies nor marines could lay legitimate claims, because oceans are absent in space. Air forces have no valid role in a vacuum. Terrestrial armies currently are organized, trained, and equipped only for operations on this planet.

A Solomon-style decision eventually will be unavoidable: senior officials must determine whether to deliver the military space "baby" intact or divide it. Careful study of complex issues should precede selection. A separate armed service with centralized control over all military space activities, for example, might avoid most doctrinal disputes. Decentralization might assure better coverage of individual missions. A wise initial pick is important, because subsequent amendments will be unlikely at any early date, if U.S. tactical air combat precedents are applicable.

STAFF ARRANGEMENTS

National and international military headquarters, uniservice and unified alike, invariably contain a command section (the commander, his deputy, executive officers, aides, secretaries) and a staff similar to that shown in Figure 7. The size and configuration of each staff reflect tasks any given organization must perform.[21]

Most functions common to land, sea, and air also apply to space. Small personal staffs in the future, like those past and present, will report directly to respective commanders. A chief of staff directs the rest. General staffs (not always under that name) fundamentally consist of four sections: personnel, intelligence, plans/operations, and logistics. Additions depend on demonstrated needs to subdivide responsibilities or to improve direction, coordination, and supervision in broad fields such as C^3. Special staffs, which feature relatively narrow administrative and technical skills, may also expand to meet demands. Command historians and installation security experts typify candidates that Figure 7 omits.[22]

Major military space headquarters, without exception, nevertheless need special staff sections that focus specifically on space. Five prospects are shown below the dotted line in Figure 7. Some apparent duplications on the diagram are deceptive. Every senior space commander, for example, employs counsel on his personal staff to handle myriad legal matters, but that does not obviate needs for specialists in space law, which embraces endless, complex issues, such as treaty interpretations, limits of national sovereignty, the legality of "keep out" zones, and technological prohibitions (particularly nuclear power in space).[23] Similar logic underpins a two-track medical staff, because general practitioners, otolaryngologists, gynecologists, and neurosurgeons are poorly prepared to deal with space-peculiar phenomena like zero gravity, ionizing radiation, respiratory poisoning, and traumatic dysbarism.*[24] Three other space-

---

*Respiratory poisoning, caused by excess oxygen, nitrogen, carbon dioxide, carbon monoxide, and other gases, may affect spacecraft crews if life-support systems fail. Partial or momentary total loss of ambient pressure causes traumatic dysbarism.

Figure 7   MILITARY SPACE COMMANDS
Typical Staff Functions

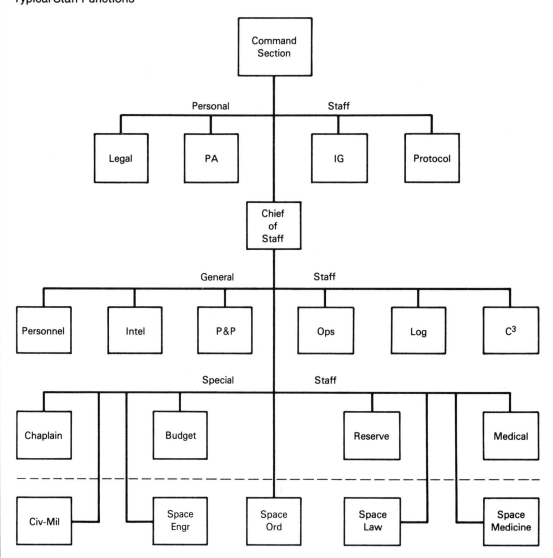

Note: Blocks above the dotted line are common to most high-level staffs. Blocks below are space specific.

Abbreviations:

C³	Command, Control, Communications	Log	Logistics
Civ-Mil	Civil-Military	Ops	Operations
Engr	Engineering	Ord	Ordnance
IG	Inspector General	PA	Public Affairs
Intel	Intelligence	P&P	Policies and Plans

specific special staff blocks in Figure 7 are worth a few words of explanation. Space system experts in an engineering section would be well positioned to advise the commander and other staff members about the technological feasibility of proposed policies, plans, and operations. They could also help integrate innovative technologies into the organization and frame requests for research. An ordnance section might perform similar functions concerning space armaments and munitions. A third group of specialists could advise each command on ways to avoid undesirable civil-military duplication, make cost-effective use of shared systems/facilities, optimize payloads with civil-military purposes,[25] and cope with militarily significant competition between public and private sectors. Enterprising companies that sell high-resolution space photographs on the open market pose serious problems in the latter instance. Unauthorized disclosures that reveal sensitive information, for example, could invalidate plans or provoke pointless international crises, if interpreted incorrectly.[26]

CHAPTER
4

Force Development Problems and Options

Military and civilian space establishments currently are indistinguishable in many respects, but dissimilar requirements inevitably will steer developments in different directions. Force planners and programmers, who write on nearly blank slates, have a rare opportunity to shape postures properly at the onset, instead of amending previous mistakes.

BENEFICIAL FORCE CHARACTERISTICS

Seven beneficial force characteristics could assist their search for suitable, feasible, and acceptable solutions: (1) capability; (2) responsiveness; (3) reliability;[1] (4) survivability; (5) simplicity; (6) flexibility; and (7) cost-effectiveness.

The first four, which underpin *effectiveness*, are interdependent and indispensable. The capability to accomplish particular missions in timely fashion under adverse conditions in hostile environments in fact is the main reason for any armed space force. Other qualities are irrelevant, if units fall short on even one count. Military space commanders, for example, seldom could tolerate prelaunch delays measured in minutes or hours, much less 32 months, the period that separated two famous U.S. shuttle flights (Challenger exploded January 28, 1986; Discovery flew September 29, 1988).[2] Long mean times between mechanical failures are essential for spacecraft on station. Wars will not wait while they seek shelter from enemy weapons or solar flares.

The last three in the list underpin *efficiency*. Simplicity makes it possible to mass produce technologically sophisticated space systems that reasonably bright individuals could operate and maintain when it is no longer possible to handpick personnel. (The selection and training of U.S. astronauts and Soviet cosmonauts initially was so restrictive that the Bionic Man might have failed some tests.)[3] Flexibility affords optional ways to cope with problems, especially the unexpected. A well-balanced blend of general and special purpose space forces accordingly seems advisable, because optimum proficiency is not always a product of specificity. Cost controls are commendable in any event, provided they do not undercut required capabilities.

MILITARY SPACE INFRASTRUCTURE

Military space infrastructure requires attention in three fundamental respects that apply to industries and installations alike: survivability, adaptability, and responsiveness. Civilian analogs that pursue commercial and scientific goals have similar needs, but failure to fulfill them does not endanger national security.

Military Space Industries

The House Armed Services Committee in a 1980 report described a U.S. industrial base "crippled by declining productivity growth, aging facilities and machinery, shortages in critical materials, increasing lead times, skilled labor shortages, inflexible government contracting procedures, inadequate defense budgets and burdensome government regulations and paperwork."[4] The U.S. military-industrial complex still experiences serious shortcomings, most of which adversely affect abilities to implement satisfactory military space programs in peacetime, much less surge in emergency or replace combat losses expeditiously.[5]

Industrial bottlenecks indicate how dependent military space forces are on a few suppliers. Avtex Fibers-Front Royal Inc., the sole source of rayon yarn for space shuttle rocket motors, briefly went out of business in November 1988, before the National Security Council encouraged the Air Force and NASA to furnish bail-out money that totalled $38 million.[6] Two plants, both in

Henderson, Nevada, produce all the ammonium perchlorate that U.S. solid fuel rockets require for combustion. Explosions leveled one on May 4, 1988; the other suspended production simultaneously, pending safety inspections. Protracted shortages as a result compelled U.S. military space officials to reschedule and otherwise revise planned launches.[7] Emphasis on offshore procurement cuts costs at the expense of self-sufficiency. Japan, for example, furnishes the United States and associates 75% of their silicon and a similar share of gallium arsenide, a prime contender for future superconductors and optically based data processors. Japan also markets most state-of-the-art random access memory (RAM) chips. Czechoslovakia, a Soviet associate, provides all high-purity silicon for computers in U.S. missile guidance systems. Monsanto, the last large U.S. silicon producer, is selling to Huels AG in West Germany.[8] Greater industrial diversification, in short, is desirable.

Adaptability and survivability both could benefit if selected industries migrated into space, where they could couple lunar resources with environments unobtainable on Earth (near vacuum, virtual freedom from gravity, and antiseptic processing conditions are three advantages). Carefully phased moves would reduce Earth-to-space lift requirements and concomitant costs, speed the perfection of many militarily useful products, and simplify logistics.[9]

Military Space Installations

Soviet military space installations are located in remote regions. Armed forces and fortifications between the Baltic and Barents seas protect Plesetsk. Neither Tyuratam nor Kapustin Yar is near an unfriendly frontier (Map 11). All three centers, reachable only by long-range delivery systems, consequently are safe from external attacks, save those that risk general nuclear war.[10]

U.S. military spacecraft, in contrast, currently launch from Cape Canaveral, Florida and Wallops Island, Virginia on the Atlantic coast, and from Vandenberg Air Force Base, California on the Pacific. All three sites are well positioned to implement peacetime safety rules, because failures fall into water, far from population clusters. Wartime vulnerability, however, is equally obvious. Seaward flanks are exposed to attacks, including limited objective operations during low intensity conflicts. Submarines that belong to hostile Third World countries could have a field day with conventional standoff weapons. Skilled saboteurs could infiltrate.[11]

Distance shields the U.S. Consolidated Space Operations Center at Peterson Air Force Base, near Colorado Springs, and

Map 11   U.S. AND SOVIET LAUNCH SITES AND CONTROL CENTERS

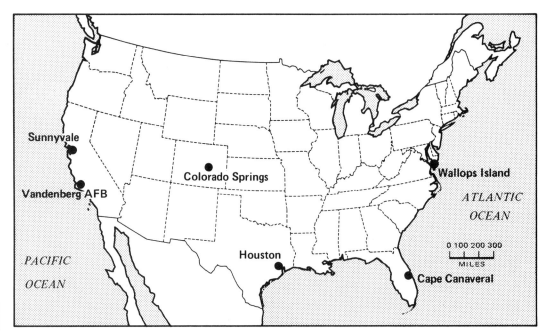

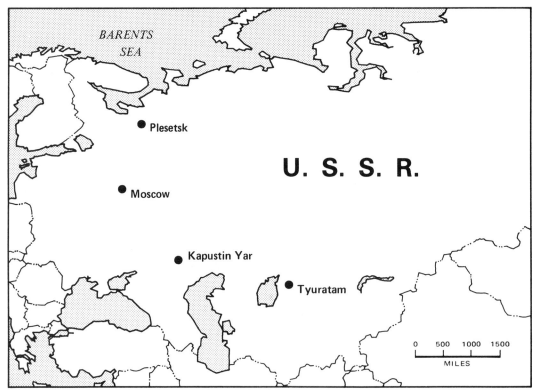

additional SPACECOM installations deep inside adjacent Cheyenne Mountain, which is hardened against nuclear strikes. The U.S. military satellite control facility and communications center at Sunnyvale, California sits on a seacoast. So does the civilian mission control close to Houston, Texas. Sunnyvale also straddles the San Andreas fault, a potential earthquake epicenter.[12]

America's defense decisionmakers accordingly might consider a better blend of fixed and mobile military space installations that incorporates increased redundancy and dispersion with greater degrees of hardness for critical elements outside Cheyenne Mountain. Offshore launch pads on modified oil-drilling rigs, which some free thinkers recommend, perhaps would be administratively advantageous,[13] but would scarcely benefit physical security. ICBM-style silos at selected launch sites ashore might serve better, as long as expendable space delivery vehicles remain in vogue. Mobile launchers and associated support probably are impractical, but land, sea, and/or air mobile C^3 elements, analogous to the National Emergency Airborne Command Post (NEACAP) and the National Emergency Command Post Afloat (NECPA), are feasible. So are subterranean supplements like the Alternate National Military Command Center at Fort Richie, Maryland. No such substitutes duplicate all C^3 capabilities available at primary headquarters, but they would be useful backups during international crises and combat.[14]

No nation, unified command, or armed service on Earth relies exclusively on centralized control for peacetime or wartime operations. On-the-spot headquarters always assist. Those precedents indicate that advance command posts almost certainly will displace into space sooner or later. It is not too soon to commence preparations and pick proper times.

DEPLOYABLE SPACE FORCES

Planners and programmers who design deployable military space forces essentially seek answers to one multipart but simple question: "How much of what is required how fast, in explicit priority, to accomplish legitimate objectives without wasting money?" Sufficient quantities, satisfactory qualities, and the best mix of manned/unmanned, offensive/defensive, combat/support forces in context with perceived threats are principal parts of such equations.

This section does not furnish specific solutions to specific problems. Instead, it lays a conceptual foundation that pertains to all.

Quantitative Sufficiency

Former U.S. Secretary of Defense Robert S. McNamara boiled quantitative sufficiency down to bare bones in an address before the American Society of Newspaper Editors on April 20, 1963. "It cannot be assumed that a new weapon would really add to our national security, no matter how attractive," he said. "You have to make a judgement on how much is enough."[15]

President Nixon put that problem in perspective several years later, when he wrote that armed forces with sufficient or greater strength "protect national security adequately. Below that level is one vast undifferentiated area of no security at all. For it serves no purpose in conflicts between nations to have been almost strong enough."[16]

Force Sizing Standards

There is no magic formula with which to figure the optimum number of military space forces in any category. All estimates are partly or completely subjective. Unambiguous objectives and sensible budgets nevertheless are useful force sizing standards. The former could help identify minimum prudent levels; the latter could locate allowable upper limits.

Objectives and Obstacles

Explicit offensive, defensive, and/or deterrent objectives, coupled with probable threats, must precede logical space force development. Officials otherwise cannot justify needs.

The U.S. strategic nuclear triad, which started from scratch and grew like Topsy, is instructive in that respect. Specific Air Force and Navy responsibilities are obscure. So are relationships between delivery vehicles, weapons, and targets. Force size often depends more on service politics than on employment policies. The Navy in 1960, for example, offered to forfeit two ballistic submarines (32 launch tubes) to finance a new aircraft carrier. Objections were minor when McNamara later cut the Polaris program from 45 to 41 submarines (64 fewer tubes), because rationales for retention were weak.[17] The U.S. bomber force has never correlated closely with Soviet air defense capabilities. Targets for our second-strike triad proliferated exponentially after the advent of MIRVs (multiple independently targetable reentry vehicles), in conformance with a precept much like Parkinson's Law: "aiming points increase in direct proportion to weapons available."[18]

U.S. Strategic Defense Initiatives (SDI), also starting from scratch, show signs that they too may copy Topsy. The announced purpose of land- and space-based components is "to deny the Soviets their objectives in an initial ballistic missile attack" against U.S. "National Command Authorities (NCA); the Command Control, and Communications (C[3]) structure; and the U.S. and Allied retaliatory forces."[19] That imprecise expression makes it virtually impossible to calculate how much is enough and obviates meaningful quests for alternatives. SDI may be the only option, if the objective is to defeat some classified percentage of Soviet warheads in flight. ICBM mobility, command post hardening, and deception might be preferable, if the mission is to protect particular C[3] sites and missile silos. Ends and means might match better if U.S. policymakers expressed aims more clearly, then coordinated the efforts of offensive and defensive force planners more closely than at present.[20]

Sensible Budgets

Budgets, as well as objectives, shape military space postures, because national defense eternally competes with domestic needs for finite funds. Space forces must further vie with land, sea, and air for their fair share of the fiscal pie.

Outlays that produce maximum capabilities at minimum expense are most cost-effective. A bit too much normally is better than a bit too little when precision is impossible, since military systems in space, like those on Earth, should be sufficient to ensure operational flexibility and cushion combat losses. A few long-lived, state-of-the-art space systems may seem cost-effective in peacetime but not in war, since commanders could neither tolerate light attrition or afford to replace super expensive spacecraft expeditiously.[21] A hi-lo mix that mingles top-of-the-line forces with simpler systems, some obsolescent but combat-effective, might foster much greater flexibility, while confining costs.[22]

Military space systems with "budget-busting" price tags, procured in small quantities for special purposes, rarely qualify as cost-effective, no matter how spectacular the technologies. The $500 million "secret" U.S. military satellite that the shuttle Atlantis lifted aloft on December 2, 1988,[23] for example, might be worth every penny if its purpose were scientific, but is extremely vulnerable to enemy ASATs and too expensive to replicate extensively. Future military space programs might avoid budgetary rebukes like those that beset B-2 stealth bombers (at least $70 + billion total),[24] if unbiased appraisals of competitive options preceded decisions to develop and deploy.[25]

Total Force concepts have been popular in the United States since the early 1970s. They count on allies and reserve components to cut costs and reduce U.S. active duty requirements.[26] Military space forces, however, cannot soon participate. Active establishments will long absorb all available weapons, equipment, and skilled personnel. Few nations likely will possess strong military space commands at any early date.

Significance of Asymmetries

Some asymmetries between similar space forces on opposing sides are important, others are immaterial. Numerical superiority is essential in certain circumstances, parity suffices in others, inferiority occasionally is acceptable. Quantitative sufficiency consequently can be measured better by abilities to accomplish missions than by "bean count" balances.[27]

Vulnerable second-strike space forces probably should outnumber opposing first-strike counterparts, if they hope to survive with ample strength intact after absorbing a surprise attack. Parity, however, appears adequate, provided forces are well defended. Quantitative equality in selected space systems may also be enough to influence foreign and domestic perceptions favorably. Superiority or parity indeed may be undesirable, if attaining either status deprives other sectors of attention and funds. Enemy anti-satellite systems illustrate that point. Acquiring many U.S. ASATs to achieve a mirror image with the Soviets, for example, probably would strengthen military space posture less than deploying additional DSATs, at identical costs. Asymmetries, in sum, are significant only on a case-by-case basis. Widely applicable rules of thumb are rare.

Qualitative Sufficiency

Requirements and technologies, conditioned by political, economic, institutional, bureaucratic, and doctrinal constraints,[28] determine the qualitative sufficiency of military space systems. Requirements, selection procedures, education, training, and experience determine the qualitative sufficiency of military space personnel.

Military space requirements expressed herein are conservative. All seem attainable during the next 25–50 years, given present and projected technologies. Unexpected breakthroughs, like many past surprises, could expedite progress.

R&D Requirements

Twenty research and development (R&D) requirements listed below indicate basic attributes that military space systems must possess to fulfill roles and accomplish security missions acceptably well. Entries exclude specific programs, such as U.S. Delta Star, On Target, Beam Aboard Rocket (BEAR), High Endo-atmospheric Defense Interceptor, Exoatmospheric Reentry Interceptor, Relay Mirror and Laser Atmospheric Compensation Experiments, Boost Surveillance Tracking System, Airborne Optical Adjunct, Starlab, and Zenith Star, to mention only a few SDI systems already undergoing, or about to begin, stringent tests.[29]

Multipurpose Prerequisites

Seven requirements apply equally well to all spacecraft and some infrastructure:

1. Improved payload-to-transport ratios

2. Spacecraft that breach transatmospheric barriers smoothly and eliminate parking orbits

3. Reliable protection against nuclear, cosmic, solar and other radiation

4. Expeditious and secure data processing

5. Real time secure communications

6. Selective automation

7. Ultrareliability under adverse conditions.

Combat Force Prerequisites

Seven combat force requirements, like the multipurpose list, are representative rather than complete. The first four pertain to offense and defense. The remainder would benefit one, but not both:

1. Abilities to maneuver weapon platforms at will, with much the same facility as fighter aircraft[30]

2. Weapon-quality lasers that easily cross transatmospheric barriers in both directions

3. Sensors able to "see" through clouds from land and space

4. Battle management C³I

5. Defense suppression abilities

6. Self-defense for spacecraft, with particular attention to protection against DEW*

7. Preferential space-based homeland defense.[31]

Logistic Support Prerequisites

Military space supply, maintenance, transportation, construction, medical support, and personnel services create unique requirements. Enumerations below include one entry each in that order:

1. Storage depots that exploit zero-g, vacuum, cold, and other properties of space to preserve food, fuel, water, and munitions indefinitely, without artificial assistance

2. Special maintenance implements for use in zero-g environments, where traditional tools will not work or are awkward[32]

3. Modular, reusable transfer vehicles, mass drivers, and tethers to facilitate military transportation anywhere in the Earth-Moon System[33]

4. Lunar structures and space stations suitable for assorted military uses

5. Instruments, techniques, and habitats suitable for zero-g aid stations and space-based installations much like mobile army surgical hospitals (MASH)[34]

6. Morale, welfare, and recreational facilities to keep military personnel in top physical and emotional condition for long periods, without frequent sojourns on Earth.

Contributory Science and Technologies

R&D requirements seldom are self-satisfying. Innovative science and technologies normally must contribute. The Aerospace Industries Association (AIA) in November 1987 identified eight high-leverage fields in a study entitled *Key Technologies for the*

---

*Satellite sensors that must help B2 stealth bombers locate mobile targets are among many defenseless systems in space that could not survive modest enemy attacks.[35]

1990s: artificial intelligence, composite materials, very large-scale integrated circuits (VLSI), software development, propulsion systems, advanced sensors, optical information processing, and ultrareliable electronics.[36]

This primer, which aggregates some candidate technologies differently, concentrates on materials, propulsion, power, electronics, optics, weapon systems, and life sciences. Successful scientific research in these six broad fields must accompany technological developments needed to fulfill high priority military space requirements. Table 4 reflects relationships.

Materials

New materials form the foundation for military progress in space, because they contribute directly or indirectly to almost every technology (everything is made of something). Experimental composites, alloys, fiber optics, and superconductors are most promising.

Composites and alloys. Stone, bronze, and iron heretofore defined the main ages of human history. The Age of Manmade Materials is now emerging.[37] Metal, ceramic, and organic polymer composites, along with new metal alloys, possess revolutionary properties preferable to materials they replace. Many are stronger, lighter, and more durable than the best steel.[38] Matrix materials within each category differ considerably, but generic attributes compare as Table 5 indicates (all terms are relative).

Every advanced composite within each type of matrix exhibits unique strengths and weaknesses. None is perfect. Carbon-carbon polymers, for example, can tolerate temperatures up to 3,000°F without expanding or weakening significantly, but tend to oxidize or burn. Ceramic coatings that convert to glass in great heat help correct that deficiency.[39] Super-hard ceramics, in turn, mold readily into complex shapes and make ball bearings far better than steel, but break rather than bend because they are so brittle. High-performance plastics consequently are more suitable for assorted applications that include exposed structures and most moving parts.[40] Composites still cannot compete with traditional materials on a price-per-pound basis. Comparatively few pounds and longer product lives compensate incompletely.[41]

Military space force planners fortunately have a rich menu of composites and alloys from which to choose. "R&D tailoring" permits scientists and technologists to start with operator-prescribed requirements, then design materials to accomplish scientific missions.[42] Lightweight shields and electronics illustrate how inventive minds are using them to solve puzzles in two complex fields. Carbon-carbon spacecraft skins have the potential to guard against laser beams and projectiles like no other

Table 4 RESEARCH AND DEVELOPMENT: RELATED TO REQUIRED PRODUCTS

Required Products	Research and Development					
	Materials	Propulsion	Power	Electronics	Optics	Munitions
Structures						
Spacecraft	X					
Lunar Installations	X					
Weapon Systems						
Explosives						
Nuclear	X					X
Conventional						X
Kinetic Energy			X			X
Lasers			X		X	
Particle Beams			X			
Missiles	X	X		X		
Guns	X		X	X		
Engines and Motors						
Boosters	X	X				
On-Board	X	X				
Mass Drivers	X		X			
Tethers	X					
Generators						
Electrochemical			X			
Nuclear	X		X			
Solar	X		X			
Intelligence Sensors						
Infrared				X	X	
Cameras	X			X	X	
Telescopes	X			X	X	
Radar			X	X		
C³ Systems						
Guidance	X			X		
Navigation	X			X		
Control	X			X		
Communications	X		X	X		
Encryption				X		
Passive Defense						
Hardening						
Radiation	X					
Weapon Effects	X					
Stealth	X	X		X		
ECM, ECCM	X			X		
Miscellaneous						
Computers	X			X		
Artificial Intelligence	X			X		
Robotics	X		X	X		
Tools	X					

Table 5 COMPOSITE MATERIAL PROPERTIES

Properties	Metal Matrix	Ceramic Matrix	Polymer Matrix
Strength		Least	Greatest
Weight	Heaviest		Lightest
Hardness		Hardest	Softest
Conductivity (elec.)	Most	Least	
Density	Most		Least
Resistance			
Wear		Most	Least
Temperature		Most	Least
Corrosion	Least	Most	
Brittleness		Most	Least
Malleability	Most		Least
Sources			
Abundance	Variable	Plentiful	Plentiful
Reliability	Variable	Good	Good

known materials. Diamond film deposits on transistors could deflect nuclear radiation. Experiments suggest that stealthy spacecraft coated with polarized polymer salts could absorb the full range of radar rays more readily than ferrite-based ceramics, which weigh ten times as much. Malleable carbon composites might also reduce broad-band radar cross sections dramatically, using thermoplastic techniques.[43]

Creative employment of new materials stimulates an electronic revolution that could satisfy many military space requirements. High-performance ceramics formed from organometallic precursors make superlative capacitors and integrated circuits. Diamond semiconductor chips, doped with impurities to carry currents, might permit an order-of-magnitude improvement over silicon.

Nickel substrates, which are relatively inexpensive, may prove the perfect match. Hermetically sealed connections, concocted from borosilicate glass and alloys with compatible coefficients of thermal expansion, already protect "black box" electronics in harsh environments; improvements seem possible. Spacecraft surfaces resistant to scratches and painted with polyanalines (plastics that approach the conductivity of copper) could become gigantic printed circuit boards, with electrical systems embedded. Savings in structural weight and room inside would be considerable.[44]

Superconductors. High temperature superconductors, a special class of ceramics that transport electricity with no resistance, deserve separate treatment, because characteristics are unique.

All once worked well only near absolute zero (–459°F; dry ice is –109°F). Scientists long believed that –419°F might be an impassable barrier, until they began experiments with ceramics, which normally are insulators instead of conductors. The first great leap forward came in 1987, when superconductivity was achieved at – 282°F, 136 degrees warmer within a few months. The search continues for superconductor materials able to function at room temperatures without constant bathing in costly liquid helium. Signs are encouraging. Ceramics mixed with readily available bismuth and thallium (a metal used as rat poison) supplement those that rely on expensive rare-earth metals like lanthanum, strontium, yttrium, and barium.[45]

Superconduction applications in space potentially are encyclopedic. Power supplies, electronics, and weaponry are likely beneficiaries. Superconductors, for example, could hasten the availability of controlled nuclear fusion energy plants for military space stations and lunar installations. Enormous solenoids could store electricity without waste, to be tapped when demands peak. More efficient electric motors for multiple purposes would become feasible. Superconductor computer circuits could switch in less than a nanosecond (ten times faster than present semiconductors), with less energy loss. Larger packing densities, combined with chips made from similar materials, would let shoebox-size computers replace room-size counterparts under those conditions. Superconducting magnets already give a big boost to microwave, millimeter-, and submillimeter-wave surveillance, guidance, and communication equipment. Inventors envisage compact, hypervelocity electromagnetic missiles and guns, as well as particle beams, long before the 50 year period of this book expires.[46]

Better semiconductors are the aim until superconductors are perfected. Gallium arsenide (GaAs) is the leading candidate to displace integrated circuits that rely on silicon. Properties include increased speed (three to ten times as fast); lower power consumption; greater resistance to radiation, including electromagnetic pulse; smaller size; lighter weight; and laser light-emitting abilities. Unhappily, however, gallium arsenide also is brittle, expensive, and harder to fabricate than silicon. Efforts to correct deficiencies continue, because rewards seem worthwhile. GaAs technologies in particular would boost spaceborne surveillance, tracking, signal processing, and other activities essential to homeland defense against ballistic missiles. Warning radars mounted on spacecraft, for example, could supplement monster land-based models.[47]

Fiber optics. Military space forces cannot function effectively without first-class communications. Fiber optics, which almost literally are developing at the speed of light, fill many needs better than other known materials.

Fiber optic systems, simply explained, convert electrical signals into light pulses that pass through special glass strands half the thickness of human hair. Small, solid-state lasers or light-emitting diodes (LED) transmit information by varying (modulating) light source intensities at prescribed intervals. Photodiode receivers at the far end of each fiber convert light pulses into electricity, which is demodulated to recreate the original signal.[48]

Fiber optic communications already cram more information into smaller cables over much longer distances with far less distortion than any other method. Halide glass fibers of great purity and immense tensile strength in the future may span 5,000 miles with a single repeater. Military space installations on Earth and moon both could benefit from fiber optic communications of all kinds, especially because they are immune to electromagnetic interference. So could spacecraft large and small, where a few lightweight fiber optic channels could replace miles of metallic wire. Chemical/biological warfare warning, temperature control, and anti-intrusion devices indicate just three among many possible protective measures that fiber optics might facilitate.[49]

Propulsion

Propulsion technology will pace the progress of future space flight. Peacetime development cycles are long (10–15 years) and initial costs enormous (multibillions in any currency). Leading edge technologies must mesh high-temperature, lightweight materials, high-performance fuels, special pumps, seals, valves, and fabrication techniques.[50]

Essentially, there are two ways to improve military space propulsion for use in the Earth-Moon System: better engines and better propellants. Propulsive capabilities are best measured by specific impulse (Isp), the ratio of engine thrust to propellant flow rate in pounds per second, minus engine drag (an Isp of 300 seconds produces 300 pounds of thrust for every pound of propellant expended each second). Higher Isp indicates higher performance. The U.S. space shuttle main engine, for example, has an Isp of about 470 seconds, compared with 1,200+ for proposed transatmospheric spacecraft. No vertically launched vehicle can defeat gravity, unless pounds of thrust are at least twice the vehicle's weight. Escape velocities from Earth and moon apparently will depend on chemical or nuclear propulsion for the predictable future. Other forms, however, are useful for less demanding duties.[51]

Liquid fuel propulsion systems. Liquid propellants contain fuel, an oxidizer, and commonly include catalysts and/or additives to increase thrust. Combustion can be started, stopped, and restarted by controlling propellant flow. Each propellant produces a particular Isp; Table 6 reflects a few.[52]

Liquid propellants ideally should be easy and inexpensive to

Table 6   SPECIFIC IMPULSE OF LIQUID PROPELLANT COMBINATIONS

Oxidizer	Fuel					
	Ammonia	RP-1	UDMH	50% UDMH and 50% Hydrazine	Hydrazine (N_2H_4)	Hydrogen*
Liquid oxygen	294	300	310	312	313	391
Chlorine trifluoride	275	258	280	287	294	318
95% hydrogen peroxide and 5% water	262	273	278	279	282	314
Red fuming nitric acid (15% NO_2)	260	268	276	278	283	326
Nitrogen tetroxide	269	276	285	288	292	341
Liquid fluorine	357	326	343		363	410

*Assumes combustion chamber pressure of 1000 pounds per square inch absolute (psia); optimum nozzle expansion ratio and ambient pressure equal 14.7 psia.
Adapted from *Space Handbook*, by Curtis D. Cochran, Dennis M. Gorman, and Joseph D. Dumoulin.

produce, safe to handle, store well for long periods, and release great energy per pound. Chemical stability and high density, coupled with low toxicity, corrosiveness, and vapor pressure, are desirable traits. Every parameter invites improvement. Cryogenic propellants, for example, generally are more energetic than fuels stored at normal temperatures, but must be refrigerated, because boiling points are low (–423°F for liquid hydrogen). Special containers and accessories, such as valves, are required at extra expense. Fluorine, available in abundance, is costly to concentrate and dangerous to handle. The most potent liquid propellants consequently are usually reserved for upper stages that use a lot less than big boosters.[53]

Liquid propulsion engines better able to pump oxidizers and fuel at specified rates, withstand thermal stress, stop, restart, and throttle in flight could do much more than boost spacecraft into orbit. Maneuverable vehicles of immense military value could become possibilities.[54]

Solid fuel propulsion systems. Shorter burning times, very limited start-stop-restart capabilities, lower specific impulse (but faster acceleration), higher density, simplicity, instant readiness, lower costs, and greater safety generally distinguish solid propellant systems from liquid competitors. Booster-to-payload weight ratios are better because heavy fuel tanks are unnecessary. The only moving parts typically are those that gimbal (swivel) nozzles.[55]

Solid propellant systems, like liquid counterparts, are subject to constant and extensive experimentation. Quests for enhanced

Isp, the "Holy Grail," involve many variables, such as superior constituents; oxidizer to fuel ratios; chemical inhibitors, which influence burning times and thrust; the size, geometric shape, and burning surface of propellant "sticks"; initial propellant temperatures and chamber pressures; assorted additives; and high-energy, rather than inert, fuel binders.[56]

Solid propellant engines generally are reliable compared with liquid systems, but combustion is complex. Segmented boosters, which facilitate transportation from factory to launch sites, eliminate the need for monster hoists and simplify inspections, but seams compromise structural integrity and risk leaky seals. Tradeoffs between convenience and quality need careful consideration.[57]

Exotic propulsion systems. Hybrid systems, which seek to combine the best attributes of liquid and solid propellants, also have limitations. Several alternatives in various phases of research and development eventually may supplement or replace chemical propulsion for some purposes, but nuclear rockets seem the most likely way to launch large payloads from Earth or moon.[58]

Scientists are just starting to investigate antimatter, solar, and laser propulsion. Prospects that they will revolutionize military space capabilities during the next few decades appear remote. Nuclear propulsion, which has many proponents, attracts little official support and few funds, because it is costly compared with chemical systems, and powerful opponents (rightly or wrongly) fear it is unsafe. International political pressure to ban such engines is great. Ion engines and solar sails "billowed" by solar winds could sustain low thrust for long periods (months, even years), but are important mainly for leisurely orbit transfers and interplanetary missions beyond the scope of this study.[59]

Some types of electric propulsion, however, are valuable in the Earth-Moon System. Auxiliary motors can keep long-duration geosynchronous satellites on station more economically than liquid- or solid-fuel models. Monetary costs and propellant mass as a percentage of spacecraft mass both can be markedly reduced.[60] Electromagnetic mass drivers, designed to develop high thrust rather than high velocities, could launch multiton loads from the moon to collection points in space, when perfected. Long service life and capacities to accelerate any material, regardless of atomic properties, are anticipated advantages; raw lunar soil or powdered space debris could serve as propellants. Big superconducting magnets would be a boon (Figure 8 depicts only one hypothetical model).[61]

Space tethers that theoretically could stretch several hundred miles may be the most ingenious form of space propulsion (Figure 9). Any spacecraft lowered below a tether's orbital center of

Figure 8   MASS DRIVER ON THE MOON

Mass drivers of assorted sizes may take many forms. The electromagnetic lunar catapult depicted launches large loads horizontally in the absence of atmosphere and presence of low gravity. The payload emerging from the muzzle at more than one mile per second is a blur. The man in the lower left corner indicates scale.

NOTE: Adapted from *Confrontation in Space* by G. Harry Stine.

mass would transfer energy and momentum to any spacecraft being raised above it, in keeping with the principle of conservation of angular momentum. Increased energy would let the top vehicle achieve a higher orbit without firing its engines, when the tether turns it loose (from GEO, say, to HEO). Decreased energy would put the bottom vehicle into a lower orbit without expending propellant to make the move (from GEO to LEO is just one possibility). "Satellites on strings" conceivably could constitute space elevators to ferry troops and cargo between transports and the lunar surface or space stations. Tethers made of conducting materials could become electric motors, energized entirely by orbital movement in the Earth's magnetic field. Tethers powdered by solar panels reportedly could provide spacecraft propellantless propulsion with a specific impulse exceeding 300,000 seconds.[62]

Supersonic combustion ramjet (scramjet) engines, one key to transatmospheric flight, are a prominent military space priority. Horizontal takeoff, single-stage-to-orbit, and high specific impulse are prerequisites. Design and engineering are complex,

Earth-based infrastructure that supports space operations is extensive and vulnerable. This photograph depicts just one launch pad at Kennedy Space Center. *NASA*.

Immense transports that move rocket boosters from assembly areas to launch pads illustrate needs for less ponderous means. Trucks on left and right indicate scale. *NASA*.

Major C³ facilities currently are tempting targets. Nearly 500 specialists man the control center shown, which is entirely above ground. *NASA.*

The U.S. space shuttle initially "piggybacks" on an expendable liquid propellant tank. Two reusable solid propellant boosters help lift that load 27 miles above Earth. Shuttle engines put it into orbit at about 70 miles, after boosters burn out and jettison. The fuel tank separates just before orbit. *NASA.*

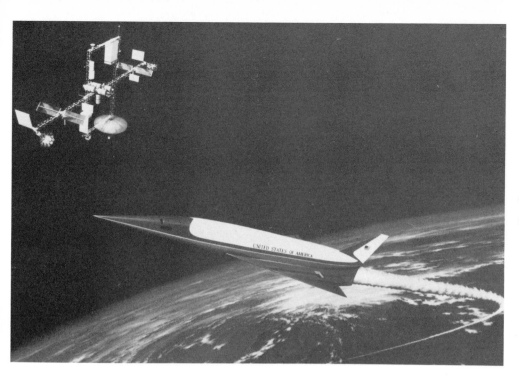

The U.S. National Aerospace Plane (NASP) is designed to take off from regular aircraft runways under its own power, reach orbit, and return to Earth routinely. The photo is an artist's depiction. *NASA*.

Typical topography on the far side of the moon. The largest crater is about 50 miles in diameter. Neighbors are smaller, but much deeper. *NASA*.

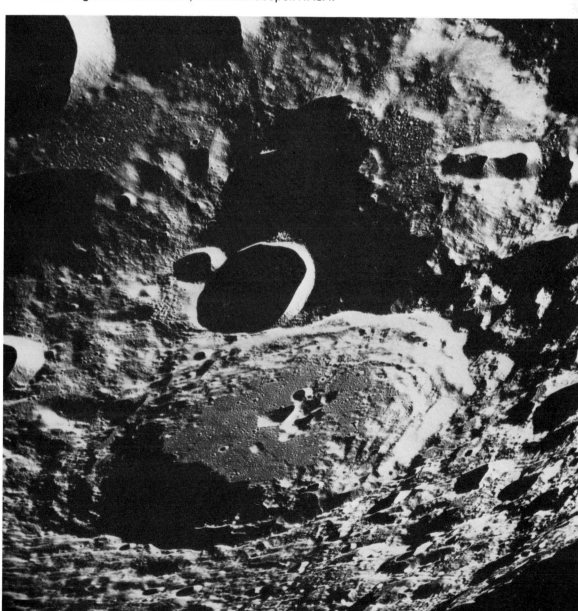

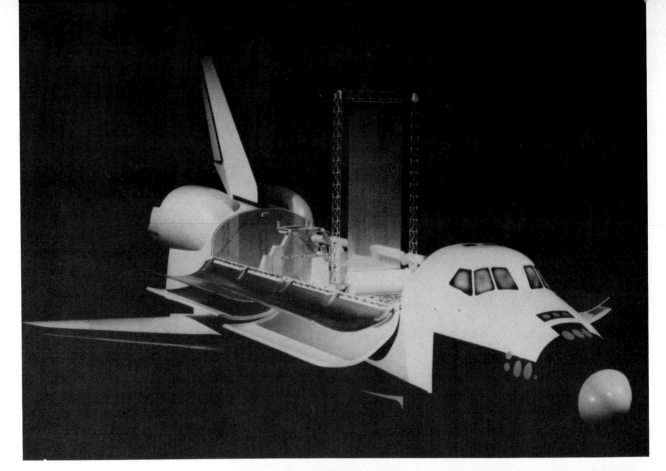

A lightweight, space-based radar antenna array aboard a space shuttle model rolls out like a window shade. Its purpose is to detect enemy missiles and differentiate warheads from decoys. *U.S. Air Force.*

An early warning satellite deployed to identify and report ICBM, SLBM, and spacecraft launches during boost phase. The barrel is an infrared telescope that searches for telltale exhaust plumes. *U.S. Air Force.*

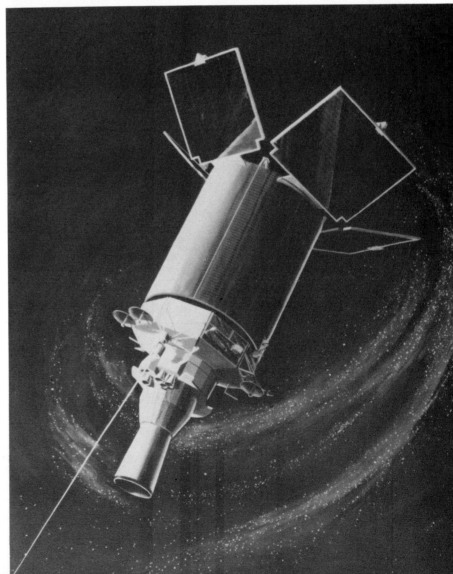

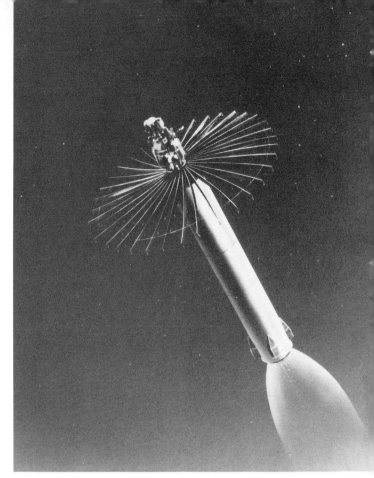

(*Left*)–An SP-100 Space Nuclear Power Generator as it might look during an orbital test. The cone radiates heat. A towed radar array is the beneficiary. (*Right*)–A nonnuclear interceptor, launched from Earth against any target in space, closing at more than 20,000 mph. Metal ribs that unfurl seconds before collision maximize the impact. *U.S. Air Force.*

Two small, hypervelocity, rocket-propelled missiles in flight. One is about to destroy a nuclear-tipped ICBM warhead. *U.S. Air Force.*

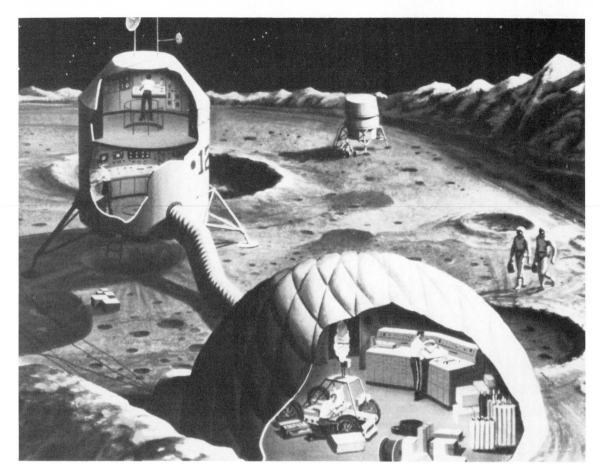

The six-man lunar outpost depicted could serve a variety of purposes. A flexible tunnel leads from the small, inflatable habitat to a lunar landing vehicle. *NASA*.

"Sky walking" outside a U.S. space shuttle. A nitrogen-propelled, hand-controlled maneuvering unit and self-contained support system eliminates any need for an "umbilical cord" between astronaut and spacecraft. *NASA*.

Routine maintenance and emergency repair are two among many tasks that astronauts may perform during periods of extravehicular activity (EVA). *NASA*.

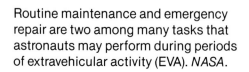

Special operations forces, including rescue crews, demand small, fast, highly maneuverable vehicles able to intercept and rendezvous readily with spacecraft in orbit. *NASA.*

A typical communications satellite. Extremely high frequencies (EHF) resist jamming. Terminals on Earth serve land, sea, and air forces. Note solar power panels. *U.S. Air Force.*

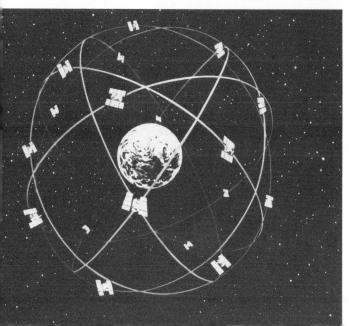

A constellation of 18 global positioning satellites in 6 circular orbits. U.S. armed forces on Earth use data derived thereby to determine their location within 50 feet. *U.S. Air Force.*

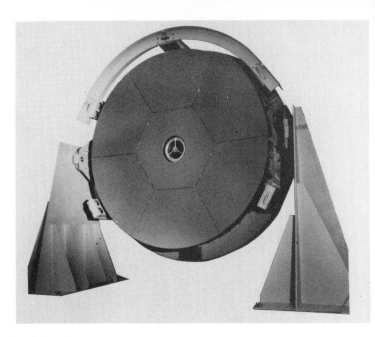

Laser mirrors come in many sizes and shapes. Actuators attached to the rear surfaces precisely configure and align the 13-foot segmented model shown. *U.S. Air Force.*

Space-based lasers must be able to acquire, track, and point at targets. Brightness and retargeting times determine effectiveness at any given range. *U.S. Air Force.*

Space-based railguns employ electromagnetic forces rather than chemical propellants to fire kinetic energy projectiles that may be "smart" or "brilliant." Velocities make rifle bullets seem slow. *U.S. Air Force.*

HYPERVELOCITY GUN

Figure 9   TYPICAL SPACE TETHER

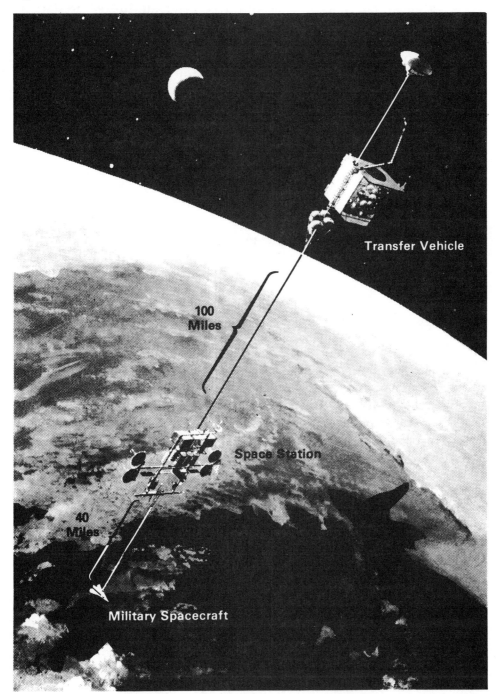

Tether lengths are illustrative. The military spacecraft will enter a lower orbit when released. The transfer vehicle will orbit at a greater altitude.

NOTE: Adapted from *Pioneering the Space Frontier*

because scramjets will not operate at slow speeds or in space. Current concepts call for air-turbo-ramjets to furnish initial impetus. Subsonic combustion ramjets* accelerate from Mach 4 to Mach 6; scramjets take over to about Mach 12. Rockets must put craft into orbit, where airbreathing engines will no longer function, and propel them thereafter until they reenter Earth's atmosphere. Aircraft configuration is critically important, since wings and scoops on the fuselage are parts of the supersonic air intake and exhaust system. Serious problems still must be solved before the first scramjet flies, but progress seems encouraging.[63]

Power Supplies

Military space forces could not survive, much less accomplish assigned missions, without electrical power supplies for multitudinous purposes that include, but are not limited to, fine-tuned flight and fire control instruments, sensors, communications, and life-support apparatus. Reduced weight and volume, coupled with long life (seven to ten years), reliability (99%+), radiation resistance, and safety are ceaseless aims for systems on spacecraft.[64]

Three sorts of space power predominate: electrochemical, solar, and nuclear. Static energy conversion systems embrace batteries and fuel cells, as well as photovoltaic, thermoelectric, and thermionic devices. Dynamic systems link electric generators with turbine or reciprocating engines that rely on thermal energy from chemical fuels, the sun, nuclear isotopes, or nuclear reactors. High-risk technologies such as antiproton annihilation and controlled fusion are still too embryonic for inclusion in this book.[65]

Some power options are competitive. Others overlap. Appropriate selections depend most of all on the type and duration of military missions they must support, but cost is a constant constraint. Custom tailoring consequently is customary.[66]

Power plant peculiarities. Power plants in space encounter a forbidding environment far different than any on Earth. On-site maintenance and repair facilities will long be scant or nonexistent. Those peculiarities impose rigorous requirements.

Gravitational extremes are severe. Spacecraft power plants first must survive vibration and the crushing force of high-g acceleration during launch. Traditional power generation processes thereafter refuse to work. Gravity, for example, cannot separate "weightless" liquids from vapors ("This Side Up" no longer applies) or help shed excess heat by convection. The

*Subsonic combustion ramjets power supersonic aircraft. Supersonic air intake slows to subsonic speed before mixing with fuel.

virtual absence of matter in space also prevents heat conduction. Radiators, which often impose severe weight and volume penalties, remain the primary recourse. Shielding is essential for several reasons. Vacuum invites cold welding, outgassing, and leakage. Solar flares and the Van Allen belts pose potentially serious electromagnetic threats to power supplies in space. Solar cells and superconductors are especially vulnerable. Chemical batteries are sensitive to temperature extremes in space, which also could shorten the useful life of other power plant components. Rotating parts require special lubricants if exposed. Kinetic perturbations also impose problems. Swiveling solar arrays and fast-rotating armatures, for example, influence spacecraft flight attitudes enough to demand costly countermeasures. Powder-fine dust could cause difficulties on the moon.[67]

Electrochemical power. Batteries presently are an indispensable source of electric power in space. Primary cells that need no recharging suffice, provided requirements range from milliwatts to one kilowatt for less than a week. Batteries, for example, furnish pyrotechnic power for explosive bolts that separate launch vehicle stages in flight. U.S. lunar modules employed batteries; Apollo command modules used them during reentry and post landing periods. Experiments suggest that lithium, magnesium, and aluminum, which are more energetic than present anode materials, might improve maximum watt-hours per pound by as much as one-third, from 100 to about 150.

Storage batteries recharged by the sun perform longer missions and replace solar arrays when spacecraft in LEO fly through Earth's shadow (as much as 40% of some orbits). Nickel-cadmium, now the preferred material, has many laudable attributes, but energy densities are no better than 15 watt-hours per pound. Continuing research investigates ambient temperatures, nonaqueous electrolytes, and ways to contain chemical reactions with standard free energies in the 100 Kcal/mole range. Inorganic electrolyte cells, in which the positive electrode reactant is also the solvent, are one promising lead.[68]

Hydrogen-oxygen fuel cells, unlike batteries, store chemical fuels and oxidants externally. Power densities of 200 to 900 watt-hours per pound are feasible for as much as three months, employing present technologies. The reaction product is potable water, when hydrogen and oxygen encounter a solution of sodium hydroxide or potassium hydroxide. Open cycle systems that last only as long as hydrogen and oxygen supplies are ideal for short-duration manned missions, like the U.S. Apollo program. Larger tanks are the price for longer missions. Regenerative systems, under investigation, could serve for years. They use solar power or other sources to reconstitute pure hydrogen and oxygen from water the fuel cells form. Lunar installations, as well as spacecraft, would find that facility useful.[69]

Solar power. Photovoltaic systems, mounted on panels, paddles, or spacecraft skins, convert solar energy to electrical power through thousands of wafer-thin, single-crystal silicon cells. Cells in series supply total voltage; subunits in parallel produce total current. Low energy densities unfortunately are unavoidable under best case circumstances. Radiation and reflection degrade performance, despite filters and protective coatings.[70]

The most efficient spacecraft arrays, which constantly reorient to face the sun, rarely exceed 10 watt-hours per pound. Many are barely able to power a kitchen toaster or hand-held hair dryer—enough for delicate spacecraft mechanisms, such as sensors, but not for laser battle stations, which may demand as much electric power as a small city. Much larger arrays are feasible, but would complicate spacecraft designs, be costly to launch, and destabilize low earth orbits due to atmospheric drag. Alternatives under review, which might improve performance several fold, include gallium arsenide cells and retractable or unfurlable panels, some similar to venetian blinds.[71]

Turboelectric, thermoelectric, and thermionic devices, which convert solar energy into electricity using paraboloidal mirrors to focus sunlight, are potentially more efficient in LEO than photovoltaic systems. Dynamic processes that depend on closed Brayton, organic Rankine, and Stirling thermodynamic cycle engines are in various stages of development. So are thermal energy storage systems that could furnish steady power during shady parts of low earth orbits.[72]

Huge solar arrays, transported piecemeal from Earth or constructed in space, would work well on the moon's light side, because few problems outlined above pertain.[73] Highly efficient superconducting transmission lines hypothetically could lead to installations in lunar shadow. They would be vulnerable to enemy attack, however, and costs could prove prohibitive.

Nuclear power. Radioisotope thermoelectric generators (RTG) are possible replacements for, or supplements to, solar power, batteries, and fuel cells. U.S. Boost Surveillance and Tracking System satellites, for example, will rely on RTGs. Low outputs, high costs, and scarce plutonium 238 nevertheless limit applications.[74]

Nuclear reactors thus remain the only known long-lived, compact source able to supply military space forces with electric power between about 10 kilowatts (kw) and multimegawatts (mmw), as Table 7 indicates.[75]

Cores no bigger than basketballs are able to produce about 100 kw, enough for "housekeeping" aboard space stations and at lunar outposts. Larger versions could meet multimegawatt needs

Table 7   SPACE POWER SYSTEM COMPARISONS

Energy Source	Conversion Type	Mission Duration	LEO	MEO	GEO	Deep Space	Power Range (bar: KW 1–10–100 | MW 1–10)
Chemical	Batteries — Primary	Short	X				▬ (≈1 KW)
	Batteries — Secondary	Medium/Long	X	X	X		▬▬▬ (≈1–10 KW)
	Fuel Cells — Primary	Short	X				▬▬ (≈1–10 KW)
	Regenerative Fuel Cell — Secondary	Medium/Long	X	X	X		▬▬▬ (≈1–10 KW)
	Dynamic*	Short	X				▬▬▬▬ (≈100 KW–1 MW)
Solar	Photovoltaic Array	Medium/Long	X	X	X		▬▬▬ (≈1–10 KW)
	Dynamic*	Long	X	X	X		▬▬▬ (≈10–100 KW)
Nuclear-Radioisotope	Thermoelectric	Long	X	X	X	X	▬▬ (≈1 KW)
	Dynamic*	Long	X	X	X	X	▬ (≈1 KW)
Nuclear-Reactor	Thermoelectric	Long	X	X	X	X	▬▬▬ (≈1–10 KW)
	Dynamic*	Long	X	X	X	X	▬▬▬▬▬▬ (≈1 KW–10 MW)
	Dynamic*	Short			X		▬▬▬ (≈1–10 MW)

*Dynamic conversion includes organic or liquid-metal Rankine, Brayton, and Stirling cycles.
Adapted from *The Evolution of Space Power Systems Technology*, by R. Rudney, J. Mullin, and D. Chaudoir.

of space-based lasers, neutral particle beams, mass drivers, and railguns. Nuclear reactors must support major bases on the moon until better options, yet unidentified, become available, because imported fossil fuels (gas and oil) would be too expensive. Hydroelectric power, a mainstay some places on Earth, is impossible.[76]

Reactor designs and operating procedures emphasize nuclear safety before, during, and after spacecraft launch, with particular attention to uncontrolled reentries that could rain radioactive debris across densely settled areas on Earth. Safety factors, rather than technological feasibility, will remain the principal impediment to nuclear power in space, unless officials convince influential critics that risks are acceptably low.[77]

Electronics

Electronics are an essential element of more military space hardware than any other constituent, except materials (see Table 4). Research and development currently concentrate most intently on three fundamental fields: supercomputers, plus associated security measures; automated systems, with special concern for artificial intelligence; and C^3 implements, especially spacecraft guidance, control, electronic sensors, and communications.

Supercomputers. Military space forces literally could not get off the ground without computers, which are inseparable parts of every spacecraft propulsion, power, navigation, intelligence collection, data processing, command/control, communication, and weapon system. Manufacturing processes, flight planning, and logistic support also depend on computers.

Computers best suited for employment on Earth and moon understandably attract the most attention from research communities. Present developments seem to justify phenomenal expectations for the near future. Parallel-processing computers that subdivide complex problems and solve each part simultaneously are a thousand times faster than computers that proceed step-by-step. An infinite number of microchip processors, each the equivalent of a standard computer, theoretically could be interconnected, but wiring would be unwieldy. One encouraging compromise arranges processors in a "hypercube" that could contain an infinite number of cubes. The most expansive experiment thus far involves 128 nodes, each of which intersects seven others (every corner of every interior cube touches the nearest corner of every neighbor). Anticipated peak speeds approximate 2 billion floating point operations (flops) per second, or 2 gigaflops; 10,000 nodes and teraflop performance are present goals.* Multiprocessor systems able to focus the efforts of tens, hundreds, even thousands of such supercomputers on otherwise insuperable tasks are conceivable.[78]

Spaceborne computer capabilities typically lag land-based equivalents by several years. That fact has militarily adverse implications, because armed forces, like chains, are limited by weak links. Parallel supercomputers during real-time laboratory experiments, for example, currently can calculate appropriate defensive moves by orbital interceptor constellations against a swarm of ASATs or reentry vehicles. Whether present generation battle management computers could duplicate that feat from platforms in space is dubious.[79]

Compact supercomputers, suitable for duty aboard spacecraft, consequently are obligatory. Repackaging to reduce size, weight, and power input, however, will not be enough. Unique requirements include reliability beyond any on Earth, resistance to radiation, safeguards against failure, and autonomous recovery, if unforeseen faults occur. Software may be the biggest stumbling block. Foolproof, flexible, affordable algorithms are scarce. Software designs often are so complex that predeployment tests cannot anticipate all possible causes of failure. Incompatible programs make it impossible for many military computers to "talk" to each other. Much improved software within a few years therefore seems a reasonable milestone for spaceborne computers.[80]

Computer security is a constant concern for military space forces that can accomplish assigned missions only if widely separated sensors, weapons, and command centers share information via networks, which, in turn, attract eavesdroppers and

---

*Bits are binary digits, the most basic unit of computer information: eight bits make one byte. Floating point operations add one byte to one byte. Teraflop operations would make 1 trillion such computations per second.

"viruses." Amateur hackers, like those who sporadically plague U.S. civilian computer nets, reportedly pose slight threats to military traffic that passwords, encryption, closed circuits, and software designs protect. Professional saboteurs, however, might interfere. Computer security specialists also worry about enemy agents and disloyal employees, who might introduce "bugs" internally, because of bribes or spite. Software moles, called "logic bombs" and "Trojan horses," could be catastrophic (the latter might remain inactive for years, then respond to instructions). Best defenses must combine built-in hardware/software shields with stringent personnel selection procedures and alert counterintelligence.[81]

Automation and autonomy. Needs for automated and/or autonomous military space systems are indisputable. Versatile robots, large and small, able to function indefinitely without food, water, or sleep, could relieve humans of heavy, hazardous, humdrum tasks, or replace them entirely in environments more adverse than any on Earth. Huge data bases hold more than human minds could handle fast enough during space combat. Machines must help sift confusing information and identify options expeditiously, despite the friction of war,* before space commanders make life or death decisions.[82]

Artificial intelligence (AI), the key to future brainy robots, is orders of magnitudes more complex than routine data management. Progress so far has been slow, partly because few companies specialize in AI, partly because no one knows precisely how people think (propositions, imagination, and mental modeling probably collaborate). Advancement accordingly must be founded as much on theoretical pioneering as on improved supercomputers and software. Microscopic motors and miniature manipulators, embedded in or etched on computer chips, may accelerate the required revolution.[83]

Two interdependent types of AI predominate: expert systems and neural networks. Speech and vision, desirable in both, would simplify communications between machines and human supervisors.[84]

Expert systems rely on rules, frames of reference, and logic to reason, reach conclusions, and explain rationales. Symbols, rather than numbers, represent information, because they admit abstractions more readily than yes/no algorithms. R&D requirements are demanding. Computer-assisted programmers first must develop expansive data banks that contain facts, hypotheses, and assumptions relevant to every conceivable contingency

---

*Clausewitz took more than two pages to define friction in war.[85] Murphy's Law states it concisely: "What can go wrong will go wrong at the worst possible moment."

in discrete mission areas. Diagnostic applications currently are most common, but robotic operations of all kinds could profit. Software must accommodate exceptions to every rule and reference frame (birds, as a rule, have feathers, lay eggs, and fly, but penguins lack plumage, roosters never lay eggs, and baby birds cannot fly). Expert system researchers also wrestle with inferential methods that might supplement propositional and predicate logic. Candidates include reasoning by analogy, case-based reasoning, and script-based reasoning.[86]

Neural networks, sometimes called cognitive or self-programming systems, are quite different, because they learn from experience. That attribute, even modestly achieved, would much reduce the required knowledge base. Pattern recognition capabilities have many potential applications that vary from simple to exceedingly complex. Neural networks, if perfected, could be trained to perform mechanical functions (weapon maintenance, sanitation) that do not justify time-consuming and costly manmade algorithms. They also could detect anomalous and changing conditions, then assess significance in light of past practice. Space commanders, for example, could strengthen their own deception plans and counter rival duplicity if neural networks exposed inconsistencies. R&D, however, is so difficult that few participants anticipate early breakthroughs.[87]

Neural networks and expert systems are complementary, not competitive. The former delivers intuitive solutions at high speed; the latter uses logic. Together, they could solve problems too tough for either to tackle alone. Users, in the final analysis, are in a better position than technologists to identify what innovative functions they need most.[88]

Command, control, and communications. C[3] systems acquire, assimilate, and disseminate data that space commanders need to plan and conduct cohesive military operations in peacetime and war. Nerve centers, most connecting links, and many countermeasures/countercountermeasures are electronic. The scope covers such diverse fields as intelligence activities (target acquisition and tracking, for example); spacecraft navigation and guidance;[89] electronic warfare;[90] and battle management for space-based ballistic missile defense.[91] Communications, which cut across the C[3] spectrum, illustrate typical problems and options. Military space force requirements for voice, video, radio-telegraph, and digital communications currently are increasing at exponential rates. The pace predictably will pick up as deployments multiply in LEO, GEO, and beyond. The number of common user and dedicated channels is not expanding commensurately. Sharing often is impractical, and bandwidths are not broad enough to fill requests. Extensive reliance on commercial satellite facilities improves peacetime flexibility, but might be worthless in war, because such systems are even less survivable than military equivalents. Land-based, sea-based, and airborne jammers able to disrupt communications between Earth and space, for example, are widely available. Low-power jammers employed at close range could overwhelm the most capable transmitters now in orbit. Room for improvement, in short, is remarkable.[92]

Objectives involve better survivability, interoperability, reliability, cross-links, and endurance. Autonomous communications satellites, able to process information onboard, would reduce Earth-to-space and return traffic, but adequate capacity in the long run likely will demand larger, more numerous satellites. Jam resistance and spoof-proofing are perennial priorities. The trend toward extremely high frequencies (EHF) helps frustrate enemy interference, because very broad bandwidths in the gigahertz range facilitate frequency hopping.[93]

Optics

Optical instruments augment military space capabilities in three important ways. Photo and quasiphoto sensors capture and record images on film or some suitable substitute, primarily for intelligence purposes. Photons supplement or replace electrons in some advanced C^3 systems that include telecommunications, in addition to information processing, storage, and display. High-energy lasers also rely on optics (see subsequent section entitled Weapon Systems for discussion).

Photographics. Infrared, visible, and ultraviolet waves activate photo and quasiphoto sensors. Passive sensors measure heat emitted by, or natural light reflected from, objects observed. Active sensors that illuminate matter artificially, most often with laser designators, rely less on chance, but are more susceptible to countermeasures because they reveal themselves to opponents. Reconnaissance and surveillance, the simplest tasks, entail abilities to detect particular items and determine locations. Precise identification, discrimination, tracking, and weapon pointing call for increased sophistication. Early warning, target acquisition, and post-attack assessments are typical purposes. Sensors that process information aboard spacecraft reduce communication loads. So do those that separate wheat from chaff (*specificity* is the technical term); some sensors, for example, compare old pictures with new, then report nothing but change.[94]

More than 100 trillion cubic miles of space separate Earth from equatorial GEO. Armed forces could monitor that expanse—indeed, all of the Earth-Moon System—with telescopes much like those used for science. Large lenses, stable platforms, and so-called active optics, which minimize atmospheric diffraction, vest land-based models with very high resolution (image fidelity). Telescopes on the moon and in orbit above Earth's atmosphere would avoid diffraction. Perpetually spotless mirrors are possible for those equipped with ultrasonic transducers and ion guns that automatically remove rocket exhaust particles, gas condensates, and molecular films. Resolution nevertheless decreases as distance increases. Larger, lighter weight lenses, achieved through novel construction techniques, therefore are topics of intense research, along with subreflectors, coatings, and means to assure superior resolution at long range under harsh conditions. Success would enable sensors in GEO and HEO to take sharp pictures of subjects on Earth without dipping low on each pass.[95]

Preferred films are monochrome, since color is less sensitive to light. Filters exclude undesirable wavelengths. Electronic imaging, however, has replaced photographic film on most optical sensors. Focal planes covered with silicon-based chips called CCDs (charge-coupled devices) convert light into digital information, which computerized receivers reassemble to form pictures that can be printed or projected on screens. CCDs are many times more sensitive than any emulsion film, and can record fine detail as well as self-develop.[96]

Infrared (IR) sensors occupy a separate niche. Night vision is a specialty. IR cannot "see" through clouds any better than sensors that record visible light reflections but, when weather is clear, they can easily unmask camouflage, which has different properties than the subject it seeks to conceal or pretends to be. Short- and middle-wave IR sensors (SWIR, MWIR) are ideally suited to spot hot missile booster exhaust. Post-boost vehicles and orbiting spacecraft are much harder to trace, because LWIR/MWIR emissions are comparatively bland when onboard engines fire briefly, and are absent when they coast. Long-wave infrared technology (LWIR) needed to pick up the scent is immature. Sensors must be cryogenically refrigerated to keep their own radiation from swamping weak signals. Discriminating "room temperature" decoys from bona fide targets is more difficult. Infrared sensors as a result leave much room for refinement.[97]

Photonics. Fiber optics are starting to invigorate long-line and intermediate point-to-point telecommunications. They feature great capacities, fewer repeaters, and freedom from electrical interference (see previous section entitled Materials). Prominent applications include high-performance cables, transmitters, and receiver modules. Optical switches and amplifiers, components for wavelength division multiplexing, low-noise avalanche photodiodes, and monolithic optical/electrical integration technologies are subjects of intense research that could benefit future military space forces, especially those based on the Earth and moon.[98]

Photonics promise to improve information processing. Almost limitless bandwidths, immunity from electronic interference, and side-by-side channels are attractive characteristics. Neural networks predicated entirely on optics attract interest, because response is so fast. Photonics make nearly perfect connections between computers (particularly multiprocessors).[99] They also work well between computers and on-line, rapid-access optical storage facilities that enthusiasts contend may surpass magnetic means by a factor of 500 or so, when laser arrays for read/write heads and high-contrast reversible materials are perfected. Cathode-ray, plasma panel, and electroluminescent displays compete with electronic technologies in most respects, but three-dimensional holograms are entirely within the province of photonics. [100]

Weapon Systems

Weapons are the trademark of every military force. Those designed expressly for space (Table 8) are unlike any employed on Earth, partly because low gravity, vacuum, and its confluence with atmosphere significantly influence effects.*

Space weapons are generally useful only against point targets. Large lethal radii are limited to nuclear radiation. Short-range space weapons (except mines) have a longer reach than most long-range arms on Earth. Lasers and particle beams make their own "munitions," then strike far distant targets at the speed of light. Many land, sea, and air systems rely on distant sensors, but none separate weapon components like space lasers and their remote mirrors. Neither do they need such elaborate generators.

Most space weapons share several characteristics. Size, weight, and costs currently are "sky" high. Power supplies are insufficient. A Soviet orbital ASAT armed with "buckshot" is the world's only operational space weapon.[101] The rest, in various stages of research and development, are mainly a mixture of laboratory experiments and prototypes. One direct-ascent ASAT that put a 35-pound miniature homing vehicle on collision course with an obsolete satellite in September 1985 thus far has been the only realistic U.S. test.[102] Projected deployment dates, with few exceptions, consequently are far in the future. [103]

Idiosyncratic space weapons nevertheless exhibit distinctive differences, as well as similarities. The following summaries emphasize a few.

Rockets, railguns, and mines. Interceptor rockets, under investigation since the late 1950s, represent the most mature space

---

*Chapter 1 describes nuclear, directed energy, chemical/biological, and conventional weapon effects in space. See section entitled Weapon Performance.

Table 8   SPACE WEAPON SYSTEM COMPARISONS

	Rockets	Railguns	Mines	Lasers[1]				Particle Beams	
				Free Electron	Excimer	Chemical	X Ray	Charged	Neutral
Location									
Earth	X			X	X			X	
Moon	X	X		X		X	X		X
Space	X	X	X	X		X	X		X
Sites per system									
One	X	X	X	X	X			X	
Many (Mirrors)				X	X	X		X	X
Munitions									
Inert Projectiles	X	X	X						
Explosives									
Conventional	X		X						
Nuclear	X		X						
Coherent Light				X	X	X	X		
Atomic, Subatomic Particles								X	X

	Rockets	Railguns	Mines	Free Electron	Excimer	Chemical	X Ray	Charged	Neutral
Lethal Force									
Blast	X		X						X
Heat				X	X	X	X	X	
Radiation	X		X					X	
Collision	X	X	X						
Impulse				X		X	X		
Eruption								X	
Current								X	
Glare				X	X	X	X		X
Maximum Range									
Longest				X[2]			X		X
Shortest	X		X			X		X	
Refire									
Yes		X		X	X	X	X	X	X
No	X		X						
Power Source									
Chemical	X		X			X			
Electrical		X		X	X			X	
Nuclear							X		X
Deployment[3]									
Early	X		X						
Mid	X			X		X		X	
Late		X			X		X		X

[1] See Table 9 for additional details.
[2] Excludes lasers located on Earth.
[3] "Early," "mid," and "late" are relative terms.

weapon technologies.*[104] Basing on Earth, moon, and orbiting spacecraft, coupled with abilities to perform many different missions, make rocket systems quite flexible. Antisatellite operations and last ditch defense against ballistic missiles are merely representative. Warheads could be nuclear, but political, legal, and military disadvantages normally make such weapons unattractive. Vacuum, for example, severely limits the lethal radii of all nuclear effects except radiation, which might endanger friendly forces and neutrals more than foes. Conventional explosives and inert projectiles consequently are preferable for most purposes. "Dumb" rockets could carry "smart rocks" or "brilliant pebbles" equipped with homing devices and/or terminal guidance. Others might detonate charges at the last moment or collide with targets at 4–5 miles per second. High-speed, exceptionally accurate rockets are essential against very hard, time-sensitive targets, such as ballistic missile reentry vehicles. Less capable systems could accomplish other missions.[105]

Space mines, unlike interceptor rockets, could precede or trail targets at close range in peacetime, perhaps for long periods, before remote controllers activate them on call, provided arms controllers and rivals allow. Payloads could comprise various explosives and kinetic energy weapons.** Directional fragmentation warheads much like Claymore mines could saturate a 100×100 yard front with 100,000 pellets from half a mile away (10 per square yard). Space mines alternatively might dispense chaff, aerosols, corner reflectors, decoys, and other deceptive devices. Electronic warfare, mainly high-power proximity jamming, is another potential mission. Salvage fusing could trigger space mines, if they were attacked.[106]

Electromagnetic launchers (EML), commonly called railguns, are closely akin to much larger mass drivers. R&D presently concentrates on two types, both embryonic. The most advanced versions transmit tremendous electronic current down one rail, through the rear of a small projectile, and back along a second rail, as shown in Figure 10. The consequent closed circuit forms a strong magnetic field that interacts with the current to create a constant outward force, which accelerates the projectile. A different EML design relies on coils, instead of rails. The projectile

*Many individual and portable crew-served weapons, such as pistols, revolvers, carbines, rifles, submachineguns, and machineguns, would work well on the moon or in free space with little or no modification. They are not "space weapons," however, in the context of this book.

**Some sources assert that space mines include orbital lasers and particle beams on spacecraft far distant from targets. They also count nuclear weapons that wait in space until detonated on command to disrupt enemy communications and intelligence sensors.[107] This study considers such systems to be standoff weapons (bombers bearing cruise missiles are analogous).

Figure 10 RAILGUN SCHEMATIC

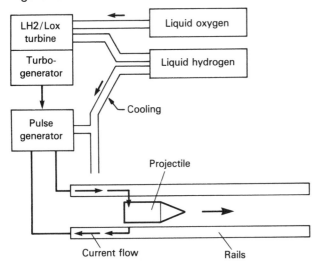

SOURCE: Office of Technology Assessment, 1988.

parts their magnetic fields when it enters; they reconnect when it passes. Acceleration occurs in the process. Both methods require monumental research before practical tests are possible. Small, "smart" projectiles (none now exist) able to tolerate terrific acceleration (several hundred thousand times greater than gravity) and compact weapon systems (most are immense) that can repeatedly fire several shots per second (one test ruins most) are typical problems. Railguns half the length of football fields, for example, would be required to launch 200,000 g projectiles at nine miles per second (15 times as fast as a rifle bullet). Large constellations to compensate for low refire rates would be costly. Superconductors, new structural materials, and compact, high current power supplies may come to the rescue, but not tomorrow.[108]

Laser weapons. Optical laser weapons presently comprise three classes: free electron, excimer, and chemical. X-ray lasers are in a class by themselves (Tables 8 and 9).

All four classes attack at the speed of light (186,000 miles per second). All four fire intense, tightly focused, unidirectional beams of coherent light that concentrate energy on target surfaces, the most absorptive of which reflect a high percentage. Very short wavelengths are most lethal, because beams spread least at long range. Atmosphere, however, interferes. Pulsed beams deposit greater energy in shorter times than steady streams of light, but power demands are prodigious. Laser weapons damage or destroy targets in three distinctive ways: dazzle disrupts optical sensors, including human eyes; thermal effects raise target temperatures enough to melt or otherwise

Table 9 LASER WEAPONS COMPARED*

	Free Electron	Excimer	Chemical	X Ray
Lasing Medium				
Gas		X	X	
Solid				X
None	X			
Pumping Mechanism				
Electric	X	X		
Chemical			X	
Nuclear				X
Operational Mode				
Continuous Wave			X	
Pulse	X	X	X	X
Wavelength				
Length (Infrared to Visible)			X	
Medium (Ultraviolet to Visible)		X		
Short (X Rays)				X
Tuneable	X			
Atmosphere **				
Penetrable	X	XeF, XeCl	DF	
Impenetrable		KrF	HF	X

*See Table 8 for additional details.

**Deuterium fluoride (DF); hydrogen fluoride (HF); krypton and fluorine (KrF); xenon and chlorine (XeCl); xenon and fluorine (XeF).

deform materials; impulse drives mechanical shock waves toward target interiors. Results depend on power amplitudes, beam size and steadiness, wavelengths, pulse lengths, polarization, angle of attack, and target hardness. Proper choices depend on weapon purposes and target characteristics.[109]

All optical lasers moreover must rely on mirrors to amplify and aim light beams. Short wavelength laser weapons outperform long wavelength weapons of equal power, because they allow longer range with the same size mirrors, or equal range with smaller ones. Resultant savings in size and weight simplify space basing. Such capabilities, however, are costly. Nearly flawless mirrors are necessary, polished almost perfectly to reflect ultraviolet (UV) light preferentially. Expensive dielectric coatings also are essential, because UV damages mirrors more readily than infrared or visible light when operators apply high power. One additional problem unrelated to wavelengths merits mention. Mirrors must be able to switch rapidly from one target to another without jiggling excessively. A single illustration is instructive in that regard. Vibrations that offset a 10-meter (33-foot) mirror 1 micrometer (40 millionths of an inch) would slice laser brightness in half.[110]

Laser weapon systems fortunately display fundamental differences, as well as similarities just described. Combined capabilities in fact could prove greater than the sum of four separate parts, if R&D specialists solve serious problems.

Free electron lasers (FEL), unlike other optical lasers that amplify light in a solid, liquid, or gas, employ a particle accelerator to pass electrons through a magnetic undulator or "wiggler." Resultant radiation creates a beam of coherent light that theoretically can be tuned to any wavelength because electron energies and magnetic periods both are variable. Present research, however, emphasizes infrared waves, which are relatively long. Power plants, accelerators, and mirrors all must be large, until technological breakthroughs diminish mass and weight. Meanwhile, space deployment seems possible, but impractical. Land-based FEL will be feasible at earlier dates only if tight beams transit the atmosphere intact, before they bounce off mirrors in space. Adaptive optics, under development, first must improve brightness many times. Relay mirrors in GEO would afford fixed aiming points, but reflectors in low earth orbits could control thermal blooming better. Tactical and technological compromises thus are required.[111]

Excimer lasers promise shorter wavelengths than experimental FELs. External energy sources, such as an electrical discharge or electron pulse, cause halogen atoms to bond briefly with noble (inert) gas atoms in a lasing chamber, then release a photon pulse in the ultraviolet to visible spectrum when they separate. Excimer lasers at this moment weigh even more and are less efficient than FELs. Land basing therefore remains the only possibility, until R&D relieves both constraints. Xenon/fluorine (XeF) and xenon/chlorine (XeCl) combinations transmit well through atmosphere, but pulse power falls well short of most mission requirements. So-called Raman cells, which seek to circumvent that problem by binding several low-power beams, have succeeded in laboratory tests. Research continues.[112]

Chemical lasers constitute a third alternative. The most mature technologies combine hydrogen (H) with fluorine (F) atoms to produce excited HF molecules that emit infrared light when they return to a stable state in the laser cavity. Potential efficiency, not yet realized, is high compared with excimer lasers and FELs. Space basing is possible at earlier dates, because HF continuous waves, as well as pulses, propagate well in a vacuum. Requirements for atmospheric compensators and relay mirrors disappear, along with redundant deployments that land-based lasers need to ensure clear shots on inclement days. Space, in addition, is an ideal place to expel huge amounts of high velocity exhaust that contains toxic waste and excess heat. Chemical laser debits, however, are considerable. Lasants, which must be replaced, impose heavy logistic loads, and power remains inadequate. Infrared beams not only demand large mirrors, but extensive and costly constellations, because dwell times are long. Research accordingly concentrates on ways to reduce wavelengths (iodine compounds are candidates) and strengthen beams. Coherent coupling techniques that create bright HF arrays are under review in the latter regard.[113]

X-ray lasers, unlike optical competitors, will be single-shot, self-destructing weapons powered by nuclear devices that demolish the entire apparatus split seconds after detonation. Bundles of laser rods (maybe 50 or more), which focus the resultant radiant energy, survive long enough to engage multiple targets simultaneously. How rapidly weapon designers will be able to harness that enormous energy, however, is debatable, because conversion, pointing, and tracking problems are exceedingly complex. Nuclear weapons in space have so many drawbacks that development may be further delayed while technologists explore conventional explosive substitutes. Space basing appears likely, if X-ray lasers reach fruition. Even rarefied atmosphere is impenetrable and "forward basing" would facilitate rapid response in emergencies. That posture, however, would violate pacts that prohibit nuclear weapons in space, and exposed battle stations would be vulnerable to preemptive attacks. "Pop-up" launches from bases on land or afloat, which seem feasible, consequently are under consideration for some close-in missions, especially ballistic missile defense.[114]

Particle beam weapons. Atomic or subatomic particles accelerated near the speed of light and properly focused produce beams which, unlike lasers, almost instantaneously deposit energy in depth, rather than initially on target surfaces. Dwell times are insignificant; thermal conduction is unimportant. Hardening spacecraft against attack normally is impractical. Current flow and heat damage or destroy structures and sensitive internal components, particularly electronics. High temperatures may ignite ballistic propellants or detonate devices that trigger nuclear weapons. Superheated spots erupt if they expand much faster than cool surrounding materials.[115]

Charged particle beams (CPB) accelerate electrons or ions, which propagate poorly through space. Such beams are too broad for weapon purposes, because particles of like charge repel each other in vacuum, and Earth's magnetic field bends them. Transmission through atmosphere is little better, unless lasers drill an ionized channel for electron beams to follow. That process, which must be proved, takes time (a critical constraint for ballistic missile defense, the most probable purpose). Range might be limited to a few hundred miles even if CPB weapons deployed in the ionosphere, where air is thin. Delayed development thus is likely.[116]

Neutral particle beams (NPB) have a brighter future. One proton and one orbiting electron normally comprise each hydrogen atom, now the most likely source of energy. Technologists tack on another electron, because accelerators accept nothing but charged particles. Negatively charged atoms (H –) accelerated, shaped, and sent through a machine that removes the excess electron, reemerge in their original neutral state. NPBs, which atmosphere would ionize, propagate well in space. Continuing research seeks to reduce weapon system size and weight. Pointing and tracking problems must still be resolved. It is difficult to know at this stage, for example, whether beams score bullseyes or misses, since target surfaces seldom show visible signs of damage. Distant assessors cannot ascertain with high confidence whether results are satisfactory or more shots are required. NPBs nevertheless enjoy widespread support and relatively high priorities.[117]

People-Oriented Programs

Military space forces surely will rely extensively on supercomputers and artifically intelligent robots a few decades hence. Maintenance, repair, and refueling are just a few among many possible functions. Complete automation nevertheless may never be practical, for reasons much like those that preclude fully mechanized armies, navies, air forces, and marine corps. Humans probably would be irreplaceable in peacetime, even if all hardware always worked perfectly. Costs to produce every imperative capability would soon become prohibitive. Sizable manned contingents probably should deploy in space, because commanders and staff far removed from crises seldom can assess situations and take appropriate actions as well as on-the-spot counterparts.

Space warfare, quite different from any peaceful pursuit, would reinforce requirements for human hearts, hands, and intellect. Spoofing and other forms of electronic warfare could shut down autonomous and remotely controlled systems more readily than those with manual overrides. Strategies, tactics, and operational art are too complex for punchcard implementation. Lucky generals may be worth more than smart ones, as Napoleon well knew. Some circumstances call for killer instincts and cunning; others call for integrity and compassion. Emotionless robots, which lack such qualities, might be more predictable to enemies than flesh and blood warriors, who have gut feelings and play hunches that often win battles, campaigns, even wars. Human minds may always be superior to the most marvelous machines in circumstances that require subjective judgments: which enemy targets to strike or spare, which friendly assets to sacrifice or safeguard.[118] No computer, for example, told Winston Churchill whether to warn Coventry or compromise Ultra, his "most secret source" of intelligence in November 1940.[119]

Space, however, is too hostile an environment for humans to survive without life-support systems, much less perform acceptably well. People-oriented programs therefore deserve high priority. Those devoted to habitats, health, safety, supply, and sanitation are particularly important.

Habitats. Small, relatively simple habitats provide occupants a "weightless" environment. Large spacecraft and lunar structures, or components thereof, may rotate slowly to produce pseudogravity through centrifugal force. Results vary from 1 g (normal on earth) to small fractions thereof, depending on habitat radii and rates of spin, as Table 10 indicates.[120]

Engineers eventually may equip tactical spacecraft with artificial gravity but, until they do so economically, crews aboard forward command centers, weapon platforms, and outposts in orbit must live and work under weightless conditions. Multicellular construction probably will characterize large space vehicles, because bulkheads distribute structural loads and provide

Table 10   HABITAT RADII RELATED TO ROTATION
(Rotation Expressed in RPM)

Radius (feet)	RPM required to produce 1 g or less			
	1.0g	0.5g	0.25g	0.1g
5	24.17	17.09	12.08	7.64
10	17.09	12.08	8.54	5.40
15	13.95	9.87	6.98	4.41
20	12.08	8.54	6.04	3.82
25	10.81	7.64	5.40	3.42
30	9.87	6.98	4.93	3.12
40	8.54	6.04	4.27	2.70
50	7.64	5.40	3.82	2.42
60	6.98	4.93	3.49	2.21
80	6.04	4.27	3.02	1.91
100	5.40	3.82	2.70	1.71
120	4.93	3.49	2.47	1.56
140	4.57	3.23	2.28	1.44
160	4.27	3.02	2.14	1.35
180	4.03	2.85	2.01	1.27
200	3.82	2.70	1.91	1.21
300	3.12	2.21	1.56	0.99
400	2.70	1.91	1.35	0.85
1000	1.71	1.18	0.85	0.54

multiple stress paths. Self-sealing pressure chambers moreover might serve much the same purpose as watertight compartments on ships. Vehicles could survive, if meteoroids or enemy weapons punctured one or more. Special accessories facilitate efficiency in weightless quarters, where cubage counts more than floor or wall space and there is no "up" or "down." Anthropometric (human body) and ergonometric (work measurement) studies help determine optimum design and placement of everything from "bathrooms" to battle stations. Data display and instrument panels able to simplify complex operations under combat conditions are subjects of special interest.[121]

Lengthy missions (several months) and/or functions that need pseudogravity justify rotating habitats, which are more difficult to devise, construct, and maintain than so-called weightless models. They also cost more. Rotational rates relieve weightlessness or remove it entirely, so food, water, pencils, paper, and other loose articles, along with crews, do not float. Artificially induced gravity, however, is not entirely normal. Occupants become disoriented if they spin too fast. Excessive gravity gradients, including those attributed to Coriolis force, may cause some individuals to become violently ill, even hallucinate. Adverse effects diminish in rotating habitats that have very large diameters. That relationship would pertain to lunar structures as well as spacecraft. Artificial gravity is greatest along the rim of any rotating habitat, least at the hub, where crews enter and exit through a near weightless vestibule. Tests will determine which individuals can tolerate frequent round trips between two totally different environments, then duties can be assigned accordingly.[122]

Personal habitats, commonly called space suits, protect personnel who venture even briefly outside orbital vehicles or lunar installations. Ideal specifications call for comfortable garments in assorted sizes that are easy to don and doff in emergency. Fully flexible, lightweight materials that resist wear and tear are mandatory. Sufficient finger dexterity to wind a watch or pick up a needle is desirable. Self-contained, dependable life-support systems must handle body heat well enough to permit prolonged exertion, prevent face plate fogging, and avoid nitrogen bubble "bends" when wearers proceed from pressurized habitats to the vacuum of space and back. Built-in devices that monitor their medical condition would also be beneficial.[123]

Health and safety. Microgravity is the source of most physiological problems peculiar to space; radiation causes the rest. Behavior abnormalities, infrequent thus far, may afflict military astronauts when missions lengthen and become more intense. Armed combat under unique conditions clearly would create unusual strains.[124]

Many debilitating effects of microgravity on human muscles, bones, and blood are major aims of life science research. So are sensory disturbances, such as motion sickness. Time-consuming exercise (two to four hours daily) retards cardiovascular deconditioning, but does not address osteoporosis, cephalic fluid shifts, or immunosuppression. Extensive exercise also detracts from important duties. So-called penguin suits that compel torso and legs to work against loads are poor substitutes for artificial gravity. Long-term drug therapy is disputatious. Rotating habitats consequently attract concerted attention. Maximum angular velocities, minimum gravity gradients, and times required to adapt are important, because they help determine how many structures of what type military space forces should deploy at considerable expense and inconvenience. It takes a lot of energy, for example, to rotate large spacecraft; docking complexities and danger of accidents increase. Scientists therefore are investigating a suite of variable-force centrifuge facilities to ascertain whether one full g or some fraction thereof is constantly essential. They could conclude that slowly rotating rooms or sleepers, occupied periodically, would suffice, but experimentation in space appears the only true way to tell.[125]

Space vehicles that orbit beyond Earth's magnetic field are exposed to intense radiation. Lunar bases would be, too. Warning signals that permit timely retreat to LEO or refuge in "storm cellars" anywhere above the Van Allen belts seem the only way for personnel to survive solar flares, but military space forces could function indefinitely in amply hardened structures under less lethal conditions. Every ounce of unnecessary shielding, however, would deprive spacecraft of precious propellant and payloads. Insufficient protection would unnecessarily imperil crews. Medical specialists need to know much more about the biological effects of high linear transfer radiation and devise better instruments to measure dosages before they can design proper protection without evadable penalties and treat casualties professionally.[126]

Space psychology, which is just starting to take shape, poses many questions for which there are as yet no answers. Most concern interplanetary travel in cramped quarters with little chance of rescue if things go radically wrong. Armed combat in space would multiply mental health problems manifold. Behavioral scientists currently strive to determine how specific individuals and small groups would likely react to various types of stress in space, identify probable limits of endurance, and develop ways to ensure effective performance. Progress is slow and study results will be tentative until manned space flights greatly expand the available data base.[127]

Supply and sanitation. Artificial environments make manned operations possible in space. Closed-loop systems that create or recycle air, water, food, and waste are particularly important, because they reduce requirements for resupply.[128]

Even seemingly simple functions are complex, compared with similar efforts on Earth. Potable water, for example, must be sterilized even if produced onboard by fuel cells. Uncontrolled bacteria otherwise would contaminate containers. Chlorination leaves a bad taste. Iodine treatment is satisfactory for short missions, but long-term solutions await further study. Candidate technologies that could purify potable, personal hygiene, and wash water include electrochemical, absorption/desorption, and molecular sieves. Filters could suppress repugnant odors and minute contaminants.[129]

Solid waste disposal is more worrisome. Crews of small spacecraft could dump feces and garbage into the void. Lunar installations could bury them. Neither practice, however, would be practical for large orbital stations. One promising experiment suggests that supercritical water oxidation at high temperatures and pressures could quickly and economically transform an aqueous slurry of organic waste into pure water, clean gas, and inert ash.[130]

The ultimate goal is to grow food on farms in space, rather than import products from Earth. Success depends on much better knowledge about the influence of gravity on plant life. Exploration of that subject is embryonic, but breakthroughs in recumbent DNA technology may facilitate manmade bioforms that could flourish outside Earth's gravitational field.[131]

CHAPTER

5

U.S. and Soviet Military Space Postures

Only two nations, the United States and Soviet Union, possess extensive military space forces. Opposing concepts, plans, programs, and deployments are similar in some respects, but composite postures are quite different (Table 11). This brief comparison takes geography, military doctrines, design philosophies, technological competence, budgetary support, and other influential factors into account.[1]

POSTURAL SIMILARITIES

U.S. and Soviet military space forces presently share several attributes. Basic objectives and mission priorities are virtually indistinguishable. C[3] structures are much alike. Both, for example, maintain primary control facilities on land, but position supplementary installations in space and afloat. Neither nation has formed a separate military service for space or a military space coalition with any country. Neither deploys extensive space combat capabilities. Space infrastructure on both sides is vulnerable to ballistic missile attacks. Satellites are poorly protected.

Table 11 U.S. AND SOVIET MILITARY SPACE POSTURES, 1989

	United States	Soviet Union
Basic Objectives		
Deter	X	X
Defend	X	X
Deny	X	X
Support Earth	X	X
Declaratory Policies		
Oppose Hegemony	X	X
Pursue Arms Control	X	X
Organization		
Military and Civilian		
Separate	X	
Inseparable		X
High Command		
Space Commands	X	
Traditional Commands		X
Infrastructure		
Industry		
Dedicated base		X
High production		X
C³ Facilities		
Homeland	X	X
Allied Territory	X	
Afloat	X	X
Space	X	X
Launch Facilities		
Inland		X
Many		X
Fixed Site	X	X
Military Space Missions		
Communications	X	X
Intelligence	X	X
Weather	X	X
Navigation	X	X
Missile Defense	X	X
Space Control	X	X
Military Space Systems		
Boosters		
Many types		X
Large quantities		X
Spacecraft		
Missions		
Mainly unipurpose	X	X
Secondary common	X	
Quantities		
Many		X
Few	X	
Technologies		
Most advanced	X	
Most costly	X	

Table 11 (cont.)

	United States	Soviet Union
Weapons		
Deployed		
Orbital ASAT		X
BMD missiles		X
Land-based lasers		X
EW	X	X
Development		
ASAT	X	
DEW	X	X
KEW	X	X
Military Space Deployments		
Main Locations		
LEO, Molniya orbits		X
LEO, GEO	X	
Duration		
Long	X	
Short		X
Manned Missions		
Many	X	
Few		X
Long		X
Short	X	
Budgetary Support		
Consistently strong		X
Inconsistent	X	
Composite Posture		
Most dependent on space	X	
Most vulnerable	X	
Best prepared		
Peacetime support	X	
Deterrence		X
Combat		X

Abbreviations: ASAT, antisatellite; BMD, ballistic missile defense; C³, command/control, communications; DEW, directed energy weapons; KEW, kinetic energy weapons; LEO, low earth orbit; GEO, geosynchronous orbit.

Basic Objectives and Policies

Official publications, disseminated openly, clearly document U.S. space objectives and supporting policies. Selected excerpts that concern national security summarize collective intent.

The Presidential Directive on National Space Policy, approved on January 5, 1988, specifies that "space leadership" is the main U.S. objective. American "preeminence in key areas of space activity critical to achieving our national security . . . and foreign policy goals" is essential. Four policies underpin that aim:[2]

The United States is committed to the exploration and use of outer space by all nations for peaceful purposes. . . . "Peaceful purposes" allow for activities in pursuit of national security goals. . . .

The United States will pursue activities in space in support of its inherent right of self-defense and its defense commitments to its allies. . . .

The United States rejects any claims to sovereignty by any nation over outer space or celestial bodies . . . and rejects any limitations on the fundamental right of sovereign nations to acquire data from space. . . .

Purposeful interference with space systems shall be viewed as an infringement on sovereign rights.

"Space activities," that document continued, "will contribute to national security objectives by (1) deterring, or if necessary, defending against enemy attack; (2) assuring that forces of hostile nations cannot prevent our own use of space; (3) negating, if necessary, hostile space systems; and (4) enhancing operations of United States and Allied forces."[3]

The U.S. Department of Defense (DOD) condensed those instructions from the Chief Executive and Commander-in-Chief, then elaborated a bit: "These goals will be achieved by providing secure, assured means for collecting and transmitting information, and by providing the means to counter aggression through space-related and strategic defense operational capabilities."[4]

Western intelligence communities and independent observers must deduce Soviet military space objectives, because authorities rarely disclose details, *glasnost* notwithstanding. Available evidence nevertheless indicates that U.S. and Soviet goals are almost identical.

Soviet General Secretary Mikhail Gorbachev in May 1987 declared that "we do not intend to relax our efforts and lose our vanguard position in the conquest of space." Semantics separate that statement from U.S. policy, which calls for "preeminence," but not by much. Defense Intelligence Agency (DIA) deductions, derived from analyses of Soviet space propaganda and deployments, parallel parts of the U.S. Presidential Directive: ". . . attain and maintain military superiority in outer space sufficient both to deny the use of outer space to other states and to assure maximum space-based military support for Soviet offensive and defensive combat operations on land, at sea, in air, and in outer space."[5] Similar findings, prepared independently and in greater detail, list five Soviet objectives:[6]

- Protect Soviet tactical and strategic strike capabilities

- Support Soviet tactical and strategic operations

- Protect Soviet and client state territories

- Prevent enemy use of space for military, political, or economic gain

• Maintain freedom of action in space to further the Soviet system.

Both countries publicly favor political cooperation in space. Neither apparently has firm plans to exploit space economically in the near future, although both are aware of potential rewards. Neither apparently plans to visit lunar libration points any time soon, to ascertain whether L4 and L5 in fact are stable, or determine how much energy spacecraft must expend to linger long at L1, L2, and L3.

Both countries publicly profess strong concerns for space arms control. That does not mean, however, that respective purposes and negotiating positions always overlap. On the contrary, serious disputes are common. The Soviets, for example, seek a comprehensive ban against the development, testing, and deployment of "space-strike arms," which include weapons associated with U.S. strategic defense initiatives (SDI). America's approach, spelled out in the 1988 Presidential Directive, is more selective: "The United States will consider and, as appropriate, formulate policy positions on arms control measures governing activities in space, and will conduct negotiations on such measures only if they are equitable, effectively verifiable, and enhance the security of the United States and its allies."[7] Mutually acceptable accords, predicated on compromise, will likely have long gestation periods, given those starting positions.

Military Missions

The United States and Soviet Union at this moment understandably concentrate on military space missions that support armed forces on Earth. Other aspects as yet attract little attention.

Intelligence collection is the most diversified mission. Reconnaissance, surveillance, target acquisition, tracking, signal interception, meteorological information, missile warning, nuclear detonation detection, and verification (arms control compliance, post-strike assessments) are prominent components. Navigational assistance that helps land, sea, and air forces locate themselves accurately is a second critical mission. Communications is a third, since findings must reach users in timely fashion. Space satellites that implement some or all of those missions are commonly called "force multipliers," because they enhance strategic and tactical capabilities of all kinds around the world, whether peace, international crises, or war prevails.[8]

Soviet leaders adamantly oppose U.S. space-based ballistic missile defense programs. Their version of SDI nevertheless predates ours by many years, and continues apace.[9] Neither side as yet assigns high priorities to space-related deterrent and denial missions in a broader context.

POSTURAL DIFFERENCES

Many differences demark U.S. from Soviet military space forces (see Table 11). The United States segregates governmental space activities from the commercial sector, and military from civilian, to much greater degrees. Our National Aeronautical and Space Administration (NASA) has no counterpart in the Soviet Union, although Glavkosmos is acquiring some similar characteristics. Military and civilian space programs in that country are virtually inseparable, with the latter being subordinate (the military share is variously estimated to be 60% to 90%, depending on definitions). U.S. military space commands (described in chapter 3) are foreign to the Soviet establishment, which emphasizes traditional command structures and centralized control. Interservice competition there is more muted.[10]

This discourse limits elaboration to two topics that set U.S. and Soviet military space postures far apart. Dissimilar programming principles guide research and development. Dissimilar deployment practices condition capabilities.

Programming Principles

U.S. and Soviet military space programming philosophies differ fundamentally in four respects. Authorities in the United States tend to favor technological sophistication over simplicity; multipurpose over unipurpose systems; quality over quantity; and quantum leaps over incremental improvements. Soviet authorities tend to reverse those orders. Exceptions occur on both sides and divergencies often are overstated, but such distinctions, by and large, are accurate.[11]

American military space technology is superior in many respects. Imagination and inventiveness are evident. The Soviets' Energiya launch vehicle, recently unveiled, looks and performs a lot like Saturn V, which put U.S. astronauts into lunar orbit on December 21, 1968. Their Mir space station is little better than America's Skylab, circa 1973. The Soviet space shuttle borrowed indirectly from U.S. blueprints. Satellites and sensors (but not weapons) generally fit that pattern.[12]

Soviet technological inferiority is not due entirely to lack of skill. They prefer simple, tried and true space systems that perform specified missions well without frills. State of the art, they feel, not only is unnecessary but, more often than not, involves avoidable risks. Soviet versions of SDI, for example, modify terminal defense technologies that were in vogue two decades ago. U.S. Phase I layered defenses, under development, demand breakthroughs of considerable magnitude. Conservative, compartmentalized programs of the sort just described limit Soviet flexibility, but U.S. complacency would be ill-advised, because steady Soviet progress is closing many gaps.[13]

Those policies permit Soviet assembly lines to mass produce relatively inexpensive space equipment and to stockpile spares. Few components, much less full systems, phase out. Only one obsolescent booster, for example, has ever retired; it flew from 1962 to 1977; ten different designs remain in service. Backup accordingly is considerable. Initial development amortization costs are nil in many instances, or nearly so. Large procurement packages keep pro rata operations and maintenance costs comparatively low.[14]

U.S. military space programs, in sharp contrast, are caught in "can't win" situations. Cutting edge technologies cost so much that procurement is strictly limited. Small buys, in turn, push price tags higher. Mass production would not always be possible, even if budgets allowed, because some hyperspecialized items are very nearly handcrafted. Spares are out of the question. American systems instead depend on redundant components aboard each spacecraft that increase life spans and guard against catastrophic failures. DOD policies "vigorously pursue new support concepts . . . aimed at substantially reducing costs while improving responsiveness, capability, reliability, availability, maintainability, flexibility and the ability to operate in peace, crisis and war." Monetary savings, however, likely will remain marginal, unless radically revised programming principles accompany new support concepts.[15]

Deployment Practices

Soviet and U.S. deployment practices differ as much or more than respective programming principles. Soviet spacecraft, for example, have little longevity compared with U.S. vehicles. Their photo reconnaissance satellites normally last no more than two months; the mean lifetime of other types is one to four years, depending on missions.[16] High quality U.S. spacecraft live longer, but modernization is relatively slow, because policymakers bypass "better" systems while they wait for the "best."

Deployments begin with reliable boosters and launch sites. The Soviets have both. They are expanding their already versatile stable of expendable and reusable launch vehicles, as shown in Figure 11. Each is optimized for particular payloads that vary from light (under 1.8 tons for SL-8) to heavy (more than 110 tons for SL-X-17, which launches the Soviet shuttle). Defense Intelligence Agency estimates that total weight-to-low earth orbit capacity could double by 1992. Approximately 20 fixed-site

Figure 11   U.S. AND SOVIET SPACE LAUNCH VEHICLES, 1989

US Space Launch Vehicles

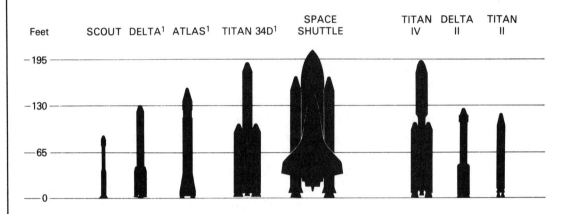

[1] Ballistic Missile Derived

Soviet Space Launch Vehicles

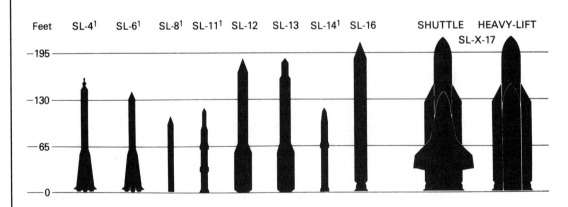

[1] Ballistic Missile Derived

Note: Adapted from *Soviet Military Power, 1988.*

launch pads are operational at Tyuratam, Kapustin Yar, and Plesetsk (Map 11). Expansion may include the first mobile launch facilities.[17]

U.S. military space forces lack equivalent launch capabilities. The fleet is small, performance erratic. No astronauts flew between 1975 and 1981, after Saturn boosters were retired. Two Titan 34D missions failed back-to-back in August 1985 and April 1986. The shuttle, our largest lift vehicle, was grounded for 32 months after the Challenger disaster in January 1986. Its peak loads approximate 30 tons. Allowable limits for Titan IV, in second place, is 10 tons less. Other boosters in late stages of development are far below those levels (Delta II, 5.5 tons; Atlas II, 7.5 tons). Space-based SDI components must deploy piecemeal, if at all, until bigger vehicles become available. Debates about such need continue.[18]

Soviet launches, which average about 100 per year, exceed the U.S. pace at a rate of 5:1. Payloads routinely are more than twice as heavy as ours. They demonstrated impressive surge capabilities during the Falkland conflict in 1982, when 28 space vehicles lifted off during a 69-day period. Potential has since improved. Turnaround times between launches at any given location can be measured in hours or days, according to one former secretary of defense, compared with U.S. times that normally take weeks or months.[19]

U.S. and Soviet military space forces launch many loads into low earth orbits (Map 12). Equatorial GEO, however, is most suitable for U.S. communication satellites. Four at that altitude (22,300 miles) can constantly cover the globe, except for high latitudes. Geosynchronous orbits also are popular for U.S. missile warning and signal intelligence missions. Equatorial GEO is less attractive to the Soviets for two reasons. Communications from that location cannot reach Arctic waters or key bases on the Kola Peninsula and Kamchatka. Soviet spacecraft bound for GEO all launch from Tyuratam, the southernmost departure site, but nevertheless sacrifice payloads for propellants, because orbital transfers and plane changes burn a lot of fuel. Most Soviet communications and early warning vehicles therefore follow eccentric Molniya orbits (apogee 25,000 miles, perigee 300 miles). Each C^3 satellite overflies the homeland at maximum altitude about eight hours daily.[20] Neither the United States nor Soviet Union deploys many spacecraft of any kind in high earth orbits much beyond GEO.

All operational weapons, other than electronic warfare devices, belong to the Soviet Union. The U.S. air-launched, direct ascent antisatellite (ASAT) system may be more sophisticated than the Soviet coorbital vehicle, but deployment is delayed indefinitely, pending congressional approval. Two Soviet land-

Map 12   U.S. AND SOVIET EARTH SUPPORT SATELLITES

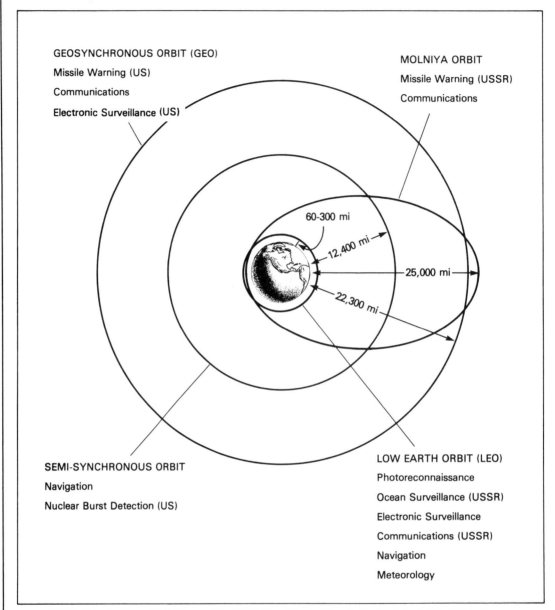

NOTE: Adapted from "Satellites and Anti-Satellites," by Ashton B. Carter, *International Security,*
Spring 1986.

based lasers at Sary Shagan possibly could blind U.S. optical sensors in space. Galosh ballistic missile defense interceptors around Moscow may have modest ASAT capabilities against spacecraft in LEO. Employment as antisatellite weapons, however, would prevent accomplishment of their primary mission, which is to protect their capital city. Even so, Soviet military space forces have some arms at their disposal; U.S. forces do not.[21]

The United States set standards for manned space flight with lunar landings between 1969 and 1972. Four Skylab missions followed in 1973; the last Apollo flight in July 1975 terminated all U.S. efforts until the shuttle Columbia lifted off in April 1981. Manned deployments during succeeding years have been few and far between. Department of Defense space policy still directs planners to "explore roles for military man-in-space," and prescribes "a mix of both manned and unmanned systems," but no approved mission for permanent human presence has emerged.[22]

Manned space flights conversely have been a Soviet specialty since 1961. Permanent manned presence for practical purposes began in 1987 aboard Mir, a modular space station. Soviet cosmonauts, who hold every endurance record except extravehicular activity ("sky walking"), have accrued three times as much experience in space as U.S. astronauts. Their current best slightly exceeds one year; ours is 84 days, set by a Skylab crew in 1973. Docking and extravehicular activity are parts of the Soviet agenda.[23]

COMPOSITE ASSESSMENTS

Composite U.S. and Soviet military space postures, when compared, indicate which establishment is best able to achieve its objectives, despite opposition by the other. Four basic balances are observable: peacetime, wartime, present, and projected.

Space forces on both sides are reasonably able to meet routine and crisis requirements. Competence in each case is improving. This assessment therefore concentrates on current and future combat capabilities.

Present Balance

Neither U.S. nor Soviet space forces are well postured for war now or in the near future. Ballistic missiles that transit circumterrestrial space are the main offensive instruments. Both sides are vulnerable, because they possess early warning devices, but little or no defense. Neither deploys many offensive forces for Earth-to-space, space-to-space, or space-to-Earth operations.

Soviet space forces nevertheless are better postured for deterrent and warfighting purposes. Launch/recovery sites, C³ centers, and logistic support facilities, far distant from hostile frontiers, are less exposed to land, sea, and air attacks that could seriously curtail, even terminate, activities in space (Map 10). Soviet forces on Earth still rely less than the United States on support from space, despite constantly increasing dependency. Few land and air forces deploy far beyond Soviet and Warsaw Pact borders; wire lines reduce their needs for satellite communications. Few naval forces stray far from home waters; satellite C^3 links would be essential to coordinate widely separated and simultaneous surprise attacks, but less useful in other circumstances.[24]

The small Soviet ASAT inventory, which some observers consider "primitive," puts defenseless U.S. satellites in potential peril, without running reciprocal risks. That advantage, coupled with diversified boosters that are highly reliable (90–95%), redundancy, and reconstitution capabilities, would serve Soviet space forces well in wartime, compared with U.S. counterparts, which could not surge, play tit-for-tat, maintain high tempo operations, or replace combat casualties expeditiously. The loss of a few Soviet satellites would not dramatically degrade performance; the loss of a few U.S. satellites could seriously curtail U.S. Space Command capabilities.[25]

Dependence on support from space, already great, is growing in the U.S. defense community. Orbital sensors increasingly supplement or supplant land-based strategic warning, surveillance, weather, and navigation systems. A handful of satellites carry something like 70% of all U.S. long-haul military communications. Commercial voice, audiovisual, radio, telephone, and data transmissions also rely on satellite links.[26]

Lack of appreciation for trends in space and their implications on Earth hampers planning in U.S. armed services. Recently unveiled Marine Corps amphibious assault doctrine, for example, relies on over-the-horizon assembly to ensure tactical surprise, although military sensors and civilian spies in the sky, who sell photographs to the highest bidder, may already have eliminated "over-the-horizon" locations.[27]

Lack of appreciation for fundamentals hampers U.S. offensive, defensive, and deterrent programs. Superboosters, the ultimate key to better capabilities, are on DOD's agenda, but progress is sluggish, because justification is unconvincing. America's experience with intercontinental ballistic missiles (ICBMs) might be instructive in that respect. American designers developed small, accurate missiles. The Soviets originally stressed raw power; precision came later. Their monster ICBMs currently carry many more warheads that have much larger yields and are more lethal than ours. Big Soviet boosters today similarly pave the way for expansion in space tomorrow.[28]

Projected Balance

The present balance between U.S. and Soviet military space forces is less important than projected postures. U.S. "preeminence," prescribed by the Presidential Directive, is possible, provided the executive branch, Congress, and the American people assign that aim a high priority and are willing to pay a high price. Second place is probable, if they are not, given Gorbachev's intent to preserve a "vanguard position," unless Soviet restructuring (*perestroika*) compels retrenchment.[29]

The prognosis is inauspicious. Gaps between U.S. ends and means are growing, despite technological superiority. Plodding pays off for the Soviets, who play tortoise to our hare. Fits and starts are U.S. specialties; theirs is persistence. We develop, they open options and deploy manned as well as unmanned systems. They are, in short, laying a much sounder foundation for military space power, in orbit, at lunar bases, or both.

RESPONSIVE PLANS AND PROGRAMS

Perceived threats to national security interests and objectives condition U.S. space strategies, tactics, and doctrines designed to cope. They also help determine quantity, type, and quality of forces the United States should deploy in particular time frames. Responsive U.S. plans and programs therefore depend on sound intelligence estimates. Best case, worst case, and intermediate appraisals are advisable, because enemy intentions and capabilities in space are most difficult to discern.

Optimistic estimates forecast political cooperation and truly peaceful competition in space (as opposed to Lenin's principle of peaceful coexistence, which continues a life or death struggle by nonmilitary means). Subscribers believe that all countries, formally or informally, will continue to honor the Outer Space Treaty of 1967, which forbids mass destruction weapons in space and military activities on the moon and other celestial bodies.[30] Arms control accords assertedly will reduce, freeze, or otherwise restrict space force quantities, characteristics, installations, and operations, including those of surface-to-surface missiles that transit space. Needs for SDI consequently will cease to exist.

Pessimistic estimates currently predict the opposite. Moscow's main interest in space is military power, according to endorsers. Interplanetary supremacy reportedly will replace world domination as the main Soviet aim; control of the Earth-Moon System will not be enough. Soviet deployments soon will feature offensive space forces that are diversified and profuse, because arms control efforts are bound to fail. No-holds-barred, winner-take-all policies inevitably prevail.

The real world almost certainly lies between those improbable poles. The key question is, Where? "Prepare for the Unexpected" seems a proper motto for U.S. planners and programmers until better answers become available.

Seven nonprovocative actions meanwhile might strengthen deterrence and improve U.S. combat capabilities, if deterrence fails.[31] The first six are nearly cost-free; the seventh is cost-effective:

1. Develop comprehensive military space doctrines applicable to the total Earth-Moon System[32]

2. Integrate military space more effectively into U.S. national security strategies

3. Emphasize verifiable arms control to confine threats

4. Reduce Army, Navy, Air Force, and Marine Corps dependency on space support by cross-training to preserve traditional skills, such as communications and navigation

5. Embellish basic research to multiply serendipitous results that might benefit military space programs

6. Employ technological expertise to produce first-class systems at acceptable costs[33]

7. Improve passive defenses for selected military space installations and vehicles, with particular attention to innovative hardening and deception.

Seven "big ticket" (some say "budget-busting") options comprise a second list. Senior U.S. officials should confirm requirements before they decide to cease research and development; continue R&D at current, reduced, or accelerated rates; and/or deploy particular quantities by any given date:

1. Survivable launch, recovery, and C^3 infrastructure

2. Heavy lift boosters

3. National Aerospace Planes (NASP) able to breach the atmospheric barrier easily and maneuver in space[34]

4. Reasonable redundancy and reconstitution capabilities for essential military space systems

5. Antisatellite systems

6. Active onboard defenses for military support satellites on a case-by-case basis

7. Land- and space-based SDI systems.

Former Secretary of State Henry A. Kissinger, at a March 1974 press conference in Moscow, asked, "What in God's name is strategic superiority?"[35] It may be unilateral control of space, which overarches Planet Earth, all occupants, and its entire contents. If so, possessors of that vantage position could overpower every opponent.[36] They might, in fact, impose their will without fighting, a feat that Sun Tzu called "the acme of skill" 25 centuries ago. U.S. military space forces therefore need means to forestall strategic surprise from space and respond successfully, unless best case estimates prove correct as events unfold.

ANNEX
A

Glossary

Ablative Shield Spacecraft skin that chars, melts, then evaporates when exposed to intense heat during reentry or laser attack. The process, which carries away some thermal energy, helps insulate vehicle subsurfaces.

Acceleration The rate velocity changes. Greatest increases, measured in units of gravity (g), occur during spacecraft launch from and return to Earth. Peak accelerations to orbit range from 3 to 8 g. Spacecraft designs minimize effects. Humans, for example, can tolerate only 2–3 g forces applied foot-to-head, but can briefly withstand about 20 g in a transverse direction. *See also* Gravity; Velocity.

Acquisition *See* Target acquisition.

Active Defense The employment of weapon systems to deter, deflect, defeat, or otherwise deal with enemy attacks. *See also* Passive defense.

Active Sensor Any device that transmits a signal, then records reflections to detect, locate, identify, and/or track targets. *See also* Passive sensor; Sensor.

Adaptive Optics Techniques to compensate for atmospheric distortion that degrades laser beams and light-sensitive sensors, such as telescopes and cameras.

Advanced Launch System *See* Heavy lift launch vehicle.

Aerodynamic Drag Atmospheric force that slows flight. It is most significant near Earth's surface. Drag above about 60 miles takes days, weeks, or months to produce significant effects.

Aerospace Plane A spacecraft able to operate effectively in atmosphere and space. *See also* National Aerospace Plane.

AI *See* Artifical intelligence.

Air *See* Atmosphere.

Anti-ASAT *See* Defensive satellite weapon.

Antisatellite Weapon Any system able to disrupt, damage, or destroy spacecraft in orbit from positions on land or sea, in air or space. Jammers and spoofers count as well as lethal weapons. *See also* Coorbital ASAT; Direct ascent ASAT.

Antisimulation *See* Dissimulation.

Apogee The maximum altitude attained by a spacecraft in elliptical orbit around Earth, its moon, or another planet. *See also* Orbit; Perigee.

Artificial Gravity Pseudo gravity that rotating spacecraft produce through centrifugal force. Its strength increases with spacecraft radii and rates of spin.

Artificial Intelligence Computers that "think." Speech, vision, intuition, logic, and abilities to learn from experience are desirable attributes.

ASAT *See* Antisatellite weapon.

Assault Actions by armed forces in physical contact to seize, secure, damage, or destroy any installation, position, or spacecraft. *See also* Standoff attack.

Atmosphere The envelope of air that surrounds Earth. Prompt effects on reentry vehicles begin about 60 miles above the surface. Prompt effects on ascending spacecraft and ballistic missiles end at the same altitude. Delayed effects extend much farther from Earth. *See also* Aerodynamic drag.

Automation Performance of particular functions by machines that partly or completely replace humans. *See also* Autonomy.

Autonomy The ability of spacecraft to perform some or all automated functions without external command, control, or support. That attribute reduces or eliminates any need for vulnerable communication links. *See also* Automation.

Ballistic Missile A pilotless projectile propelled into space from land, sea, or air. Velocity, gravity, and aerodynamic drag largely determine its trajectory after powered flight ceases. Mid-course corrections and terminal guidance permit only minor modifications to the flight path.

Ballistic Missile Defense All measures to intercept and destroy hostile ballistic missiles, or otherwise neutralize them. Systems include weapons; target acquisition, tracking, and guidance sensors; and ancillary installations. *See also* Ballistic missile.

Base *See* Lunar base.

Battle Management C³I procedures and equipment, especially computers and data displays, that help commanders make sound decisions expeditiously and direct implementation during armed combat. *See also* Command, control, and communications.

Biosphere An environment that sustains life within its confines, especially humans, animals, and plants. *See also* Closed Ecology Life-Support System; Life-support system.

Blackout Disruption of radio and radar transmissions for minutes or hours after one or more nuclear explosions in space ionizes Earth's atmosphere. Short-wave, high-frequency propagations are most susceptible. Short interruptions also occur when reentering spacecraft ionize the air.

Booster A launch vehicle that propels a payload into orbit from Earth, its moon, or another planet. *See also* Heavy lift launch vehicle.

Boost Phase The powered flight of a ballistic missile from launch until the final rocket stage burns out. Elapsed time typically is 3–5 minutes, but fast burners may take 100 seconds or less. *See also* Midcourse phase; Post-boost phase; Rocket stage; Terminal phase.

"Brilliant" Pebble A kinetic energy projectile with all essential homing devices embedded or on board, which is much smaller and more sophisticated than a "smart" rock. *See also* "Smart" rock.

Burn Consumption of propellant by engines that propel spacecraft or by thrusters that correct attitudes and directions.

Bus *See* Post-boost vehicle.

C³ *See* Command, control, and communications

Celestial Body Any planet other than Earth; any moon; any asteroid; any star. *See also* Planet.

Celestial Sphere An imaginary, nonrotating orb of infinite radius, with its center at Earth's core. Its equator is a projection of Earth's equator. Various features comprise a frame of reference for locating orbital objects in space. *See also* Declination; Right ascension.

Charged Particle Beam A stream of electrons accelerated to nearly the speed of light. *See also* Neutral particle beam; Particle beam weapon.

Chemical Laser An intense beam of coherent light produced by chemical actions in a device designed to generate and control it. *See also* Laser weapon.

Circumterrestrial Space A region that abuts Earth's atmosphere at an altitude of about 60 miles and extends to about 50,000 miles. Most military space activities currently occur therein. Sometimes called inner space.

Cislunar Space Wedge-shaped territory between Earth and its moon. One point touches Earth's atmosphere; others touch lunar libration point L4, the moon, and L5.

Closed Ecology Life-support System A self-sufficient (closed loop) biosphere that creates or recycles air, water, and food to sustain human life aboard spacecraft, at lunar installations, or on other planets. *See also* Biosphere; Life-support system.

Command, Control, and Communications An arrangement of facilities, equipment, personnel, and procedures used to acquire, process, and disseminate data that decisionmakers need to plan and direct operations. *See also* Battle management.

Command Guidance Precomputed and/or event-driven instructions, transmitted in real time, that steer and otherwise control spacecraft from remote locations. Reliable communication links are required.

Concealment Actions and conditions that prevent enemy observation, but provide no protection against weapon effects. Clouds, camouflage, and stealth technology are representative. *See also* Cover.

Constellation Multiple spacecraft that orbit in dispersed formation for offensive, deterrent, defensive, or support purposes.

Coorbital ASAT An antisatellite interceptor that duplicates the flight path of its target in space, then attacks without delay. *See also* Direct ascent ASAT; Space mine.

Cosmic Radiation High-energy corpuscular rays that originate with the sun or sources outside the solar system. Solar flares pose the main danger to manned spacecraft. *See also* Solar flares.

Cover Physiographic conditions that protect targets against enemy weapons and adverse environments. They also prevent observation. Terrain masks and subterranean installations on Earth, its moon, or another planet are representative. *See also* Concealment; Hardening.

CPB *See* Charged particle beam.

Critical Node Any element that causes complete system failure if it becomes ineffective for any reason. Spacecraft launch sites and irreplaceable communications satellites are representative.

Critical Terrain *See* Key terrain.

Dazzle Temporary blinding of astronauts or sensors by lasers or nuclear explosions.

Deception Measures designed to deceive enemies. They may build faith in false images or increase ambiguities, so foes do not know what to believe. *See also* Decoy; Dissimulation; Simulation.

Declination The astronomical analog of latitude. The angular distance north or south of the celestial equator, measured along a great circle route that passes through the celestial poles. *See also* Celestial sphere; Right ascension.

Decoy An object that simulates a particular type target (spacecraft; missile warhead), employed to deceive enemy sensors, and thereby divert attacks. *See also* Deception; Dissimulation; Simulation.

Deep Space   Interplanetary space beyond the Earth-Moon System. *See also* Circumterrestrial space; Outer space.

Defense in Depth   *See* Layered defenses.

Defense Suppression   The employment of lethal weapons to neutralize enemy armed forces that protect intended targets. *See also* Penetration aid.

Defensive Satellite Weapon   Any system able to disrupt, damage, or destroy enemy antisatellite (ASAT) weapons from positions on land or sea, in air or space. The term commonly is reserved for weapons designed specifically for that purpose.

Delta Vee   A standard measurement of spacecraft potential to maneuver. It indicates the maximum change in velocity possible in the absence of external forces. Gravity, aerodynamic drag, and other environmental factors influence actual velocity change. Spacecraft with enough delta vee to escape Earth's gravity en route to the moon, for example, need little more velocity to reach Mars. *See also* Velocity.

Deposition Region   A dense radioactive layer that accumulates 25–30 miles above the Earth when a cascade of gamma rays from any nuclear explosion in space collides with the upper atmosphere. Resultant charge imbalances create electromagnetic pulse. *See also* Electromagnetic pulse.

DEW   *See* Directed energy weapon.

Direct Ascent ASAT   Any weapon launched or fired from Earth, moon, or another planet to intercept an orbiting spacecraft without delay. *See also* Coorbital ASAT.

Directed Energy Weapon   An intense, tightly focused, precisely aimed beam of atomic/subatomic particles or electromagnetic energy designed to attack far distant targets at or nearly at the speed of light. *See also* Laser weapon; Particle beam weapon.

Discrimination   The ability to differentiate genuine targets from decoys and other harmless objects. *See also* Decoy; Target.

Dissimulation   Deceptive measures that make targets seem like decoys. *See also* Deception; Decoy; Simulation; Target.

Drag   *See* Aerodynamic drag.

DSAT   *See* Defensive satellite weapon.

Early Warning   *See* Tactical warning.

Earth-Moon System   Space and all its contents within an imaginary sphere that extends approximately 480,000 miles in every direction from Earth's center. The moon and earth-crossing asteroids are the most prominent visible features. Atmosphere, gravity, and the Van Allen radiation belts typify invisible, but immensely important, features.

Eccentric Orbit   Extremely elongated or squashed elliptical orbits. *See also* Elliptical orbit.

ECCM *See* Electronic countercountermeasures.

ECM *See* Electronic countermeasures.

Electromagnetic Launcher Any device that employs electromagnetic power to accelerate kinetic energy projectiles. *See also* Mass driver; Railgun.

Electromagnetic Pulse Prodigious current that results from a nuclear explosion in space, peaks 100 times faster than lightning, then bolts toward Earth. Unshielded electronics within several hundred miles of the epicenter may be disabled. *See also* Deposition region; System-generated electromagnetic pulse.

Electromagnetic Radiation A wavelike phenomenon that consists of a variable electric and variable magnetic field that combine to transport energy through the vacuum of space. Flux per unit area is greatest near our sun and the stars. *See also* Cosmic radiation; Electromagnetic spectrum; Solar flares; Van Allen belts.

Electromagnetic Spectrum A continuum of electromagnetic energy waves that range from about 10^4 hertz to about 10^{24} hertz. Secondary cosmic rays and gamma rays possess the highest frequencies and shortest wavelengths. X rays, ultraviolet light, visible light, infrared, microwaves, and ever longer radio waves descend the scale in that order. *See also* Electromagnetic radiation.

Electronic Countercountermeasures A form of electronic warfare employed to retain effective use of the electromagnetic spectrum, despite enemy ECM interference. *See also* Electromagnetic spectrum; Electronic countermeasures, Electronic warfare.

Electronic Countermeasures A form of electronic warfare that prevents or degrades enemy use of the electromagnetic spectrum. Jamming is a typical tactic. *See also* Electromagnetic spectrum; Electronic countercountermeasures; Electronic warfare.

Electronic Warfare Use of the electromagnetic spectrum to degrade enemy capabilities, and activities that prevent opponents from using the electromagnetic spectrum effectively for offensive or defensive purposes. *See also* Electromagnetic spectrum.

Elliptical Orbit Any non-circular, closed flight path in space. *See also* Eccentric orbit.

Embedded Equipment Any built-in sensor or other component that is inseparable from a spacecraft or weapon. Electronic circuits molded into spacecraft skin are representative. *See also* On-board equipment; "Smart" skin.

EMP *See* Electromagnetic pulse.

Endoatmospheric Weapon Any device designed to intercept spacecraft or missile warheads within Earth's atmosphere. *See also* Exo-atmospheric weapon.

Excimer Laser A contraction of "excited dimer." A photonic beam weapon that pumps diatomic (two-atom) molecules, usually a noble (inert) gas such as krypton or xenon, combined with chlorine or fluorine. *See also* Laser weapon.

Exoatmospheric Weapon Any device designed to intercept spacecraft or missile warheads in space. *See also* Endoatmospheric weapon.

Exosphere The upper limits of Earth's atmosphere, which begins about 300 miles above the surface and terminates in hard vacuum at an altitude that exceeds 2,000 miles.

Extremely High Frequencies Part of the electromagnetic spectrum between 300 and 3000 gigahertz. EHF decrease effects of nuclear scintillation/absorption on radio and radar transmissions. They also allow narrower beams. *See also* Electromagnetic spectrum.

Faraday Cage Grounded parallel conductors which form an electrostatic screen that prevents induced currents (such as EMP) from circulating through electronic equipment, or limit destructive effects.

Fast-Burn Booster A ballistic missile engine that functions for 100 seconds or less after launch. Employment makes boost-phase defense most difficult. *See also* Boost phase.

Free Electron Laser A photonic beam weapon that collimates and accelerates electrons not bound to atoms. A magnetic undulator (wiggler) forms a coherent stream of radiant energy from the resultant stream, which theoretically can be tuned to any desired wavelength. *See also* Laser weapon.

Functional Kill *See* Soft kill.

GEO *See* Geosynchronous earth orbit.

Geostationary Earth Orbit The only geosynchronous orbit that circles Earth 22,300 miles above the equator. Spacecraft on that path appear to stand still when seen from the surface because they maintain the same relative position. *See also* Geosynchronous earth orbit.

Geosynchronous Earth Orbit Any elliptical flight path that makes a figure eight around Earth from a center line over the equator at an average ground track altitude of 22,300 miles. Spacecraft on any such path complete precisely one trip per day, because their 24-hour period is the time it takes Earth to rotate once. *See also* Geostationary earth orbit; Orbital period.

Gravity A force of mutual attraction between bodies as a result of their mass. Earth and moon influence all matter within their respective fields. Earth's much stronger field dominates a much larger area. Effects of both fields diminish with the square of distance from the source. One g is equivalent to the acceleration of gravity on a body at sea level. *See also* Acceleration; Gravity well.

Gravity Well Imaginary, funnel-shaped walls, steep at the bottom, but level at the top. Greater energy is required to climb out (gravity hinders) than to maneuver at the top (where gravity is slight) or return (gravity helps). *See also* Gravity.

Habitat   *See* Space habitat.

Hardening   Passive, manmade measures that mitigate effects of enemy weapons and adverse environments. Heat shields, electronic surge arresters, and fortifications are representative. *See also* Cover.

Hard Kill   Weapon effects that forcibly break the surface of animate or inanimate targets, then damage or destroy their contents. Violence is evident to distant observers. Explosives and kinetic projectiles are representative instruments. *See also* Soft kill.

Heavy Lift Launch Vehicle   Any rocket or other space transport designed to put very large payloads (100 tons or more) into orbit from Earth or moon. SL-X-17, the current Soviet version, deployed in 1989. The U.S. Advanced Launch System (ALS) is still in development. *See also* Booster.

HEO   *See* High earth orbit.

High Earth Orbit   A flight path in circumterrestrial space above geosynchronous altitude, between 22,300 and 50,000–60,000 miles from Earth's surface.

High Energy Transfer   Any orbital change that alters direction and/or altitude expeditiously along short and/or steep routes. Such maneuvers expend propellant rapidly. *See also* Minimum energy transfer.

High Frequency   Part of the electromagnetic spectrum between 3 and 30 megahertz. Diurnal changes in the ionosphere determine bandwidth at any given time over a particular path. Communication blackouts occur when sunspot activity or nuclear explosions in space cause ionospheric disturbances. *See also* Electromagnetic spectrum.

Homing Device   Embedded and/or on-board instruments that vector any type weapon toward a target and assist interception.

Housekeeping   *See* Spacecraft "housekeeping."

Hypervelocity Gun   *See* Electromagnetic launcher; Mass driver; Railgun.

Impulse   *See* Impulse kill; Specific impulse.

Impulse Kill   Destruction caused by any directed energy weapon that delivers a pulse intense enough to vaporize the target surface. The resultant shock wave attacks internal components, and may cause structural collapse. *See also* Directed energy weapon.

Inclination   *See* Orbital inclination.

Infrared Sensor   Any device designed to detect, locate, identify, and/or track targets by recording radiation those targets emit or reflect on wavelengths longer than visible light (0.72 to 1,000 microns).

Inner Space   *See* Circumterrestrial space.

Interceptor   *See* Space interceptor.

Ionosphere   A region of electrically charged (ionized) thin air layers that begins about 30 miles above Earth's atmosphere and overlaps the lower exosphere. The maximum concentration of electrons occurs at about 375 miles. Effects on HF radio propagation are important. *See also* Exosphere.

IR   *See* Infrared sensor.

Jamming   Degrading or drowning out enemy electronic transmissions (radio and radar signals, for example) by electronic warfare devices and tactics. *See also* Electronic warfare.

Keep Out Zone   A negotiated or unilaterally established security area declared off limits to unauthorized spacecraft. The main purpose is to reduce dangers of surprise attack. Such restrictions are potentially useful for arms control purposes.

KEW   *See* Kinetic energy weapon.

Key Terrain   Physical features, natural and artificial, the seizure, retention, destruction, or indirect control of which would confer a marked advantage on a country or coalition. Critical installations and orbits are representative.

Kill Assessment   *See* Post-strike assessment.

Kinetic Energy   A capacity for work derived from the motion of any object. *See also* Kinetic energy weapon.

Kinetic Energy Weapon   A device that launches, fires, or otherwise propels nonexplosive projectiles designed to damage or destroy targets. "Brilliant" pebbles, railguns, and "smart" rocks are representative. *See also* Electromagnetic launcher; Kinetic energy; Rocket weapon.

L1, L2, L3, L4, L5.   *See* Lunar libration points.

Lasant   Solids, liquids, gases, and plasmas that can be stimulated to create laser light. Hydrogen, fluorine, krypton, iodine, and xenon are typical ingredients. *See also* Laser weapon.

Laser Weapon   An optical or X-ray device that projects a beam of coherent light designed to attack far distant targets in space almost instantaneously. The beam deposits energy first on target surfaces, then penetrates. Thermal and impulse kills are most common. *See also* Chemical laser; Excimer laser; Free electron laser; Impulse kill; Lasant; Thermal kill; X-ray laser.

Launch Vehicle   Any rocket or other space transport designed to put payloads into orbit from Earth or moon. *See also* Heavy lift launch vehicle.

Launch Window   The time period during which a spacecraft or missile must be launched to achieve the intended orbit, encounter, rendezvous, or impact. Orbital mechanics, which determine the proper time, deal with launch vehicle delta vees; relative positions of departure site and destination; and assorted perturbations, especially gravity, atmospheric drag, and electromagnetic forces. *See also* Delta vee; Orbital mechanics.

Layered Defenses   Protective measures in successive positions along the axis of enemy advance, as opposed to a single line of resistance. Designed to absorb and progressively weaken enemy attacks. Boost phase, mid-course, and terminal defenses against ballistic missiles are representative.

LEO   *See* Low earth orbit.

Lethality   The capability of a particular type weapon to incapacitate a particular type of target with kinetic, explosive, radiant energy, or other force.

Libration Points   *See* Lunar libration points.

Life-Support System   An artificial environment that permits humans to function effectively in space. Elementary requirements include air, water, and food; temperature and pressure control; provisions for personal hygiene; and waste disposal. Space suits, which afford only a few of those necessities, are for short-term use only. *See also* Biosphere; Closed Ecology Life-Support System.

Liquid Propellant   Any combination of fluid fuel and oxidizer that a rocket engine burns. Combustion can be started, stopped, and restarted by controlling propellant flow. *See also* Rocket; Solid propellant.

Low Earth Orbit   Any flight path in circumterrestrial space between sensible atmosphere and the bottom of the Van Allen belts (60–250 miles in altitude), with leeway in both directions. Elliptical orbits may dip in and out of LEO on each trip around Earth.

Lunar Base   A relatively large, permanent or semipermanent installation on Earth's moon. Sophisticated life-support systems are essential. *See also* Lunar outpost.

Lunar Libration Points   Five three-dimensional positions in space, all under the influence of gravitational fields that surround Earth and moon. L1, L2, and L3, on a line with Earth and moon, are considered unstable. Spacecraft probably would have to expend propellants to remain long at those locations. L4 and L5, 60° ahead of and behind the moon in its orbit, are considered stable. Spacecraft presumably could remain at those locations indefinitely without expending fuel, because gravitational fields are in balance.

Lunar Outpost   A small, usually temporary installation on Earth's moon. Relatively simple life-support systems are essential. *See also* Lunar base.

Mach   The speed of sound, which is 762 mph at sea level and 660 mph at 36,100 feet. That figure stays constant to about 95,000 feet, then increases. Not measurable in space, because sound does not exist in a vacuum.

Magnetosphere   A vast region dominated by Earth's magnetic field, which traps charged particles, including those in the Van Allen belts. It begins in the upper atmosphere, where it overlaps the ionosphere, and extends several thousand miles farther into space. *See also* Van Allen belts.

Maneuver   Ability to change directions rapidly. Installations on Earth and moon are mainly static, but may have maneuverable components. All spacecraft can maneuver to some degree, if they expend sufficient propellant. *See also* Mobility.

Mass Driver   An electromagnetic catapult designed to launch large payloads (perhaps multitons) into space, primarily from the moon or a planet other than Earth. Potential uses as very heavy artillery are debatable, particularly moon-to-Earth applications. *See also* Electromagnetic launcher.

Medium Earth Orbit   Any flight path in circumterrestrial space between low earth orbits (about 250 miles in altitude) and geosynchronous orbits at an average altitude of 22,300 miles. *See also* Geosynchronous orbit; Low earth orbit.

MEO   See Medium earth orbit.

Mesosphere   Earth's atmosphere 30–50 miles above its surface. Temperature inversions that occur in the stratosphere cease. Readings of $-100°F$ are normal.

Meteor   Any meteoroid that enters Earth's atmosphere and glows from frictional heat. *See also* Meteorite; Meteoroid.

Meteorite   Any meteor that strikes Earth's surface. *See also* Meteor.

Meteoroid   Tangible matter indigenous to free space, made of metal and stone. Most, called micrometeoroids, are smaller than dust particles, but some weigh many tons. Speeds vary from 30,000 mph to 160,000 mph. *See also* Meteor; Meteorite.

Midcourse Phase   The ballistic trajectory of ICBM and SLBM reentry vehicles from the time they separate from the bus until warheads hit Earth's atmosphere (20 minutes or less). *See also* Boost phase; Post-boost phase; Post-boost vehicle; Terminal phase.

Military Base   A relatively large, permanent or semipermanent installation operated by armed forces on Earth, moon, or another planet. *See also* Lunar base.

Mine   See Space mine.

Minimum Energy Transfer   Any orbital change that alters direction and/or altitude gradually. Such maneuvers conserve propellants. See *also* High energy transfer.

Mobility   Ability to change locations. Installations on Earth and moon are mainly static, but may have mobile components. All spacecraft in orbit are mobile. *See also* Maneuver.

Molniya Orbit An eccentric, stable flight path, inclined 63.4° to Earth's equator, with perigee about 300 miles above the surface, and apogee of about 25,000 miles. Soviet forces put communications and early warning satellites on that track.

Multiprocessor A system able to integrate the efforts of several (maybe many) supercomputers. *See also* Parallel processor.

NASP *See* National Aerospace Plane.

National Aerospace Plane A high priority DOD–NASA program that involves leading-edge technologies in materials, propulsion, computational fluid dynamics, and other fields needed to produce spacecraft able to operate effectively in atmosphere and space.

Neutral Particle Beam A stream of hydrogen atoms, accelerated to nearly the speed of light and stripped of an artificially added charge. The resultant device propagates well in space. *See also* Charged particle beam; Particle beam weapon; Soft kill; Thermal kill.

NPB *See* Neutral particle beam.

On-Board Equipment Any sensor or other component that is part of, but separable from, a spacecraft or weapon. Radio transceivers and infrared cameras are representative. *See also* Embedded equipment.

Orbit The path of any object that flies through space in accord with physical laws of energy and momentum. Spacecraft that orbit Earth, for example, must maintain sufficient velocity to counterbalance gravity, but not enough to overcome its pull. *See also* Eccentric orbit; Elliptical orbit; Geostationary orbit; Geosynchronous orbit; High earth orbit; Low earth orbit; Molniya orbit; Selenostationary orbit; Semi-synchronous orbit; Stable orbit; Unstable orbit.

Orbital Inclination The angle of a flight path in space relative to the equator of Earth, moon, or another planet. Equatorial paths are 0° for flights headed east, 180° for those headed west. Polar paths are 90°. All other paths overfly equal parts of the northern and southern hemispheres (from 50° N latitude to 50° S, for example).

Orbital Mechanics Physical laws that control spacecraft flight paths and missile trajectories through space. Conservation principles of angular momentum and energy in a gravitational field figure prominently.

Orbital Period The time it takes a spacecraft or other object to circumnavigate Earth, moon, or another planet. High altitude circuits take longer to complete than low ones. Elliptical and circular orbits have equal periods, if the average of apogee and perigee altitudes is the same.

Orbital Plane An imaginary two-dimensional surface (infinite height and length, but no breadth) that contains all points on a flight path in space. Spacecraft that gain or lose altitude, or fly more or less elliptical paths, remain on the original plane. Those that alter direction change planes. Spacecraft launched at different times from Earth, moon, or another planet on identical paths are on different planes that may be as little as 1° or as much as 180° apart, due to global rotation.

Orbital Transfer   *See* High energy transfer; Minimum energy transfer.

Outer Space   All of the Earth-Moon System except circumterrestrial space. It extends from about 50,000 miles above Earth's surface to about 480,000 miles (twice the distance from Earth to moon). *See also* Circumterrestrial space; Deep space.

Outpost   *See* Lunar outpost.

Parallel Processor   A supercomputer that subdivides problems and solves all parts simultaneously instead of step-by-step. *See also* Multiprocessor.

Parking Orbit   Spacecraft bound from Earth to MEO or beyond commonly launch first into LEO, circle the globe while awaiting a "window," then transfer the payload (but not the launch vehicle) to the final path at a greater altitude. That process expends less propellant than direct ascent with the total load. Parking orbits also are used to check out spacecraft systems before they commit to a high risk orbit transfer. *See also* High energy transfer; Launch window; Minimum energy transfer.

Particle Beam Weapon   An intense, tightly focused, precisely aimed stream of atomic or subatomic particles designed to attack far distant targets at nearly the speed of light. The stream deposits energy in depth, rather than on target surfaces. Heat and current generation generally cause most damage. *See also* Charged particle beam; Neutral particle beam.

Passive Defense   All measures, other than armed force, to deter, deflect, defeat, or otherwise deal with enemy attacks. Cover, concealment, hardening, mobility, dispersion, and deception are representative. *See also* Active defense.

Passive Sensor   Any device designed to detect, locate, identify, and/or track targets without disclosing its own position. Target emissions, such as infrared radiation and reflected sunlight, are their sole sources of information. *See also* Active sensor; Sensor.

Payload   Crews and cargo aboard any spacecraft or missile. Arms, munitions, guidance/control instruments, sensors, and communications are representative.

Penetration Aid   Any non-lethal device that misdirects enemy defenses or otherwise makes it easier for spacecraft or ballistic missiles to attack defended targets. Decoys, jammers, and spoofers are illustrative. *See also* Decoy; Defense suppression.

Perigee   The minimum altitude attained by a spacecraft in elliptical orbit around Earth, its moon, or another planet. Spacecraft in LEO attain maximum velocity at that point where Earth's gravitational pull is strongest.

Period.   *See* Orbital period.

Perturbation Natural forces that cause orbits to deviate from ideal elliptical paths. Drag, influences of a nonspherical Earth, luni-solar gravity, solar winds, and various electromagnetic forces are typical.

Plane *See* Orbital plane.

Planet One of nine large celestial bodies that revolve around the sun in our solar system; specifically Mercury, Venus, Earth, Mars, Jupiter, Saturn, Uranus, Neptune, and Pluto.

Pointing Aiming with sufficient accuracy that sensors can detect, locate, identify, and/or track targets, and that weapons can engage them. *See also* Tracking.

Polar Orbit An orbit with a 90° inclination. Spacecraft on that path potentially could pass over every point below as they loop around Earth, its moon, or another planet. *See also* Orbital inclination.

Pop-Up Launch Short-notice deployment of any spacecraft from its base on Earth, moon, or another planet to a predetermined position in space from which it can expeditiously accomplish an immediate mission.

Post-Boost Phase The course of a ballistic missile from the time powered flight ceases until the post-boost vehicle (bus) dispenses all warheads and penetration aids (normally 3–5 minutes, but may be less). *See also* Boost phase; Midcourse phase; Post-boost vehicle; Terminal phase.

Post-Boost Vehicle Part of a ballistic missile payload that dispenses one or more warheads and penetration aids during the post-boost phase. It imparts minor changes in velocity and direction to put each on a precise trajectory that maximizes accuracy. *See also* Post-boost phase.

Post-Strike Assessment The acquisition and evaluation of data that indicate the success of an attack and thereby assist subsequent decisionmaking.

Power System *See* Spacecraft power system.

Preferential Defense The concentration of combat power against selected enemy forces in ways that safeguard critical targets in order of priority, and (if need be) sacrifice less important assets.

Prograde Orbit Any flight path in space with an inclination between 0° and 90°. *See also* Inclination; Retrograde orbit.

Propellant *See* Spacecraft propulsion.

Propulsion System *See* Spacecraft propulsion.

Radar An active sensor that transmits radio waves, then records reflections. Returns (echoes) indicate target locations, range, velocity, and sometimes shape. Phased array radar (PAR) with electronically steerable beams can track many objects at great distances. *See also* Active sensor; Radar cross section.

Radar Cross Section The ratio between incident energy and radar energy reflected by a target. The size of the object, its structural shape, refractory characteristics of surface materials, and target location with regard to receiver determine the image. *See also* Radar.

Radiation *See* Electromagnetic pulse; Electromagnetic radiation; Solar flares; Van Allen belts.

Railgun An electromagnetic weapon designed to launch kinetic energy projectiles against enemy targets. Very fast muzzle velocities reduce leads needed to engage spacecraft at long range. *See also* Electromagnetic launcher; Mass driver.

Ramjet A jet engine that relies on forward motion, rather than a mechanical device for compression. Air enters through an intake, slows to subsonic speed, mixes with fuel, ignites, and escapes through a rear nozzle. Inoperable until the aircraft attains about Mach 1 and after it reaches about Mach 6. *See also* Scramjet.

Reconnaissance Intelligence operations to collect information about opponents or territory through visual, aural, or technological observation, while patrolling a specified area. *See also* Surveillance.

Reconstitution Ability to replace assets rapidly from standby deployments or stocks. *See also* Redundancy.

Redout The blinding or dazzling of infrared sensors by intense infrared radiation in Earth's upper atmosphere after a nuclear explosion. *See also* Infrared sensor.

Redundancy Proliferative or alternative means of accomplishing any mission. *See also* Reconstitution.

Reentry The return through Earth's atmosphere of any object originally launched from Earth. *See also* Reentry vehicle.

Reentry Vehicle Any spacecraft, missile warhead, or kinetic energy projectile designed to survive intense and rapid heating when it encounters Earth's atmosphere upon return from space. *See also* Reentry.

Restricted Area *See* Keep out zone.

Retrograde Orbit Any flight path in space with an inclination between 90° and 180°. *See also* Orbital inclination; Prograde orbit.

Right Ascension The astronomical analog of longitude. The constellation Aries, against which spectators on Earth see the sun when it crosses Earth's equator in spring (the vernal equinox), defines the prime meridian. Angular positions in space are measured east from that celestial counterpart of Greenwich Observatory. *See also* Celestial sphere; Declination.

Rilles Echeloned ridges and canyons on Earth's moon. Some are straight, but most are sinuous. They crosshatch to form a lunar grid.

Rocket A vehicle that can operate outside Earth's atmosphere, because it carries its own oxidizer, as well as fuel. Solid and liquid propellants are preferable. Even large, bulky tanks can hold little compressed gas in comparison. *See also* Rocket stage; Rocket staging; Rocket transport; Rocket weapon; Vertical launch.

Rocket Stage   One of two or three rocket segments that separate at predetermined times. The bottom segment is largest; the smallest, on top, carries the payload. Each is equipped with an engine. *See also* Rocket; Rocket staging.

Rocket Staging   Incremental increases in spacecraft or missile velocity between liftoff and final orbit are economical. The first stage provides energy needed to overcome inertia, gravity, and (on Earth) atmospheric drag. Less weight must be lifted after that stage terminates thrust and drops off. A smaller engine on the second stage then ignites. It puts the payload into ultimate orbit, unless a third stage is required. *See also* Rocket; Rocket stage.

Rocket Transport   Any rocket used to launch into orbit any cargo. *See also* Rocket; Rocket weapon.

Rocket Weapon   Any rocket designed to attack enemy targets after launch from Earth, moon, another planet, or an orbiting spacecraft. Earth-to-space, space-to-space, and space-to-Earth delivery of explosives and inert projectiles are possible. *See also* Rocket.

Salvage Fused Weapons   A missile warhead, space mine, or other explosive device that detonates automatically when attacked.

Satellite   *See* Space satellite.

Scintillation   Unwelcome transient alterations in the carrier frequency of a telecommunication wave.

Scramjet.   *See* Supersonic combustion ramjet.

Selenostationary Orbit   The lunar equivalent of a geostationary flight path, but because the moon rotates so slowly (once every 27.3 days), no spacecraft would seem to stand still when seen from the lunar surface. *See also* Geostationary earth orbit.

Semi-Synchronous Orbit   A flight that completes exactly two circuits per day.

Sensor   Any instrument designed to measure some physical phenomenon, such as electromagnetic radiation. Military space forces employ most such devices to detect, locate, identify, and/or track targets; to home in on targets; and to assist post-strike assessments. *See also* Active sensor; Passive sensor.

Shuttle   *See* Space shuttle.

Signature   Distinctive signals (such as electromagnetic radiation) that any object emits or reflects, which sensors use to detect, locate, identify, and/or track targets. Each type of ballistic missile, for example, trails a characteristic exhaust "plume" during powered flight. *See also* Sensor.

Simulation   Deceptive measures that make decoys seem like targets. *See also* Deception; Decoy; Dissimulation; Target.

Slew Time   The minimum time it takes to repoint any weapon from one target to another.

"Smart" Rock   A kinetic energy projectile, much larger and less sophisticated than a "brilliant" pebble, which requires external guidance to locate targets. Embedded or on-board homing devices then direct interception. *See also* "Brilliant" pebble.

"Smart" Skin   External spacecraft surfaces that embed sensors, which are inseparable from the vehicle structure. *See also* Embedded equipment.

Soft Kill   Weapon effects that penetrate targets without breaking the surface, then damage or destroy internal components. Violence is not evident to observers. Electromagnetic pulse and neutral particle beams are representative instruments. *See also* Hard kill.

Solar Flares   Spectacular, pervasive outbursts of energy that emanate periodically from our sun, accompanied by high-speed protons that comprise a potentially lethal radiation hazard to any unshielded form of life in space. Intense and sudden ionospheric disturbances also occur, with fadeouts and other debilitating effects on long-range telecommunications. Major flares may last from a few minutes to several hours. *See also* Solar wind.

Solar Wind   A constant plasmic flow of low-energy charged particles in all directions from our sun. Velocities and densities vary with sunspot activity. Radiation hazards are significant, but minor compared with solar flares. *See also* Solar flares.

Solid Propellant   Any combination of fuel and oxidizer other than gases or liquids that energize a rocket engine. Burning occurs on exposed surfaces of each "stick." Inhibitors bonded to the combustion chamber wall insulate the wall. Internal diaphragms and propellant wafers can provide some start-stop-restart capabilities. *See also* Liquid propellant.

Space   The universe and all its contents, except Earth and its atmosphere. *See also* Circumterrestrial space; Cislunar space; Deep space; Outer space; Translunar space.

Space Command   Any headquarters and subordinate elements designed to plan, program, budget for, and operate armed forces that pursue their primary missions anywhere except on Earth or in its atmosphere.

Spacecraft   Any manned or unmanned vehicle intended primarily for operations beyond Earth and its atmosphere. *See also* Space interceptor; Space mine; Space satellite; Space shuttle; Space station.

Spacecraft "Housekeeping"   Actions taken on board or from remote locations to keep a spacecraft in orbit and able to accomplish assigned missions. Craft in low earth orbits require almost constant attention;

others normally need less. Typical tasks turn thrusters, power plants, sensors, and other instruments on and off; point solar panels in the proper direction; and correct spacecraft attitude for pitch, yaw, and roll. *See also* Stationkeeping.

Spacecraft Power System "Housekeeping" in space requires energy. Static energy systems include batteries, fuel cells, and photovoltaic, thermoelectric, and thermionic devices. Dynamic systems presently link electric generators with turbines or reciprocating engines that run on thermal energy from chemical fuels, the sun, nuclear isotopes, or nuclear reactors. Adequate supplies are easiest to provide on our moon or on planets, because mass and weight impose more limitations aboard space vehicles. *See also* Spacecraft "housekeeping."

Spacecraft Propulsion Engines and propellants that boost space vehicles into orbit from Earth, moon, or another planet. Others provide the energy needed to change orbits. *See also* Liquid propellant; Ramjet; Rocket; Scramjet; Solid propellant.

Space Habitat Any artificial environment designed to sustain life in space. *See also* Biosphere; Closed Ecology Life-Support System; Life-support system; Space suit.

Space Interceptor Any offensive or defensive spacecraft launched from Earth, moon, or another planet to rendezvous with an enemy spacecraft for any purpose (identify, deter, deflect, destroy). *See also* Coorbital ASAT; Direct ascent ASAT.

Space Mine (1) Any offensive space weapon that coorbits near its intended target, then attacks on command or in accord with pre-programmed instructions. (2) One of several or many orbital weapons positioned to form a protective field in space. *See also* Coorbital ASAT; Salvage fused weapon.

Space Satellite Any unmanned spacecraft that has one or more missions. Primary purposes are to support activities of any kind on Earth, moon, or another planet. Reconnaissance, surveillance, navigation, and communications are illustrative.

Space Shuttle Any space transport designed to deliver personnel and/ or cargo from Earth, moon, or another planet to destinations in space, then return for additional loads.

Space Station Any spacecraft designed to maintain a manned presence in orbit for any purpose. Small vehicles accommodate as few as two or three crew members. Large vehicles may accommodate tens, hundreds, even thousands.

Space Suit Apparel that protects and facilitates activities of personnel who venture temporarily outside orbital vehicles or installations in space. Portable life-support systems are indispensable. Custom tailoring and flexible materials are desirable. *See also* Life-support system.

Space Tether A long line (perhaps several hundred miles) of great tensile strength used to transfer payloads from one orbit to another or ferry personnel/cargo between the moon or planets and space transports. Loads lowered below the tether's orbital center of mass shift energy to loads being raised above. *See also* Transfer vehicle.

Space Vehicle   *See* Spacecraft.

Specific Impulse (Isp)   The ratio of engine thrust to propellant flow rate in pounds per second, minus engine drag. Isp measures how well an engine coverts chemical energy into velocity. High Isp increases vehicle delta vee for a given mass ratio or decreases the mass ratio necessary to achieve a given delta vee. *See also* Delta vee.

Spoofing   A form of ECM or ECCM deception that fools enemy command and control systems by sending false electronic signals. *See also* Deception; Electronic countercountermeasures; Electronic countermeasures.

Stable Orbit   Ability to fly through space indefinitely on a prescribed path while expending little or no propellant. *See also* Unstable orbit.

Stage   *See* Rocket stage.

Staging   *See* Rocket staging.

Standoff Attack   Actions by armed forces not in physical contact to damage or destroy enemy targets. Long-range engagement by all but DEW allow defenders some time to improve their posture. *See also* Assault.

Stationkeeping   Actions taken on board or from remote locations to keep a spacecraft in orbit. Guidance and orbit control tasks predominate. *See also* Spacecraft "housekeeping."

Stealth   Technologies and techniques that make it difficult for sensors to detect spacecraft in flight. Structural designs, nonmetallic materials, absorptive coatings, heat shields, emission controls, passive guidance, and electronic countermeasures contribute.

Strategic Defense Initiative (SDI)   U.S. plans and programs for an Earth- and space-based ballistic missile defense system to protect targets primarily in the United States. Commonly called "Star Wars."

Strategic Warning   Notification that enemy offensive operations of any kind may be impending. The alert may be received minutes, hours, days, or longer before hostilities commence. *See also* Tactical warning.

Stratosphere   Earth's atmosphere 10–30 miles above its surface. Life-support systems are essential. Temperatures decrease with altitude in lower layers, but inversions occur at the top, where maximum readings reach about 45°F.

Suborbital Flight   Spacecraft velocity after liftoff from Earth, moon, or another planet that is too slow to overcome gravity. *See also* Orbit.

Sun-Synchronous Orbit   A retrograde flight path in space, inclined about 98° to Earth's equator, constantly maintains the same relative position to the sun. Spacecraft on that path, which pass over the same spots on Earth at the same local time each day, are particularly useful for reconnaissance, because unnatural changes in shadow length or position indicate human activities.

Supersonic Combustion Ramjet (Scramjet)   A jet engine suitable for transatmospheric flight. Unlike ramjets, air compression occurs at supersonic speeds. Ramjets are required until the vehicle reaches about Mach 6. Rockets must take over at about Mach 12, where air is too thin for scramjets to function. *See also* Ramjet; Rocket.

Surface-to-Surface Missile   Any projectile launched from Earth, moon, or another planet on a suborbital, fractional orbit, or orbital path to strike a target anywhere else on that sphere.

Surveillance   Intelligence operations to collect information through visual, aural, or technological observation (often clandestine), while following the subject or maintaining close watch. *See also* Reconnaissance.

System-Generated Electromagnetic Pulse   A sudden surge of electronic current that originates when energetic gamma rays from a nuclear explosion strike solids, instead of atmosphere. Effects are confined within objects that are struck (such as spacecraft). Solid state circuits are especially vulnerable. *See also* Electromagnetic pulse.

Tactical Warning   Notice that enemy offensive operations of any kind are in progress. The alert may be received at any time from the moment the attack is launched until its effect is felt. *See also* Strategic warning.

Target   Property that a belligerent plans to capture or destroy; areas a belligerent plans to control or deny to opponents; a country, area, agency, installation, person, or group against which intelligence/counterintelligence activities are directed. *See also* Target acquisition.

Target Acquisition   Detection, location, identification, and (in the case of mobile targets) tracking any object with sufficient accuracy for armed forces to strike it. *See also* Target.

Terminal Phase   The final trajectory of ballistic missile reentry vehicles from the time they encounter Earth's atmosphere until impact, a period that normally approximates a minute. *See also* Boost phase; Midcourse phase; Post-boost phase; Reentry vehicle.

Tether   *See* Space tether.

Thermal Kill   Destruction of a target by a directed energy weapon that heats structures and/or internal components until they vaporize, melt, or otherwise deform. *See also* Laser weapon; Particle beam weapon.

Thermosphere   Earth's thin atmosphere 50–300 miles above its surface. Tremendous inversions cause temperatures to increase dramatically. Peak readings near the top may reach 2,250°F. Diurnal variations probably are several hundred degrees.

Third Body Problem   Orbital mechanics become exceedingly complex when they deal with three mutually attracting masses: a spacecraft and its interactions with two overlapping gravitational fields, such as those of Earth and moon or another planet and the sun. Complications multiply where no field is clearly dominant. The only mathematical solution to resultant problems involves restrictive assumptions. Computer calculations otherwise are required. *See also* Orbital mechanics; Two body problem.

Thrust   The force a rocket engine exerts to overcome inertia and accelerate a vehicle to required velocity. *See also* Acceleration; Thrust vector control; Velocity; Vertical launch.

Thrust Vector Control   Actions to correct the attitude and direction of a rocket during powered flight. Liquid propulsion systems deflect or swivel engines. Solid propulsion systems employ many techniques, of which movable nozzles, adjustable nozzle vanes, and slip rings or collars at nozzle mouths are typical. *See also* Thrust.

Tracking   The use of sensors to plot the course of targets. Defenders can predict ballistic trajectories, provided the vehicles observed cannot maneuver. *See also* Pointing.

Transatmospheric Vehicle   *See* Aerospace plane; National Aerospace Plane.

Transfer   (1) Any maneuver that changes a spacecraft orbit. (2) Any delivery of personnel and/or cargo from one orbiting spacecraft to another. (3) Any delivery of personnel and/or cargo between an orbiting spacecraft and the moon or a planet. *See also* High energy transfer; Minimum energy transfer.

Transfer Vehicle   Any craft designed to deliver personnel and/or cargo short distances in space. Trips between orbiting spacecraft and between spacecraft and the moon are typical. *See also* Space tether.

Translunar Space   Technically, any territory beyond Earth's moon. Specifically, from a military standpoint, the narrow strip concealed from Earth, which contains L2. *See also* Cislunar space; Lunar libration points.

Troposphere   Earth's atmosphere from the surface to about 10 miles above the equator and half that altitude near the poles. This is where most clouds, winds, precipitation, and other weather effects occur.

Two Body Problem   Orbital mechanics commonly deal with only two mutually attracting masses: a spacecraft and its interactions with Earth or moon or another planet, each of which controls or strongly influences spacecraft behavior wherever its gravitational field is dominant. Straightforward mathematical solutions solve resultant problems. *See also* Third body problem.

Ultra High Frequency   Part of the electromagnetic spectrum between 300 and 3,000 megahertz. *See also* Electromagnetic spectrum.

Unified Command   A top-echelon U.S. combatant organization with regional or functional responsibilities, which normally includes forces from two or more military services. It has a broad, continuing mission and is established by the President, through the Secretary of Defense, with the advice and assistance of the Joint Chiefs of Staff. When authorized by the JCS, commanders of unified commands established by the President may form one or more subordinate unified commands within their jurisdictions. *See also* Space command.

Unstable Orbit Flight through space that requires constant or periodic expenditures of propellant to maintain the prescribed path. *See also* Stable orbit.

Van Allen Belts Two intense radiation layers trapped in Earth's magnetosphere from 45°N to 45°S latitude. The lower layer begins between 250 and 750 miles above the Earth's surface and tops at 6,200 miles. A low particle slot separates it from the upper layer, which terminates at 37,000–52,000 miles, depending on solar activity. Protons are most prominent at 2,200 miles. Electron flux peaks at approximately 9,900 miles. Spacecraft need shielding to transit safely.

Vehicle *See* Spacecraft.

Velocity Speed is the distance traveled in a particular unit of time (the speed of light is 186,000 miles per second). Velocity, a vector quantity, is speed in a particular direction (the speed of a spacecraft in circular orbit is constant, but velocity constantly changes with changes in direction). *See also* Delta vee.

Vertical Launch Spacecraft that take off on flight paths perpendicular to Earth must develop at least twice as many pounds of thrust as the vehicle weighs. Acceleration and velocity initially are low, but increase rapidly because the weight lifted decreases as the engines expend propellant, gravity exerts progressively less influence, and atmospheric drag diminishes. *See also* Aerodynamic drag; Gravity; Thrust; Velocity.

Vulnerability Weakness of any kind that any competitor could exploit by any means to reduce present or projected security capabilities of an opponent.

Warhead An explosive weapon delivered by any ballistic missile or rocket. *See also* Ballistic missile; Rocket.

Warning *See* Strategic warning; Tactical warning.

Waveguide Cutoff A device that helps protect very high frequency electronic equipment against potentially lethal radiant energy surges, particularly electromagnetic pulse. *See also* Electromagnetic pulse.

Weightlessness Spacecraft and their contents float, not because they are weightless, but because all free fall at identical rates in a gravitational field. Physical and psychological effects on humans range from inconvenience to severe debilities.

Window *See* Launch window.

X Rays Electromagnetic radiation with wavelengths shorter than 10 nanometers (10 billionths of a meter). Nuclear explosions are one potent source. *See also* Electromagnetic radiation; X-ray laser.

X-Ray Laser A single-shot, self-destructing beam weapon that can engage many far distant targets simultaneously at the speed of light. The nuclear explosion that furnishes power also demolishes the device. *See also* Laser weapon.

ANNEX B

Abbreviations and Acronyms

ABM	Antiballistic missile
AI	Artificial intelligence
ALS	Advanced launch system
ASAT	Antisatellite
BMD	Ballistic missile defense
BW	Bacteriological warfare
C^3	Command, control, and communications
CELSS	Closed Ecology Life-Support System
CINCSPACE	Commander in Chief, Space
CPB	Charged particle beam
CW	Chemical warfare
DEW	Directed energy weapon
DOD	Department of Defense
DSAT	Defensive satellite
ECM	Electronic countermeasures
ECCM	Electronic countercountermeasures
EHF	Extremely high frequency
EML	Electromagnetic launcher
EMP	Electromagnetic pulse
EVA	Extravehicular activity
EW	Electronic warfare
Excimer	Excited dimer
FEL	Free electron laser
g	Gravity

GEO	Geosynchronous orbit
GSO	Geostationary orbit
HEL	High energy laser
HEO	High earth orbit
HF	High frequency
HPM	High power microwave
ICBM	Intercontinental ballistic missile
IR	Infrared
Isp	Specific impulse
KEW	Kinetic energy weapon
KKV	Kinetic kill vehicle
kw	Kilowatt
L1 to L5	Lunar libration points
Ladar	Laser radar (same as lidar)
Laser	Light amplification by stimulated emission
LEO	Low earth orbit
Lidar	Light detecting and ranging
LOX	Liquid oxygen
LWIR	Long wave infrared
MARV	Maneuverable reentry vehicle
MEO	Medium earth orbit
MHV	Miniature homing vehicle
MILSAT	Military satellite
MIRV	Multiple independently targetable reentry vehicle
MMW	Multimegawatt
Mph	Miles per hour
MV	Miniature vehicle
mw	Megawatt
MWIR	Medium wave infrared
NASA	National Aeronautical and Space Administration
NASP	National Aerospace Plane
NATO	North Atlantic Treaty Organization
NPB	Neutral particle beam
PBV	Post-boost vehicle
Psyop	Psychological operations
R&D	Research and development
Radar	Radio detection and ranging
RDT&E	Research, development, test, and evaluation
Rpm	Revolutions per minute
RTG	Radioisotope thermoelectric generators
SACSPACE	Supreme Allied Commander, Space
Scramjet	Supersonic combustion ramjet
SDI	Strategic Defense Initiative
SDIO	Strategic Defense Initiative Office
SGEMP	System generated electromagnetic pulse
SLBM	Submarine-launched ballistic missile
SPACECOM	Space command

TNT	Trinitrotoluene
UHF	Ultra high frequency
UN	United Nations
UV	Ultraviolet
VLSI	Very large scale integration

A N N E X
C

Treaty on
Outer Space

Text of the Treaty on Principles Governing the Activities of States in the Exploration and Use of Outer Space, including the Moon and Other Celestial Bodies; Signed at Washington, London and Moscow on January 27, 1967; Ratification advised by the Senate, April 25, 1967; Ratification by the President of the United States May 24, 1967; Ratifications of the Governments of the United States, the United Kingdom and the Union of Soviet Socialist Republics deposited with the said Governments at Washington, London and Moscow October 10, 1967; Proclaimed by the President October 10, 1967; Entered into Force October 10, 1967

The States Parties to this Treaty,

Inspired by the great prospects opening up before mankind as a result of man's entry into outer space.

Recognizing the common interest of all mankind in the progress of the exploration and use of outer space for peaceful purposes,

Believing that the exploration and use of outer space should be carried on for the benefit of all peoples irrespective of the degree of their economic or scientific development,

Desiring to contribute to broad international cooperation in the scientific as well as the legal aspects of the exploration and use of outer space for peaceful purposes,

Believing that such cooperation will contribute to the development of mutual understanding and to the strengthening of friendly relations between States and peoples,

Recalling resolution 1962 (XVIII), entitled "Declaration of Legal Principles Governing the Activities of States in the Exploration and Use of Outer Space," which was adopted unanimously by the United Nations General Assembly on 13 December 1963,

Recalling resolution 1884 (XVIII), calling upon States to refrain from placing in orbit around the Earth any objects carrying nuclear weapons or any other kinds of weapons of mass destruction or from installing such weapons on celestial bodies, which was adopted unanimously by the United Nations General Assembly on 17 October 1963,

Taking account of United Nations General Assembly resolution 110 (II) of 3 November 1947, which condemned propaganda designed or likely to provoke or encourage any threat to the peace breach of the peace or act of aggression, and considering that the aforementioned resolution is applicable to outer space,

Convinced that a Treaty on Principles Governing the Activities of States in the Exploration and Use of Outer Space, including the Moon and Other Celestial Bodies, will further the Purposes and Principles of the Charter of the United Nations,

Have agreed on the following:

ARTICLE I

The exploration and use of outer space, including the moon and other celestial bodies, shall be carried out for the benefit and in the interests of all countries, irrespective of their degree of economic or scientific development, and shall be the province of all mankind.

Outer space, including the moon and other celestial bodies, shall be free for exploration and use by all States without discrimination of any kind, on a basis of equality and in accordance with international law, and there shall be free access to all areas of celestial bodies.

There shall be freedom of scientific investigation in outer space, including the moon and other celestial bodies, and States shall facilitate and encourage international cooperation in such investigation.

ARTICLE II

Outer space, including the moon and other celestial bodies, is not subject to national appropriation by claim of sovereignty, by means of use or occupation, or by any other means.

ARTICLE III

States Parties to the Treaty shall carry on activities in the exploration and use of outer space, including the moon and other celestial bodies, in accordance with international law, including the Charter of the United Nations, in the interest of maintaining international peace and security and promoting international cooperation and understanding.

ARTICLE IV

States Parties to the Treaty undertake not to place in orbit around the Earth any objects carrying nuclear weapons or any other kinds of weapons of mass destruction, install such weapons on celestial bodies, or station such weapons in outer space in any other manner.

The moon and other celestial bodies shall be used by all States Parties to the Treaty exclusively for peaceful purposes. The establishment of military bases, installations and fortifications, the testing of any type of weapons and the conduct of military maneuvers on celestial bodies shall be forbidden. The use of military personnel for scientific research or for any other peaceful purposes shall not be prohibited. The use of any equipment or facility necessary for peaceful exploration of the moon and other celestial bodies shall also not be prohibited.

ARTICLE V

States Parties to the Treaty shall regard astronauts as envoys of mankind in outer space and shall render to them all possible assistance in the event of accident, distress, or emergency landing on the territory of another State Party or on the high seas. When astronauts make such a landing, they shall be safely and promptly returned to the State of registry of their space vehicle.

In carrying on activities in outer space and on celestial bodies, the astronauts of one State Party shall render all possible assistance to the astronauts of other States Parties.

States Parties to the Treaty shall immediately inform the other States Parties to the Treaty or the Secretary-General of the United Nations of any phenomena they discover in outer space, including the moon and other celestial bodies, which could constitute a danger to the life or health of astronauts.

ARTICLE VI

States Parties to the Treaty shall bear international responsibility for national activities in outer space, including the moon and other celestial bodies, whether such activities are carried on by governmental agencies or by non-governmental entities, and for assuring that national activities are carried out in conformity with the provisions set forth in the present Treaty. The activities of non-governmental entities in outer space, including the moon and other celestial bodies, shall require authorization and continuing supervision by the appropriate State Party to the Treaty. When activities are carried on in outer space, including the moon and other celestial bodies, by an international organization, responsibility for compliance with this Treaty shall be borne by the international organization and by the States Parties to the Treaty participating in such organization.

ARTICLE VII

Each State Party to the Treaty that launches or procures the launching of an object into outer space, including the moon and other celestial bodies, and each State Party from whose territory or facility an object is launched, is internationally liable for damage to another State Party to the Treaty or to its natural or juridical persons by such object or its component parts on the Earth, in air space or in outer space, including the moon and other celestial bodies.

ARTICLE VIII

A State Party to the Treaty on whose registry an object launched into outer space is carried shall retain jurisdiction and control over such object, and over any personnel thereof, while in outer space or on a celestial body. Ownership of objects launched into outer space, including objects landed or constructed on a celestial body, and of their component parts, is not affected by their presence in outer space or on a celestial body or by their return to the Earth. Such objects or component parts found beyond the limits of the State Party to the Treaty on whose registry they are carried shall be returned to that State Party, which shall, upon request, furnish identifying data prior to their return.

ARTICLE IX

In the exploration and use of outer space, including the moon and other celestial bodies, States Parties to the Treaty shall be guided by the principle of co-operation and mutual assistance and shall conduct all their activities in outer space, including the moon and other celestial bodies, with due regard to the corresponding interests of all other States Parties to the Treaty. States Parties to the Treaty shall pursue studies of outer space, including the moon and other celestial bodies, and conduct exploration of them so as to avoid their harmful contamination and also adverse changes in the environment of the Earth resulting from the introduction of extraterrestrial matter and, where necessary, shall adopt appropriate measures for this purpose. If a State Party to the Treaty has reason to believe that an activity or experiment planned by it or its nationals in outer space, including the moon and other celestial bodies, would cause potentially harmful interference with activities of other States Parties in the peaceful exploration and use of outer space, including the moon and other celestial bodies, it shall undertake appropriate international consultations before proceeding with any such activity or experiment. A State Party to the Treaty which has reason to believe that an activity or experiment planned by another State Party in outer space, including the moon and other celestial bodies, would cause potentially harmful interference with activities in the peaceful exploration and use of outer space, including the moon and other celestial bodies, may request consultation concerning the activity or experiment.

ARTICLE X

In order to promote international co-operation in the exploration and use of outer space, including the moon and other celestial bodies, in conformity with the purposes of this Treaty, the States Parties to the Treaty shall consider on a basis of the equality any requests by other States Parties to the Treaty to be afforded an opportunity to observe the flight of space objects launched by those States.

The nature of such an opportunity for observation and conditions under which it could be afforded shall be determined by agreement between the States concerned.

ARTICLE XI

In order to promote international co-operation in the peaceful exploration and use of outer space, States Parties to the Treaty conducting activities in outer space, including the moon and other celestial bodies, agree to inform the Secretary-General of the United Nations as well as the public and the international scientific community to the greatest extent feasible and practicable, of the nature, conduct, locations and results of such activities. On receiving the said information, the Secretary-General of the United Nations should be prepared to disseminate it immediately and effectively.

ARTICLE XII

All stations, installations, equipment and space vehicles on the moon and other celestial bodies shall be open to representatives of other States Parties to the Treaty on a basis of reciprocity. Such representatives shall give reasonable advance notice of a projected visit, in order that appropriate consultations may be held and that maximum precautions may be taken to assure safety and to avoid interference with normal operations in the facility to be visited.

ARTICLE XIII

The provisions of this Treaty shall apply to the activities of States Parties to the Treaty in the exploration and use of outer space, including the moon and other celestial bodies, whether such activities are carried on by a single State Party to the Treaty or jointly with other States, including cases where they are carried on within the framework of international inter-governmental organizations.

Any practical questions arising in connection with activities carried on by international inter-governmental organizations in the exploration and use of outer space, including the moon and other celestial bodies, shall be resolved by the States Parties to the Treaty either with the appropriate international organization or with one or more States members of that international organization, which are Parties to this Treaty.

ARTICLE XIV

1. This Treaty shall be open to all States for signature. Any State which does not sign this Treaty before its entry into force in accordance with paragraph 3 of this article may accede to it at any time.

2. This Treaty shall be subject to ratification by signatory States. Instruments of ratification and instruments of accession shall be deposited with the Governments of the United States of America, the United Kingdom of Great Britain and Northern Ireland, and the Union of Soviet Socialist Republics, which are hereby designated the Depositary Governments.

3. This Treaty shall enter into force upon the deposit of instruments of ratification by five Governments including the Governments designated as Depositary Governments under this Treaty.

4. For States whose instruments of ratification or accession are deposited subsequent to the entry into force of this Treaty, it shall enter into force on the date of the deposit of their instruments of ratification or accession.

5. The Depositary Governments shall promptly inform all signatory and acceding States of the date of each signature, the date of deposit of each instrument of ratification of and accession to this Treaty, the date of its entry into force and other notices.

6. This Treaty shall be registered by the Depositary Governments pursuant to Article 102 of the Charter of the United Nations.

ARTICLE XV

Any State Party to the Treaty may propose amendments to this Treaty. Amendments shall enter into force for each State party to the Treaty accepting the amendment upon their acceptance by a majority of the States Parties to the Treaty and thereafter for each remaining State Party to the Treaty on the date of acceptance by it.

ARTICLE XVI

Any State Party to the Treaty may give notice of its withdrawal from the Treaty one year after its entry into force by written notification to the Depositary Governments. Such withdrawal shall take effect one year from the date of receipt of this notification.

ARTICLE XVII

This Treaty, of which the English, Russian, French, Spanish and Chinese texts are equally authentic, shall be deposited in the archives of the Depositary Governments. Duly certified copies of this Treaty shall be transmitted by the Depositary Governments to the Governments of the signatory and acceding States.

IN WITNESS WHEREOF the undersigned, duly authorized, have signed this Treaty.

DONE in triplicate, at the cities of Washington, London and Moscow, this twenty-seventh day of January one thousand nine hundred sixty-seven.

A N N E X
D

Treaty between the United States of America and the Union of Soviet Socialist Republics on the Limitation of Anti-Ballistic Missile Systems, With Associated Protocol

Signed May 26, 1972; ratification advised by the Senate August 3, 1972; ratified by the President and entered into force October 3, 1972

The United States of America and the Union of Soviet Socialist Republics, hereinafter referred to as the Parties,

Proceeding from the premise that nuclear war would have devastating consequences for all mankind,

Considering that effective measures to limit anti-ballistic missile systems would be a substantial factor in curbing the race in strategic offensive arms and would lead to a decrease in the risk of outbreak of war involving nuclear weapons,

Proceeding from the premise that the limitation of anti-ballistic missile systems, as well as certain agreed measures with respect to the limitation of strategic offensive arms, would contribute to the creation of more favorable conditions for further negotiations on limiting strategic arms,

Mindful of their obligations under Article VI of the Treaty on the Non-Proliferation of Nuclear Weapons,

Declaring their intention to achieve at the earliest possible date the cessation of the nuclear arms race and to take effective measures toward reductions in strategic arms, nuclear disarmament, and general and complete disarmament,

Desiring to contribute to the relaxation of international tension and the strengthening of trust between States,

Have agreed as follows:

ARTICLE I

1. Each Party undertakes to limit anti-ballistic missile (ABM) systems and to adopt other measures in accordance with the provisions of this Treaty.

    2. Each Party undertakes not to deploy ABM systems for a defense of the territory of its country and not to provide a base for such a defense, and not to deploy ABM systems for defense of an individual region except as provided for in Article III of this Treaty.

ARTICLE II

1. For the purpose of this Treaty an ABM system is a system to counter strategic ballistic missiles or their elements in flight trajectory, currently consisting of:

    (a) ABM interceptor missiles, which are interceptor missiles constructed and deployed for an ABM role, or of a type tested in an ABM mode;

    (b) ABM launchers, which are launchers constructed and deployed for launching ABM interceptor missiles; and

    (c) ABM radars, which are radars constructed and deployed for an ABM role, or of a type tested in an ABM mode.

2. The ABM system components listed in paragraph 1 of this Article include those which are:

    (a) operational;

    (b) under construction;

    (c) undergoing testing;

    (d) undergoing overhaul, repair or conversion; or

    (e) mothballed.

ARTICLE III

Each party undertakes not to deploy ABM systems or their components except that:

    (a) within one ABM system deployment area having a radius of one hundred and fifty kilometers and centered on the Party's national capital, a Party may deploy: (1) no more than one hundred ABM launchers and no more than one hundred ABM interceptor missiles at launch sites, and (2) ABM radars within no more than six ABM radar complexes, the area of each complex being circular and have a diameter of no more than three kilometers; and

(b) within one ABM system deployment area having a radius of one hundred and fifty kilometers and containing ICBM silo launchers, a Party may deploy: (1) no more than one hundred ABM launchers and no more than one hundred ABM interceptor missiles at launch sites, (2) two large phased-array ABM radars comparable in potential to corresponding ABM radars operational or under construction on the date of signature of the Treaty in an ABM system deployment area containing ICBM silo launchers, and (3) no more than eighteen ABM radars each having a potential less than the potential of the smaller of the above-mentioned two large phased-array ABM radars.

ARTICLE IV

The limitations provided for in Article III shall not apply to ABM systems or their components used for development or testing, and located within current or additionally agreed test ranges. Each Party may have no more than a total of fifteen ABM launchers at test ranges.

ARTICLE V

1. Each Party undertakes not to develop, test, or deploy ABM systems or components which are sea-based, air-based, space-based, or mobile land-based.

2. Each Party undertakes not to develop, test, or deploy ABM launchers for launching more than one ABM interceptor missile at a time from each launcher, nor to modify deployed launchers to provide them with such a capability, nor to develop, test, or deploy automatic or semi-automatic or other similar systems for rapid reload or ABM launchers.

ARTICLE VI

To enhance assurance of the effectiveness of the limitations on ABM systems and their components provided by this Treaty, each Party undertakes:

(a) not to give missiles, launchers, or radars, other than ABM interceptor missiles, ABM launchers, or ABM radars, capabilities to counter strategic ballistic missiles or their elements in flight trajectory, and not to test them in an ABM mode; and (*b*) not to deploy in the future radars for early warning of strategic ballistic missile attack except at locations along the periphery of its national territory and oriented outward.

ARTICLE VII

Subject to the provisions of this Treaty, modernization and replacement of ABM systems or their components may be carried out.

ARTICLE VIII

ABM systems or their components in excess of the numbers or outside the areas specified in this Treaty, as well as ABM systems or their components prohibited by this Treaty, shall be destroyed or dismantled under agreed procedures within the shortest possible agreed period of time.

ARTICLE IX

To assure the viability and effectiveness of this Treaty, each Party undertakes not to transfer to other States, and not to deploy outside its national territory, ABM systems or their components limited by this Treaty.

ARTICLE X

Each Party undertakes not to assume any international obligations which would conflict with this Treaty.

ARTICLE XI

The Parties undertake to continue active negotiations for limitations on strategic offensive arms.

ARTICLE XII

1. For the purpose of providing assurance of compliance with the provisions of this Treaty, each Party shall use national technical means of verification at its disposal in a manner consistent with generally recognized principles of international law.

2. Each Party undertakes not to interfere with the national technical means of verification of the other Party operating in accordance with paragraph 1 of this Article.

3. Each Party undertakes not to use deliberate concealment measures which impede verification by national technical means of compliance with the provisions of this Treaty. This obligation shall not require changes in current construction, assembly, conversion, or overhaul practices.

ARTICLE XIII

1. To promote the objectives and implementation of the provisions of this Treaty, the Parties shall establish promptly a Standing Consultative Commission, within the framework of which they will:

(a) consider questions concerning compliance with the obligations assumed and related situations which may be considered ambiguous;

(b) provide on a voluntary basis such information as either Party considers necessary to assure confidence in compliance with the obligations assumed;

(c) consider questions involving unintended interference with national technical means of verification;

(d) consider possible changes in the strategic situation which have a bearing on the provisions of this Treaty;

(e) agree upon procedures and dates for destruction or dismantling of ABM systems or their components in cases provided for by the provisions of this Treaty;

(f) consider, as appropriate, possible proposals for further increasing the viability of this Treaty, including proposals for amendments in accordance with the provisions of this Treaty;

(g) consider, as appropriate, proposals for further measures aimed at limiting strategic arms.

2. The Parties through consultation shall establish, and may amend as appropriate, Regulations for the Standing Consultative Commission governing procedures, composition and other relevant matters.

ARTICLE XIV

1. Each Party may propose amendments to this Treaty. Agreed amendments shall enter into force in accordance with the procedures governing the entry into force to this Treaty.

2. Five years after entry into force of this Treaty, and at five year intervals thereafter, the Parties shall together conduct a review of this Treaty.

ARTICLE XV

1. This Treaty shall be of unlimited duration.

2. Each Party shall, in exercising its national sovereignty, have the right to withdraw from this Treaty if it decides that extraordinary events related to the subject matter of this Treaty have jeopardized its supreme interests. It shall give notice of its decision to the other Party six months prior to withdrawal from the Treaty. Such notice shall include a statement of the extraordinary events the notifying Party regards as having jeopardized its supreme interests.

ARTICLE XVI

1. This Treaty shall be subject to ratification in accordance with the constitutional procedures of each Party. The Treaty shall enter into force on the day of the exchange of instruments of ratification.

2. This Treaty shall be registered pursuant to Article 102 of the Charter of the United Nations.

Done at Moscow on May 26, 1972, in two copies, each in the English and Russian languages, both texts being equally authentic.

For the United States of America:
> RICHARD NIXON,
> *President of the United States of America.*

For the Union of Soviet Socialist Republics:
> L. I. BREZHNEV,
> *General Secretary of the Central Committee of the CPSU.*

Protocol to the Treaty Between the United States of America and the Union of Soviet Socialist Republics on the Limitation of Anti-Ballistic Missile Systems

Signed at Moscow July 3, 1974; ratification advised by the Senate, November 10, 1975; entered into force May 24, 1976

The United States of America and the Union of Soviet Socialists Republics, hereinafter referred to as the Parties,

Proceeding from the Basic Principles of Relations between the United States of America and the Union of Soviet Socialist Republics signed on May 29, 1972,

Desiring to further the objectives of the Treaty between the United States of America and the Union of Soviet Socialist Republics on the Limitation of Anti-Ballistic Missile Systems signed on May 26, 1972, hereinafter referred to as the Treaty,

Reaffirming their conviction that the adoption of further measures for the limitation of strategic arms would contribute to strengthening international peace and security,

Proceeding from the premise that further limitation of anti-ballistic missile systems will create more favorable conditions for the completion of work on a permanent agreement on more complete measures for the limitation of strategic offensive arms,

Have agreed as follows:

ARTICLE I

1. Each Party shall be limited at any one time to a single area out of the two provided in Article III of the Treaty for deployment of anti-ballistic missile (ABM) systems or their components and accordingly shall not exercise its rights to deploy an ABM system or its components in the second of the two ABM system deployment areas permitted by Article III of the Treaty, except as an exchange of one permitted area for the other in accordance with Article II of this Protocol.

2. Accordingly, except as permitted by Article II of this Protocol: the United States of America shall not deploy an ABM system or its components in the area centered on its capital, as permitted by Article III(a) of the Treaty, and the Soviet Union shall not deploy an ABM system or its components in the deployment area of intercontinental ballistic missile (ICBM) silo launchers permitted by Article III(b) of the Treaty.

ARTICLE II

1. Each Party shall have the right to dismantle or destroy its ABM system and the components thereof in the area where they are presently deployed and to deploy an ABM system or its components in the alternative area permitted by Article III of the Treaty, provided that prior to initiation of construction, notification is given in accord with the procedure agreed to by the Standing Consultative Commission, during the year beginning October 3, 1977, and ending October 2, 1978, or during any year which commences at five year intervals thereafter, those being the years for periodic review of the Treaty, as provided in Article XIV of the Treaty. This right may be exercised only once.

2. Accordingly, in the event of such notice, the United States would have the right to dismantle or destroy the ABM system and its components in the deployment area of ICBM silo launchers and to deploy an ABM system or its components in an area centered on its capital, as permitted by Article III(a) of the Treaty, and the Soviet Union would have the right to dismantle or destroy the ABM system and its components in the area centered on its capital and to deploy an ABM system or its components in an area containing ICBM silo launchers, as permitted by Article III(b) of the Treaty.

3. Dismantling or destruction and deployment of ABM systems or their components and the notification thereof shall be carried out in accordance with Article VIII of the ABM Treaty and procedures agreed to in the Standing Consultative Commission.

ARTICLE III

The rights and obligations established by the Treaty remain in force and shall be complied with by the Parties except to the extent modified by this Protocol. In particular, the deployment of an ABM system or its components within the area selected shall remain limited by the levels and other requirements established by the Treaty.

ARTICLE IV

This Protocol shall be subject to ratification in accordance with the constitutional procedures of each Party. It shall enter into force on the day of the exchange of instruments of ratification and shall thereafter be considered an integral part of the Treaty.

DONE at Moscow on July 3, 1974, in duplicate, in the English and Russian languages, both texts being equally authentic.

For the United States of America:

RICHARD NIXON,

President of the United States of America.

For the Union of Soviet Socialist Republics:

L. I. BREZHNEV,

General Secretary of the Central Committee of the CPSU.

Source Notes

Background, Purpose, and Scope

1. *Pioneering the Space Frontier: Report of the National Commission on Space*, New York, Bantam Books, 1986, pp. 5, 7, 10, 59–60, 75–92; Edward Teller, "The Lunar Laboratory," and Gregg E. Maryniak, "Living Off the Land—The Use of Resources in Space for Future Civilian Space Operations," both in *America Plans For Space*, Washington, National Defense University Press, June 1986, pp. 33–44 and 53–80; Daniel O. Graham, *High Frontier*, Washington, High Frontier, Inc., 1982, pp. 37–47, 89–98; Lou Cannon, "Reagan Says U.S. Should Lead Colonization of Space," *Washington Post*, September 23, 1988, p. A3.
2. Hans Mark, "Warfare in Space," in *America Plans for Space*, pp. 13–15.
3. Halford J. Mackinder, "The Geographical Pivot of History," *Geographical Journal*, Vol. 23, 1904, pp. 421–444, and *Democratic Ideals and Reality*, London, Constable & Co., 1919.
4. *Public Papers of the Presidents of the United States: John F. Kennedy, 1961*, Washington, U.S. GPO, 1962, pp. 403, 405.
5. *Pioneering the Space Frontier*, pp. 65, 66–67, 134.

Chapter 1.   Area Analysis of Earth-Moon System

1. *Webster's Third New International Dictionary of the English Language*, s.v. "geography."
2. *Space Handbook*, ed. by Curtis D. Cochran, Dennis M. Gorman, and Joseph D. Dumoulin, Maxwell Air Force Base, AL, Air University Press, January 1985, pp. 2-27 through 2-29.

3. John M. Collins, *U.S.-Soviet Military Balance, 1980–1985*, New York, Pergamon-Brassey's, 1985, p. 140; Wernher Von Braun, and Frederick I. Ordway III, *History of Rocketry and Space Travel*, New York, Thomas Y. Crowell, 1969, pp. 234, 238.

4. *Space Handbook*, p. 1-3; Robert G. Fleagle, "Atmosphere," *Encyclopedia Americana: International Edition*, 1978.

5. *Space Handbook*, pp. 1-3, 1-4; G. Harry Stine, *Handbook for Space Colonists*, New York, Holt, Rinehart and Winston, 1985, pp. 47–63.

6. *Aviation Weather: For Pilots and Flight Operations Personnel*, Washington, Depts. of Transportation and Commerce, 1975, pp. 79–124; "Atmosphere," *Encyclopedia Americana*; Kathy Sawyer, "At Cape, Did Lightning Strike Twice?," *Washington Post*, April 9, 1987, p. 3; "Astronauts Oppose Launches Into Clouds," *Washington Post*, April 15, 1987, p. A-24; telephone conversations with range control officials at Patrick AFB and Cape Canaveral, Florida, April 14, 1987.

7. "Atmosphere," *Enclyclopedia Americana*.

8. G. Harry Stine, *Handbook for Space Colonists*, pp. 65–79; Frederick C. Durant III, "Space Exploration," *New Encyclopedia Britannica*, 15th edn.; *Space Handbook*, Chapter 8 and Appendix A.

9. *Ibid*; comments on a draft of this study by Patrick A. Grieco, USAF.

10. William M. Kaula, "Earth, Gravitational Field of," *New Encyclopedia Britannica*; Jesse W. Beams, "Gravitation," *New Encyclopedia Britannica*; "Space Exploration," *New Encyclopedia Britannica*.

11. Telephone conversation with Sean K. Collins, W. J. Schafer Associates, April 15, 1987.

12. "Motion," *Encyclopedia Americana*.

13. "Space Exploration," *New Encyclopedia Britannica*; *Space Handbook*, pp. 3-1 through 3-12; David Baker, *The Shape of Wars to Come*, New York, Stein and Day, 1982, pp. 35, 36–37; Graham Yost, *Spy-Tech*, New York, Facts on File Publications, 1985, pp. 56–57.

14. Stine, *Handbook for Space Colonists*, pp. 81–95.

15. Baker, *The Shape of Wars to Come*, pp. 33–34, 35; "Space Exploration," *New Encyclopedia Britannica*.

16. "Weightlessness," *New Encyclopedia Britannica: Micropedia*, 1983; telephone conversation with Sean K. Collins.

17. Ibid.

18. "Space Exploration," *New Encyclopedia Britannica*; Yost, *Spy-Tech*, pp. 57, 59–60; Baker, *The Shape of Wars to Come*, pp. 37–38.

19. Burrows, *Deep Black*, pp. 58–59; Baker, *The Shape of Wars to Come*, p. 38.

20. "Space Exploration," *New Encyclopedia Britannica*; telephone conversation with Sean K. Collins, April 20, 1987.

21. Ashton B. Carter, "Satellites and Anti-Satellites," *International Security*, Spring 1986, pp. 50, 52, 62, 64; Yost, *Spy-Tech*, pp. 58–59; Baker, *The Shape of Wars to Come*, pp. 35–36, 38–39; *Space Handbook*, pp. 2-43, 2-44.

22. Peter Mackenzie Millman, "Meteor," *New Encyclopedia Britannica*; *Space Handbook*, p. 1-6; G. Harry Stine, *Confrontation in Space*, Englewood Cliffs, NJ, Prentice-Hall, 1981, pp. 79–80.

23. "Atmosphere," *Encyclopedia Americana; Space Handbook*, pp. 1-4, 1-6.

24. Isaac Asimov, "Sound," *Encyclopedia Americana; Space Handbook*, pp. 1-4, 1-5; comments on a draft of this study by Patrick A. Grieco, USAF.

25. *Space Handbook*, pp. 1-8, 1-13, 2-41 through 2-47; "Space Exploration," *New Encyclopedia Britannica*; R. Grant Athay, "Sun," *Encyclopedia Americana*; "Skylab Program," *New Encyclopedia Britannica: Micropedia*.

26. Colin O. Hines, "Ionosphere," *New Encyclopedia Britannica*; "Atmosphere," *Encyclopedia Americana*; "Sun," *Encyclopedia Americana; Space Handbook*, pp. 1-5, 1-10, 11, 12.

27. *Space Handbook*, pp. 1-9, 10, 13, 14; Wilmot N. Hess, "Van Allen Radiation Belts," *New Encyclopedia Britannica*; N. C. Gerson, "Van Allen Radiation Belts," *Encyclopedia Americana*.

28. *Pioneering the Space Frontier: Report of the National Commission on Space*, New York, Bantam Books, 1986, p. 34; *Space Handbook*, pp. 1-8, 9, 10, 11, 12, and Chapter 7; Stine, *Confrontation in Space*, pp. 79, 80, 81; "Sun," *Encyclopedia Americana*.

29. Carter, "Satellites and Anti-Satellites," pp. 48–66; Robert B. Giffen, *U.S. Space System Survivability: Strategic Alternatives for the 1990s*, Washington, National Defense University Press, 1982, pp. 6–8; Stine, *Confrontation in Space*, p. 64.

30. Giffen, *U.S. Space System Survivability*, pp. 6–8.

31. Ibid., p. 12; *Space Handbook*, pp. 2-37 through 2-40; Burrows, *Deep Black*, p. 57; telephone conversations with Sean K. Collins, April 29, 1987.

32. *Space Handbook*, p. 2-40; Giffen, *U.S. Space System Survivability*, p. 12.

33. *Space Handbook*, p. 2-40.

34. Ibid., pp. 2-18, 2-41, 3-13; Gilbert Fielder, "Moon," *New Encyclopedia Britannica*; Victor G. Szebehely, "Mechanics, Celestial," *New Encyclopedia Britannica*; James D. Burke, "Moon," *Encyclopedia Americana*.

35. "Moon," *New Encyclopedia Britannica*; "Moon," *Encyclopedia Americana*.

36. Ibid.

37. Peter H. Schultz, *Moon Morphology*, Austin, University of Texas Press, 1976; *Apollo Over the Moon: A View From Orbit*, ed. by Harold Masursky, G.W. Colton, and Farouk El-Baz, Washington, National Aeronautical and Space Agency, 1978; "Moon," *New Encyclopedia Britannica*; "Moon," *Encyclopedia Americana*.

38. "Moon," *New Encyclopedia Britannica*.

39. Ben Bova, "Moonbase Orientation Manual 1: Transport and Manufacturing," *Analog*, June 1987, pp. 75, 76, 81–84; Gerard K. O'Neill, *The High Frontier: Human Colonies in Space*, New York, Morrow, 1977, p. 144; *Pioneering the Space Frontier*, pp. 7, 14, 85–86; Sally K. Ride, *Leadership and America's Future in Space: A Report to the Administrator*, Washington, NASA, August 1987, pp. 29–31.

40. O'Neill, *The High Frontier*, pp. 128–130; *Pioneering the Space Frontier*, pp. 131–132.

41. *Pioneering the Space Frontier*, pp. 131–132; Stine, *Confrontation in Space*, pp. 59–60.

42. O'Neill, *The High Frontier*, pp. 128–130; Roman Smoluchowski, *The Solar System: The Sun, Planets, and Life*, New York, Scientific American Library, 1983, p. 125; telephone conversation with Gregg E. Maryniak, Space Studies Institute, Princeton, NJ, May 12, 1987.

43. Stine, *Confrontation in Space*, pp. 64–65.

44. Charles Olivier, "Asteroid," *Encyclopedia Americana*; *Pioneering the Space Frontier*, p. 65; Ben Bova, "Moonbase Orientation Manual 1," pp. 72, 73.

45. Appendix 1, "Analysis of the Area of Operations," *Field Manual (FM) 101-5: Staff Organization and Procedure*, Washington, D.C., Headquarters, Department of the Army, June 1968, pp. I-1 through I-13.

46. Ibid., p. I-5; *FM 100-5: Operations*, Washington, D.C., Headquarters, Department of the Army, May 5, 1986, p. 80.

47. For discussion of gravity wells and sources of Map 8, see Stine, *Confrontation in Space*, pp. 56–58, 86; *Pioneering the Space Frontier*, pp. 60–61. Clausewitz addresses the importance of high ground in *On War*, ed. by Michael Howard and Peter Paret, Princeton, NJ, Princeton University Press, 1976, pp. 352–354.

48. Telephone conversation with Sean K. Collins, May 25, 1987.

49. *Pioneering the Space Frontier*, pp. 132, 133–134.

50. Ibid., p. 132; Stine, *Confrontation in Space*, pp. 72–73.

51. Stine, *Confrontation in Space*, pp. 57, 58, 60–61, 86–87; O'Neill, *The High Frontier*, pp. 133, 135, 141–143, summarizes some economic benefits.

52. Arthur C. Clarke, *Of Time and Stars*, London, Victor Gollancz, Ltd., 1972, p. 126.

53. Ibid., p. 117; Robert Salkeld, *War and Space*, Englewood Cliffs, NJ, Prentice-Hall, 1970, pp. 48, 51, 55, 69.

54. Quotation is from Stine, *Confrontation in Space*, pp. 61–62.

55. Salkeld, *War and Space*, pp. 50, 56.

56. Ibid., pp. 59–61, 65–66.

57. Ibid., pp. 66–67; telephone conversation with Sean K. Collins, June 5, 1987.

58. Salkeld, *War and Space*, p. 66; *Space Handbook*, p. 1-5.

59. Salkeld, *War and Space*, pp. 63, 74, 75.

60. *The Effects of Nuclear Weapons*, ed. by Samuel Glasstone and Philip J. Dolan, 3d ed., Washington, Dept. of Defense and Dept. of Energy, 1977, pp. 1–2, 7–8, 80–86, 154–157, 194–195, 226–227; telephone conversations with Defense Nuclear Agency officials, June 1987.

61. *The Effects of Nuclear Weapons*, pp. 46, 73–75, 281–282, 315–316.

62. Ibid., pp. 324–325, 463–489; David J. Lynch, "DNA Studying Nuclear Blasts in Space for SDI," *Defense Week*, June 29, 1987, p. 2.

63. *The Effects of Nuclear Weapons*, pp. 46, 47.

64. *The Effects of Nuclear Weapons*, pp. 24–25, 40, 74, 315, 469, 474, 476; *Nuclear Effects Testing*, Washington, Defense Nuclear Agency, undated [1987].

65. Ibid., pp. 514–520; Anthony P. Trippe, "The Threat of Electromagnetic Pulse," *National Defense*, December 1984, pp. 23–25; Eric J. Lerner, "Mushrooming Vulnerability to EMP" *Aerospace America*, August 1984, p. 74; Jorg C. Lippert, "The Hidden Destroyer: EMP—Disturbances From Space," *NATO's Sixteen Nations*, May 1983, pp. 38, 39–40, 41; Daniel L. Stein, "Electromagnetic Pulse—The Uncertain Certainty," *Bulletin of the Atomic Scientists*, March 1983, p. 52; "EMP: Short-Circuit Could Cause Defense Blackout," *Defense Week*, May 11, 1981, pp. 4–5.

66. *The Effects of Nuclear Weapons*, pp. 522–540; Trippe, "The Threat of Electromagnetic Pulse," pp. 24–25; Stein, "Electromagnetic Pulse—The Uncertain Certainty," pp. 53–54.

67. *The Effects of Nuclear Weapons*, pp. 521–522; Lerner, "Mushrooming Vulnerability to EMP," pp. 74–75; Stine, *Confrontation in Space*, pp. 97–98; Lippert, "The Hidden Destroyer: EMP," p. 39; Stein, "Electromagnetic Pulse—The Uncertain Certainty," p. 53.

68. Cosmo DiMaggio, *Directed Energy Weapons Research: Status and Outlook*, Washington, Congressional Research Service, August 30, 1985; Dietrich Schroeer, *Directed-Energy Weapons and Strategic Defense: A Primer*, Adelphi Papers 221, London, International Institute for Strategic Studies, Summer 1987; *Report to the Congress on the Strategic Defense Initiative*, Washington, Dept. of Defense, June 1986, pp. VII-C-7,8; Graham, *High Frontier*, pp. 135–136, 138, 139; Stine, *Confrontation in Space*, pp. 104–105; *Space Handbook*, p. 9-25.

69. *Space Handbook*, pp. 9-1 through 9-21; "Report to the APS of the Study Group on Science and Technology of Directed Energy Weapons: Executive Summary and Major Conclusions," *Physics Today*, May 1987, pp. S-3–S-10; Graham, *High Frontier*, pp. 136, 139, 140.

70. Kosta Tsipis, "Laser Weapons," *Scientific American*, December 1981, p. 54; Vickie M. Graham, "Defense at the Speed of Light," *Airman*, December 1986, p. 13; Graham, *High Frontier*, p. 138.

71. "Report to the APS on Directed Energy Weapons," pp. S-11, S-12; Tsipis, "Laser Weapons," pp. 54–55, 56, 57 (figure modifies his diagram on p. 56); *Space Handbook*, p. 9-14.

72. *Space Weapons and International Security*, ed. by Bhupendra Jasani for Stockholm International Peace Research Institute (SIPRI), Oxford, Oxford University Press, 1987, pp. 25–26; Joyce E. Larson and William C. Bodie, *The Intelligent Layperson's Guide to "Star Wars,"* New York, National Strategy Information Center, 1986, pp. 13, 15, 16; *Report to the Congress on the Strategic Defense Initiative*, p. VII-C-2,4; "Report to the APS on Directed Energy Weapons," pp. S-8, S-10, S-11, S-12; *Space Handbook*, p. 9-22; Stine, *Confrontation in Space*, p. 106; comments on a draft of this study by John Albertine, U.S. Space and Naval Warfare Systems Command.

73. *Space Weapons and International Security*, pp. 26, 28; Graham, *High Frontier*, pp. 136, 141, 142.

74. *Space Handbook*, pp. 9-25 through 9-42, 9-50, 9-51, 9-54; "The DOD Particle Beam Technology Program," *Defense Science & Electronics*, May 1983, pp. 49–50; *Report to the Congress on the Strategic Defense Initiative*, p. VII-C-7; Graham, *High Frontier*, pp. 136, 140–141.

75. Stine, *Confrontation in Space*, pp. 113–114, 115; *Space Handbook*, pp. 9-25, 9-33, 9-41; *Report to the Congress on the Strategic Defense Initiative*, p. VII-C-7; Graham, *High Frontier*, pp. 136, 141; "Report to the APS on Directed Energy Weapons," pp. S-8, S-10, Larson and Bodie, *The Intelligent Layperson's Guide to "Star Wars,"* p. 17.

76. E.M. Kallis, *Chemical Warfare: A Primer on Agents, Munitions, and Defensive Measures*, Washington, Congressional Research Service, April 27, 1981, pp. 3–4; *Field Manual (FM) 21-40*, "Chemical, Biological and Nuclear Defense," Washington, Department of the Army, October 14, 1977, pp. 1-13 through 1-18; *ABC Warfare Defense Ashore*, Technical Publications PL-2, Washington, Bureau of Yards and Docks, Department of the Navy, revised April 1960, pp. 2-21 through 2-24, 3-5, 3-16 and 3-17; *The Problem of Chemical and Biological Warfare*, Vol. II, "CB Weapons Today," Stockholm International Peace Research Institute, New York, Humanities Press, 1973, pp. 33–35, 42–43, 47–48; Amoretta M. Hoeber, *The Chemistry of Defeat: Asymmetries in U.S. and Soviet Chemical Warfare Postures*, Cambridge, MA, Institute for Foreign Policy Analysis, 1981, pp. 21–23, 25–28, 42, 47–48; Charles J. Dick, "Soviet Chemical Warfare Capabilities," *International Defense Review*, January 1981, pp. 31, 33, 34, 36, 37, and "The Soviet Chemical and Biological Warfare Threat," *Royal United Services Institute (RUSI)*, March 1981, pp. 48, 50–51; David Rosser-Owen, "NBC Warfare and Anti-NBC Protection," *Armada International*, January 1984, pp. 78, 80, 82, 84.

77. *Army Technical Manual (TM) 3-216, Air Force Manual (AFM) 355-6*, "Military Biology and Biological Agents," Washington, Departments of the Army and Air Force, March 1964, pp. 1, 5–6, 11–16, 36, 86; *FM 21-40*, pp. 1-9 through 1-13; *ABC Warfare Defense Ashore*, pp. 2-17, 2-18, 3-5, 3-16, 3-17, 4-3, 4-9 through 4-12; A.G. Vicary and J. Wilson, "Nuclear, Biological and Chemical Defense," *Royal United Services Institute (RUSI)*, December 1980, pp. 7, 9–10; David M. Saunders, "The Biological/Chemical Warfare Challenge," *U.S. Naval Institute Proceedings*, September 1965, pp. 47–48; Rosser-Owen, "NBC Warfare and Anti-NBC Protection," pp. 86–87; Dick, "The Soviet Chemical and Biological Threat," pp. 47–48.

78. Stine, *Confrontation in Space*, pp. 157–158.

79. Decontamination difficulties on earth are described in *FM 21-40*, pp. 5-26 through 5-32; Dick, "Soviet Chemical Warfare Capabilities," pp. 31, 35; Joseph D. Douglass, Jr., "Chemical Weapons: An Imbalance of Terror," *Strategic Review*, Summer 1982, pp. 37–38; K.G. Benz, "NBC Defense—An Overview, Part II, Detection and Decontamination," *International Defense Review*, February 1984, pp. 162–163; Kallis, *Chemical Warfare*, pp. 10–11; Hoeber, *The Chemistry of Defeat*, pp. 9–10; C.N. Donnelly, "Winning the NBC War: Soviet Army Theory and Practice," *International Defense Review*, August 1981, pp. 994–995; Betty Chapman, "Navy CW Defense," *National Defense*, April 1983, pp. 54–57 and "Chemical Warfare: The Dirty Weapon," *National Defense*, June 1980, p. 36; Helmut Stelzmueller, "NBC Defense—NATO Needs New Devices," *Military Technology*, February 1983, pp. 26, 31–35.

80. Stine, *Confrontation in Space*, pp. 78–79; Clarke, *Of Time and Stars*, p. 128.

81. Stine, *Confrontation in Space*, pp. 95–96.

82. Ibid., pp. 78–80, 86; T.A. Heppenheimer, "Electromagnetic Rail Guns," *Popular Science*, August 1987, pp. 54–57; William Bogle, "Rail Guns and Smart Rocks," *National Defense*, March 1986, p. 18; Larson and Bodie, *The Intelligent Layperson's Guide to "Star Wars,"* pp. 11–12; Craig Covault, "SDI Delta Intercept Yields Data on Space Collision Shock Waves," *Aviation Week & Space Technology*, June 8, 1987, p. 26; Clarence A. Robinson, Jr., "Defense Developing Orbital Guns," *Aviation Week & Space Technology*, July 23, 1984, pp. 61, 65; O'Neill, *The High Frontier*, pp. 138–140.

83. *Space Handbook*, pp. 11-1 through 11-3, 11-5 through 11-8; Arnold E. Nicogossian and James F. Parker, Jr., *Space Physiology and Medicine*, Washington, NASA, 1982, pp. 127–140; *Fundamentals of Aerospace Medicine*, ed. by Roy L. DeHart, Philadelphia, Lea & Febiger, 1985, pp. 847, 852; Christopher H. Dodge, in U.S. Congress, Senate, *Soviet Space Programs: 1976–1980* (with supplementary data through 1983), Part 2, Committee on Commerce, Science, and Transportation, 98th Cong., 2d Sess., Washington, U.S. GPO, October 1984, pp. 724–725; Stine, *Handbook for Space Colonists*, pp. 175–193, 225–243.

84. Dodge, in *Soviet Space Programs: 1976–1980*, p. 698; *Fundamentals of Aerospace Medicine*, p. 854.

85. Dodge, in *Soviet Space Programs: 1976–1980*, pp. 703–704, 707, 708; *Space Handbook*, p. 11-12; Stine, *Handbook for Space Colonists*, pp. 133–151, 211–223.

86. Dodge, in *Soviet Space Programs: 1976–1980*, pp. 704–706, 707, 708, 714–716; *Space Handbook*, pp. 11-3, 11-12, 11-13, 11-16; *Fundamentals of Aerospace Medicine*, p. 847.

87. Nicogossian and Parker, *Space Physiology and Medicine*, pp. 285–292; Dodge, in *Soviet Space Programs: 1976–1980*, pp. 708, 710; *Space Handbook*, p. 11-3.

88. Stine, *Handbook for Space Colonists*, pp. 113–131; *Space Handbook*, p. 11-3; Dodge, in *Soviet Space Programs: 1976–1980*, p. 726.

89. Nicogossian and Parker, *Space Physiology and Medicine*, pp. 293–299; Dodge, in *Soviet Space Programs: 1976–1980*, pp. 728–730; *Space Handbook*, pp. 11-3, 11-4; *Pioneering the Space Frontier*, p. 34.

90. Stine, *Confrontation in Space*, pp. 80–81; *Pioneering the Space Frontier*, p. 72; Nicogossian and Parker, *Space Physiology and Medicine*, pp. 300–302; Dodge, in *Soviet Space Programs: 1976–1980*, pp. 726–727; *Space Handbook*, p. 11-5; comments on a draft of this study by Robert L. Civiak, Congressional Research Service.

91. *Fundamentals of Aerospace Medicine*, pp. 840, 861; Kathy Sawyer, "Research on Weightlessness Holds Key to Mars Mission," *Washington Post*, July 6, 1987, pp. A1, A21; Nicogossian and Parker, *Space Physiology and Medicine*, pp. 141–155; Dodge, in *Soviet Space Programs: 1976–1980*, pp. 699, 722–724.

92. Stine, *Handbook for Space Colonists*, pp. 97–111; "Weightlessness," *New Encyclopedia Britannica: Micropedia*; Dodge, in *Soviet Space Programs: 1976–1980*, p. 721.

93. *Fundamentals of Aerospace Medicine*, pp. 843–844, 845–847; Dodge, in *Soviet Space Programs: 1976–1980*, pp. 460, 461, 695, 696, 697, 706; Nicogossian and Parker, *Space Physiology and Medicine*, pp. 165–219; *Space Handbook*, pp. 11-9, 11-10; Sawyer, "Research on Weightlessness Holds Key to Mars Mission," p. A-21.

94. *Space Handbook*, p. 11-10; Stine, *Handbook for Space Colonists*, pp. 232–239.

95. Dodge, in *Soviet Space Programs: 1976–1980*, pp. 697, 698–699; *Space Handbook*, p. 11-9; *Fundamentals of Aerospace Medicine*, p. 854; Stine, *Handbook for Space Colonists*, pp. 153–211, 245–257.

96. Dodge, in *Soviet Space Programs: 1976–1980*, pp. 693–695; *Space Handbook*, p. 11-9; Nicogossian and Parker, *Space Physiology and Medicine*, pp. 160–162.

97. *Space Handbook*, p. 11-9; Dodge, in *Soviet Space Programs: 1976–1980*, p. 694.

98. Dodge, in *Soviet Space Programs: 1976–1980*, pp. 695, 697; *Space Handbook*, p. 11-10.

Chapter 2. Strategic Problems and Options

1. J.C. Wylie compares and critiques land, sea, and air schools of strategic thought in *Military Strategy: A General Theory of Power Control*, New Brunswick, NJ, Rutgers University Press, 1967, pp. 37–57, 65–75. The U.S. Army, Navy, and Air Force delineate respective doctrines in *Field Manual (FM) 100-5: Operations*, Washington, Dept. of the Army, May 1986; *Naval Warfare Publication (NWP) 1 (Rev. A): Strategic Concepts of the U.S. Navy*, Washington, Dept. of the Navy, May 1978; *Air Force Manual (AFM) 1-1: Basic Aerospace Doctrine of the United States Air Force*, Washington, Dept. of the Air Force, January 1984.

2. For U.S. and Soviet views of various interests, see John M. Collins, *U.S.-Soviet Military Balance: Concepts and Capabilities, 1960–1980*, Washington, McGraw-Hill Publications, 1980, pp. 17–19, 22.

3. Gerard K. O'Neill, *The High Frontier: Human Colonies in Space*, New York, Morrow, 1977. See also *Pioneering the Space Frontier: Report of the National Commission on Space*, New York, Bantam Books, 1986, pp. 2, 3, 5, 9–10, 71.

4. Literature on space exploration is voluminous. See, for example, U.S. National Aeronautics and Space Administration Solar System Exploration Committee, *Planetary Exploration Through Year 2000: A Core Program*, Washington, U.S. GPO, 1983; U.S. National Academy of Sciences, National Research Council, Astronomy Survey Committee, *Astronomy and Astrophysics for the 1980's*, Washington, National Academy Press, 1982. See also *Pioneering the Space Frontier*, pp. 5, 8–9, 26–57.

5. *Charter of the United Nations and Statute of the International Court of Justice*, New York, United Nations, 1945, especially Articles 1, 55, 56; Appendix 1, "Treaties and Treaty Proposals . . . ," in *Space Weapons and International Security*, ed. by Bhupendra Jasani, Oxford, Oxford

University Press, 1987, pp. 312–315 (Outer Space Treaty) and 322–327 (Moon Treaty).

6. U.S. and Soviet declaratory statements are contained in Appendix F, "United States Space Policy," in *Aeronautics and Space Report of the President: 1982 Activities*, Washington, U.S. GPO, 1983, p. 98; U.S. Congress, Senate, *National Aeronautics and Space Act of 1958 . . .* , Committee on Commerce, Science, and Transportation, 95th Cong., 2d Sess., Washington, U.S. GPO, December 1978, pp. 1, 10–11; Appendix 1, "Treaties and Treaty Proposals," in *Space Weapons and International Security*, p. 330 (Soviet proposal to the UN General Assembly concerning international cooperation in the peaceful exploitation of outer space under conditions of its non-militarization, 1985).

7. *Pioneering the Space Frontier*, p. 3; Daniel O. Graham, *High Frontier: A New National Strategy*, Washington, High Frontier, Inc., 1982, pp. 40, 90.

8. *Pioneering the Space Frontier*, pp. 81–89; Graham, *High Frontier*, pp. 40–42, 89–91; Ben Bova, "Moonbase Orientation Manual I: Transport and Manufacturing," *Analog*, June 1987, pp. 65–70, 77, 80–87; Gregg E. Maryniak, "Living Off the Land—The Use of Resources in Space," in *America Plans for Space*, Washington, National Defense University Press, 1986.

9. *Antarctic Politics and Marine Resources: Critical Choices for the 1980s*, Kingston, RI, Center for Ocean Management Studies, 1985; *Antarctic Treaty System: An Assessment*, Washington, National Academy Press, 1986.

10. Paul B. Stares, *Space and National Security*, Washington, Brookings Institution, 1987, pp. 45–72; Robert B. Giffen, *U.S. Space System Survivability*, Washington, National Defense University Press, 1982, p. 2; Thomas C. Brandt, "The Military Uses of Space," in *America Plans for Space*, pp. 81–91.

11. *Arms Control in Space: Workshop Proceedings*, Washington, Office of Technology Assessment, OTA-BP-ISC-28, May 1984, pp. 2, 15, 16, 20–21, 39; Alex Glicksman, "Options for Space Arms Control," in *America Plans for Space*, p. 166.

12. Robert M. Bowman, "Arms Control in Space," Colin S. Gray, "Space and Arms Control," and Henry F. Cooper, "Space Arms Control," all in *America Plans for Space*, pp. 118–119, 134, 179.

13. "Treaty on Outer Space," in U.S. Congress, *Legislation on Foreign Relations Through 1985*, Vol. III, Joint Committee Print, Senate Committee on Foreign Relations and House Committee on Foreign Affairs, Washington, U.S. GPO, August 1986, p. 1065.

14. Ibid., pp. 71, 77.

15. *Arms Control in Space: Workshop Proceedings*, pp. 4, 13, 16, 21–22, 35–43; Bowman, "Arms Control in Space" and Glicksman, "Options for Space Arms Control," in *America Plans for Space*, pp. 119–120, 131, 161, 164–166.

16. Carl von Clausewitz, *On War*, ed. and trans. by Michael Howard and Peter Paret, Princeton, NJ, Princeton University Press, 1976, pp. 487, 595–597, 619; James J. Schneider and Lawrence L. Izzo, "Clausewitz's Elusive Center of Gravity," *Parameters*, September 1987, pp. 46–57; *FM 100-5: Operations*, pp. 179–180.

17. Robert D. Heinl, Jr., *Dictionary of Military and Naval Quotations*, Annapolis, MD, U.S. Naval Institute Press, 1966, p. 311.

18. André Beaufre, *An Introduction to Strategy*, New York, Praeger, 1965, pp. 22–24, 35–36.

19. Sun Tzu, *The Art of War*, trans. by Samuel B. Griffith, New York, Oxford University Press, 1963, p. 77; Basil H. Liddell Hart, *Strategy: The Indirect Approach*, London, Faber and Faber, 1967, pp. 339, 365.

20. Giffen, *U.S. Space System Survivability*, pp. 6–11; Geoffrey E. Perry, "Recoverable Kosmos Satellites for Military Reconnaissance," in U.S. Congress, Senate, *Soviet Space Programs, 1971–75*, Vol. I (staff report prepared for the Committee on Aeronautical and Space Sciences), Washington, U.S. GPO, August 30, 1976, pp. 457–478.

21. Graham Yost, *Spy-Tech*, New York, Facts on File Publications, 1985, pp. 120–121.

22. Stefan T. Possony and J.E. Pournelle, *The Strategy of Technology: Winning the Decisive War*, Cambridge, MA, Dunellen, 1970, pp. 4–12, 55.

23. George Heilmeier, "Guarding Against Technological Surprise," *Congressional Record*, June 22, 1976, p. S10139; Jack Swift, "Strategic Superiority Through SDI," *Defense & Foreign Affairs*, December 1985, p. 17; David A. Brinkley and Andrew W. Hull, *Estimative Intelligence*, Washington, Defense Intelligence School, August 1979, p. 258; Klaus Knorr and Oskar Morgenstern, *Science and Defense: Some Critical Thoughts on Military Research and Development*, Princeton, NJ, Princeton University Press, 1965, pp. 19–27.

24. *FM 30-102: Opposing Forces Europe*, Washington, Dept. of the Army, November 18, 1977, pp. 2-26 through 2-32; Collins, *U.S.-Soviet Military Balance: Concepts and Capabilities, 1960–1980*, pp. 312–313.

25. *FM 100-5: Operations*, p. 9-11.

26. For sample assumptions on Earth, see William J. Stewart, "Strategy: A Proposed Model for Its Formulation," in *The Art and Practice of Military Strategy*, Washington, National Defense University Press, 1984, p. 13. Also John M. Collins, *U.S.-Soviet Military Balance: 1980–1985*, New York, Pergamon-Brassey's, 1985, pp. 9, 61, 64, 74, 104, and *Grand Strategy*, p. 21.

27. Sun Tzu, *The Art of War*, p. 85.

28. Ashton B. Carter, "Satellites and Anti-Satellites," *International Security*, Spring 1986, p. 81; Hans Mark, "Warfare in Space," in *America Plans for Space*, pp. 18–19, 24.

29. Collins, *U.S.-Soviet Military Balance: Concepts and Capabilities, 1960–1980*, pp. 221–223.

30. Michael Collins, "CSIS Resources, Technology, and Future Space Battlefields" (paper presented at a Center for Strategic and International Studies conference, Washington, October 27–29, 1987), pp. 3, 14–16, "Launch Sites at Risk in Conventional War," *Navy News and Undersea Technology*, September 5, 1988.

31. Nicholas L. Johnson, *Soviet Military Strategy in Space*, London, Jane's Publishing Co., 1987, pp. 202, 216.

32. Ibid., p. 201; Carter, "Satellites and Anti-Satellites," p. 78; John L. Pio-

trowski, "A Soviet Space Strategy," *Strategic Review*, Fall 1987, pp. 56, 57–58.

33. Johnson, *Soviet Military Strategy in Space*, p. 201; Carter, "Satellites and Anti-Satellites," pp. 67–68, 69–70, 78.

34. Giffen, *U.S. Space System Survivability*, p. 31.

35. Collins, "CSIS Resources, Technology, and Future Space Battlefields," pp. 2, 3, 4, 12.

36. Giffen, *U.S. Space System Survivability*, pp. 25–31; *Arms Control in Space: Workshop Proceedings*, pp. 42–44.

37. Collins, "CSIS Resources, Technology, and Future Space Battlefields," pp. 6, 15; Stares, *Space and National Security*, p. 77; Giffen, "U.S. Space System Survivability," pp. 29–30; John M. Collins, *Green Berets, SEALS, and Spetsnaz*, New York, Pergamon-Brassey's, 1987, pp. 84–86.

38. Conversation with Jonathan E. Medalia, Congressional Research Service, August 15, 1988; Giffen, "U.S. Space System Survivability," pp. 27, 28; Collins, "CSIS Resources, Technology, and Future Space Battlefields," p. 17.

39. Giffen, "U.S. Space System Survivability," pp. 26, 27, 30; Stares, *Space and National Security*, pp. 81–82; Collins, "CSIS Resources, Technology, and Future Space Battlefields," pp. 13–14; Carter, "Satellites and Anti-Satellites," pp. 76–77.

40. Giffen, *U.S. Space System Survivability*, pp. 27, 30–31; Carter, "Satellites and Anti-Satellites," pp. 71, 85; Robert Salkeld, *War and Space*, Englewood Cliffs, NJ, Prentice-Hall, 1970, pp. 64, 65; David J. Lynch, "DNA Studying Nuclear Blasts in Space for SDI," *Defense Week*, June 29, 1987, p. 2; Mark, "Warfare in Space," in *America Plans for Space*, pp. 18–19.

41. Offensive maneuver forms are described in *Field Manual (FM) 100-5: Operations*, pp. 101–106.

42. Carter, "Satellites and Anti-Satellites," pp. 74–75, 82; Mark, "Warfare in Space," in *America Plans for Space*, pp. 19–20.

43. Salkeld, *War and Space*, pp. 72–74; Carter, "Satellites and Anti-Satellites," pp. 79, 80.

44. Sun Tzu, *The Art of War*, pp. 66–67; *Strategic Military Deception*, ed. by Donald C. Daniel and Katherine L. Herbig, New York, Pergamon Press, 1981, pp. 3–176; Bernard E. Trainor, "Deception," *Marine Corps Gazette*, October 1986, pp. 57–61; Michael I. Handel, "Intelligence and Deception," *Journal of Strategic Studies*, March 1982, pp. 122–154; Thomas A. Savoie, "Deception at the Operational Level of War," *Army*, April 1987, pp. 30–40.

45. Many studies describe deterrence. See, for example, Y. Harkabi, *Nuclear War and Nuclear Peace*, Jerusalem, Israel Program for Scientific Translations, 1966, pp. 9–40, 124–133; Morton A. Kaplan, "The Calculus of Deterrence," *World Politics*, October 1958, pp. 20–44; William W. Kaufmann, "The Requirements of Deterrence," in *Military Policy and National Security*, ed. by William W. Kaufmann, Princeton, NJ, Princeton University Press, 1956, pp. 12–38; Glenn H. Snyder, *Deterrence and Defense: Toward a Theory of National Security*, Princeton, NJ, Princeton University Press, 1961, pp. 3–51.

46. Geoffrey Blaney, *The Causes of War*, New York, Free Press, 1973, p. 278; Karl W. Deutsch, *The Analysis of International Relations*, 2d ed., Englewood Cliffs, NJ, Prentice-Hall, 1978, pp. 132–164; R.J. Rummel, *Understanding Conflict and War, Vol. 4: War, Power, Peace*, Beverly Hills, CA, Sage Publications, 1979, pp. 241–315; John G. Stoessinger, *Why Nations Go to War*, 2d ed., New York, St. Martin's, 1978, p. 246; David Abshire and Brian Dickson, "War by Miscalculation: The Forgotten Dimension," *Washington Quarterly*, Autumn 1983, pp. 114–124; Jack S. Levy, "Misperception and the Causes of War: Theoretical Linkages and Analytical Problems," *World Politics*, October 1983, pp. 76–99.

47. John M. Collins, "Principles of Deterrence," *Air University Review*, November-December 1979, pp. 21–22.

48. Piotrowski, "A Soviet Space Strategy," p. 57.

49. Ibid., pp. 57–58, 61; Giffen, *U.S. Space System Survivability*, pp. 33–34, 49; "White House Message on Anti-Satellite Arms," *New York Times*, August 21, 1985, p. 10; Paul B. Stares, "ASAT Weapons: Why Restraint Makes Sense," *Brookings Review*, Fall 1987, p. 4; *Arms Control in Space: Workshop Proceedings*, p. 20.

50. Piotrowski, "A Soviet Space Strategy," p. 62.

51. Swift, "Strategic Superiority Through SDI," pp. 17, 36; Mary C. Fitzgerald, "The Soviet Military on SDI," *Studies in Comparative Communism*, Autumn/Winter 1986, pp. 177–191; David B. Rivkin, "What Does Moscow Think?," *Foreign Policy*, Summer 1985, pp. 95–99.

52. U.S. Congress, Senate, *Nuclear Risk Reduction*, Hearings Before the Committee on Foreign Relations, 98th Congress, 2nd Session, Washington, U.S. GPO, 1984; Sam Nunn and John W. Warner, "Reducing the Risk of Nuclear War," *Washington Quarterly*, Spring 1984, pp. 3–7; Steven A. Hildreth, *Nuclear Risk Reduction Measures*, Washington, Congressional Research Service, September 26, 1986, p. 19; Richard K. Betts, "A Joint Nuclear Risk Control Center," *Parameters*, Spring 1985, pp. 39–51.

53. A tree of arguments that summarizes relationships between deterrence and defense is contained in *Arms Control and Civil Defense*, ed. by Donald G. Brennan, Croton, NY, Hudson Institute, 1963, p. 25. Polarized approaches are exemplified by Charles L. Glenn, "Why Even Good Defenses May Be Bad," *International Security*, Fall 1984, pp. 92–123, and Richard B. Foster, "From Assured Destruction to Assured Survival," *Comparative Strategy*, Vol. 2, No. 1, 1980, pp. 53–74.

54. Giffen, *U.S. Space System Survivability*, p. 26.

55. "USAF, Northrup Unveil B-2 Next Generation Bomber," *Aviation Week & Space Technology*, November 28, 1988, pp. 20–27; Steven Ashley and C. P. Gilmore, "Stealth!" *Popular Science*, July 1988, pp. 46–51; Marvin Leibstone, "Stealth: The U.S. Advanced Technology Bomber," *Military Technology*, September 1986, pp. 219–222; Jay H. Goldberg, "The Technology of Stealth," *Technology Review*, May/June 1989, pp. 33–39; Malcolm W. Browne, "Vision Chemical Found to Absorb Radar," *New York Times*, August 18, 1987, p. C-1; Bill Sweetman, "And Now, the Stealth-Defeating Radar!," *Interavia*, April 1987, pp. 331–333; "Stealth Aircraft 'Seen' in Tracking Experiment," *Military Avionics*, August 19, 1988, p. 5.

56. Collins, "CSIS Resources, Technology, and Future Space Battlefields," p. 13.

57. Giffen, *U.S. Space System Survivability*, pp. 35–36, 38, 42–43; Mark, "Warfare in Space," and Bowman, "Arms Control in Space," in *America Plans for Space*, pp. 22–23, 25–26, 115.

58. Defensive maneuver forms are described in *Field Manual (FM) 100-5: Operations*, pp. 134–137, 153–160.

59. Comments on a draft of this study by Patrick A. Grieco, USAF.

60. Carter, "Satellites and Anti-Satellites," pp. 80, 90; Stares, *Space and National Security*, p. 82; Giffen, *U.S. Space System Survivability*, pp. 37, 39, 50.

61. *Ballistic Missile Defense*, ed. by Ashton B. Carter and David N. Schwartz, Washington, Brookings Institution, 1984; *The Technology, Strategy, and Politics of SDI*, ed. by Stephen J. Cimbala, Boulder, CO, Westview Press, 1987; *Ballistic Missile Defense Technologies*, Washington, Office of Technology Assessment, U.S. GPO, September 1985; Harold Brown, "Is SDI Technically Feasible?," *Foreign Affairs* ("America and the World"), 1985, pp. 435–454; Zbigniew Brzezinski, Robert Jastrow, and Max M. Kampelman, "Defense in Space is Not 'Star Wars'," *New York Times Magazine*, January 27, 1985, pp. 28–29, 46, 51; Cosmo DiMaggio, Arthur F. Manfredi, Jr., and Stephen A. Hildreth, *The Strategic Defense Initiative: Program Description and Major Issues*, Washington, Congressional Research Service, January 7, 1986; Jeffrey Cooper, Charles Peña, and Kara Bue, *How Defenses Work and the Implications for Strategic Defense Architectures*, Washington, SRS Technologies, July 1987; William A. Davis, Jr., *Regional Security and Anti-Tactical Ballistic Missiles: Political and Technical Issues*, New York, Pergamon-Brassey's, 1986; Roger J. Sullivan, Wender M. Heller, and E.C. Aldridge, Jr., *Candidate U.S. Civil Defense Programs*, Washington, System Planning Corporation, March 1978, pp. 9–30.

62. Aadu Karemaa, "What Would Mahan Say About Space Power?," *U.S. Naval Institute Proceedings*, April 1988, pp. 48–49; Johnson, *Soviet Military Strategy in Space*, p. 203.

63. Stares, *Space and National Security*, p. 77, mentions booby traps. Open-source discussion of space mines almost all concerns offensive applications.

64. G. Harry Stine, *Confrontation in Space*, Englewood Cliffs, NJ, Prentice-Hall, 1981, pp. 132–143.

65. Giffen, *U.S. Space System Survivability*, pp. 35, 36, 51.

66. Ibid, pp. 35, 37; Stares, *Space and National Security*, pp. 81–82.

67. David Lupton, "Space Doctrines," *Strategic Review*, Fall 1983, p. 42; Giffen, *U.S. Space System Survivability*, pp. 36, 40, 50, 51; Stares, *Space and National Security*, p. 83.

68. Johnson, *Soviet Military Strategy in Space*, p. 215; Giffen, *U.S. Space System Survivability*, pp. 36, 40, 42, 51.

69. Stares, *Space and National Security*, pp. 83–84; Mark, "Warfare in Space," in *America Plans for Space*, p. 26.

Chapter 3. Organizational Problems and Options

1. B. Bruce-Briggs, "The Army in Space: New High Ground or Hot Air Balloon?" *Military Review*, December 1986, p. 49.

2. Marcia S. Smith, Statement for the Committee on Armed Services, U.S. House of Representatives, Washington, Congressional Research Service, November 10, 1983, p.10, updated orally, November 2, 1988. No edition of *Soviet Military Power*, published annually by the U.S. Department of Defense since September 1981, mentions a Soviet military space command.

3. U.S. Congress, House, *Title 10, United States Code, Armed Forces* (as amended through April 21, 1987), Committee Print No. 4, Prepared for the Use of the Committee on Armed Services, 100th Congress, 1st Session, Washington, U.S. GPO, June 1987, pp. 48–49.

4. *United States Space Command*, Fact Sheet, Peterson AFB, CO, Hq. Space Command, Public Affairs, April 1986; "All About Space Command," *Military Times News Magazine*, November 1983, pp. 8–13, 18–19; *United States Air Force Space Command*, Fact Sheet, Peterson AFB, CO, Hq. Space Command, Public Affairs, April 1986; *Naval Space Command: Supporting the Fleet of the Future*, Dahlgren, VA, Naval Space Command, undated [1984]; Thomas B. Allen, "A Measure of Infinity," *Sea Power*, February 1984, pp. 23–30; Pat Gagan, "The Army Space Command," *Military Review*, March 1988, pp. 45–51; Craig Covault, "Ground Troops to Benefit From Army Space Command," *Aviation Week & Space Technology*," April 25, 1988, pp. 80–82.

5. *Title 10, United States Code, Armed Forces*, pp. 48–49.

6. Ibid., pp. 51–53.

7. Many sources note that interservice rivalry has spread to space. See, for example, "Pentagon not Prepared to Form 'Space Command'," *Defense Daily*, February 23, 1982, pp. 275–276; Richard Halloran, "Military Divided Over Space Policy," *New York Times*, July 5, 1983; p.11; Marcia S. Smith, Statement for the Committee on Armed Services, U.S. House of Representatives, p. 9; "DOD Studies 'Truly Unified' Space Command," *Military Space*, July 18, 1988, p. 1.

8. Current concentration on circumterrestrial space is evident in John L. Piotrowski, Statement on Space Control Before the Subcommittee on Research and Development, Committee on Armed Services, House of Representatives, March 10, 1988, pp. 1, 2, 4, 5; *Air Force Manual (AFM) 1-6: Miltary Space Doctrine*, Washington, Dept. of the Air Force, October 15, 1982, pp. 2, 3, 5, 8–9; C.R. Davis, "U.S. Space Command," *Marine Corps Gazette*, June 1986, pp. 76–80; Nicholas L. Johnson, *Soviet Military Strategy in Space*, London, Jane's Publishing Co., 1987, pp. 191–219.

9. George Liska, *Nations in Alliance: The Limits of Interdependence*, Baltimore, Johns Hopkins University Press, 1968; Robert E. Osgood, *Alliances and American Foreign Policy*, Baltimore, Johns Hopkins University Press, 1968, pp. 17–31; Caspar W. Weinberger, *Report on Allied Contributions to the Common Defense: A Report to the United States Congress*, Washington, Dept. of Defense, 1987; David Dickson, "Space:

It Is Expensive in the Major Leagues," *Science*, September 4, 1987, pp. 110–111.

10. Bernard Weinraub, "Argentine Assails U.S. at O.A.S. Talks," *New York Times*, May 28, 1982, p. 1; "Ex-Navy Chief Says U.S. Aid Crucial in Falklands War," *Philadelphia Inquirer*, May 30, 1988, p. 3.

11. Smith, Statement for the Committee on Armed Services, p.8.

12. Reasons to consider a separate military service for space are contained in Charles D. Friedenstine, "The Uniqueness of Space Doctrine," *Air University Review*, November-December 1985, pp. 13–23. Robert T. Herres advanced reasons to reject when he was USCINCSPACE. See "The Future of Military Space Forces," *Air University Review*, January-March 1987, pp. 40–47.

13. Harriet Fast Scott and William F. Scott, *The Armed Forces of the USSR*, Boulder, CO, Westview Press, 1979, pp. 133–141.

14. "An Air Force Almanac," *Air Force*, May 1988, p. 79; *United States Air Force Statistical Digest*, 1948, Vol. 1, p. 2, and Vol. 2, p. 20.

15. Herman S. Wolk, *Planning and Organizing the Post War Air Force: 1943–1947*, Washington, Office of the Air Force Historian, 1984; Robert F. Futrell, *Ideas, Concepts, Doctrine: A History of Basic Thinking in the United States Air Force, 1907–1964*, Maxwell AFB, AL, Air University Press, 1971, pp. 95–134; Perry McCoy Smith, *The Air Force Plans for Peace, 1943–1945*, Baltimore, Johns Hopkins University Press, 1970, pp. 15–26.

16. "Navy Retains Aviation Arm Under Merger," *Naval Aviation News*, September 1947, p. 8; *Secretary of the Navy Letters*, 46-2211 (Washington, U.S. Naval Historical Center) December 2, 1946, 7 pp., 47-57, January 21, 1947, 16 pp., and 47-522, August 11, 1947, 16 pp.; Allan R. Millett, *Semper Fidelis: The History of the United States Marine Corp.*, New York, Macmillan, 1980, pp. 445–474; Robert Debs Heinl, *Soldiers of the Sea*, Annapolis, MD, U.S. Naval Institute Press, 1962, pp. 510–536.

17. *Air Force Manual (AFM) 1-1: Basic Aerospace Doctrine of the United States Air Force*, Washington, Hq. U.S. Air Force, January 5, 1984, pp. 2-8, 2-20; Carl E. Mundy, "Employment of Amphibious and Fleet Marine Forces" (Briefing at Center for Naval Analyses Forum), November 3, 1986, pp. 44–49; *JCS Pub. 26: Joint Doctrine for Theater Counterair Operations (From Overseas Land Areas)*, Washington, Joint Chiefs of Staff, April 1, 1986, pp. 3–4; Thomas A. Cardwell, "The Quest for Unity of Command," *Air University Review*, May-June 1984, pp. 25–29.

18. Barbara Amouyal, "AF Haunted by Amendment Questioning Commitment to Close Air Support," *Defense News*, October 24, 1988, p. 7; David C. Morrison, "Pentagon Dogfighting," *National Journal*, October 8, 1988, pp. 2524–2528; Brooke Nihart, "Sixty Years of Unresolved Problems," *Armed Forces Journal*, April 1970, pp. 19–24; Mark Thompson, "Army and Air Force Battle on Air Support for Infantry," *Philadelphia Inquirer*, October 30, 1988, p. 9.

19. Marcia S. Smith, *Space Activities of the United States, Soviet Union and Other Launching Countries/Organizations: 1957–1982*, Washington, Congressional Research Service, March 15, 1983, pp. 8, 24–25, 65.

20. Richard C. Gross, "SPACECOM: Space Service of Future?," *Defense Science & Electronics*, December 1985, p. 7; "Pentagon Not Prepared to Form 'Space Command'," *Defense Daily*, pp. 275–276.

21. A review and recommendations concerning USSPACECOM and its staff are contained in *Review of Unified and Specified Command Headquarters* (Derek J. Vander Schaaf, Chairman, Study Team), Washington, Dept. of Defense, February 1988, pp. 34–35 and Annex G.

22. *JCS Pub 1: Dictionary of Military and Associated Terms*, Washington, Joint Chiefs of Staff, June 1, 1987, pp. 158, 340.

23. Military space law is commonly explored in *Journal of Space Law*, a U.S. quarterly publication and *Proceedings of . . . Colloquium[s] on The Law of Outer Space*, published annually by the International Institute of Space Law of the International Aeronautical Federation.

24. G. Harry Stine, *Handbook for Space Colonists*, New York, Holt, Rinehart, and Winston, 1985, pp. 104–111, 127–131, 218–223; Curtis D. Cochran, Dennis M. Gorman, and Joseph D. Dumoulin, *Space Handbook*, Maxwell AFB, AL, Air University Press, January 1985, pp. 11-1 through 11-11.

25. Sample problems that call for civil-military cooperation are contained in Carolyn Meinel and Tom Blair, "Military Space Launch Today," *Military Technology*, November 1988, pp. 137–140; Michail Cassutt, "Classified Astronauts," *Space World*, November 1988, pp. 6–8; "GAO Questions NASA's Ability to Provide Military Mission Security," *Aerospace Daily*, April 9, 1987, p. 50; "Space Reassessment," *Defense Technology Viewpoint*, October 12, 1987, pp. 3–4; Phillip M. Boffey, "U.S. Rules Out Weapons on Planned Space Station," *New York Times*, February 6, 1987, p. 17.

26. Ann M. Florini, "The Opening Skies: Third Party Imaging Satellites and U.S. Security," *International Security*, Fall 1988, pp. 91–123; U.S. Congress, Office of Technology Assessment (OTA), *Commercial Newsgathering From Space*, OTA-TM-ISC-40, Washington, U.S. GPO, May 1987; William J. Broad, "U.S. Ends Curb on Photographs From Satellites," *New York Times*, January 21, 1988, pp. Al, A23; Craig Covault, "Photographs Spot Secret Base for USSR Nuclear Submarines," *Aviation Week & Space Technology*, July 20, 1987, p. 18.

Chapter 4.   Force Development Problems and Options

1. For ways to measure spacecraft reliability, see Cochran, Gorman, and Dumoulin, *Space Handbook*, Chapter 10.

2. "Challenger & Crew Lost at Launch," *Defense Daily*, January 29, 1986, pp. 145–146; "Discovery Flies Despite Shifting Winds, Blown Fuses," *Aerospace Daily*, September 30, 1988, pp. 505–506.

3. Christopher H. Dodge, "Selection and Training of Astronauts" in U.S. Congress, House, *United States Civilian Space Programs, 1958–1978*, Report Prepared for the Subcommittee on Space Science and Applications of the Committee on Science and Technology, Serial D, Vol. 1, 97th Cong., 1st Sess., Washington, U.S. GPO, January 1981, pp. 647–659;

Mae Mills Link, N.N. Gurovskiy, and I.I. Bryanov, "Selection and Training of Astronauts [and Cosmonauts]," in *Foundations of Space Biology and Medicine*, Vol. III, ed. by Melvin Calvan and Oleg G. Gazenko, Washington, NASA, 1975, pp. 419–450.

4. U.S. Congress, House, *The Ailing Defense Industrial Base: Unready for Crisis*, Report of the Defense Industrial Base Panel of the Committee on Armed Services, 96th Congress, 2d Session, Washington, U.S. GPO, 1980, pp. 5–6, 11, 18–23.

5. Norman Polmar, John T. Correll, Scott C. Truver, and Robert L. Anderson, *Lifeline in Danger: An Assessment of the United States Defense Industrial Base*, Arlington, VA, Aerospace Education Foundation, September 1988; U.S. Congress, Office of Technology Assessment, *Holding the Edge—Maintaining the Technology Base*, Washington, U.S. GPO, April 1989; "U.S. Defense Industrial Base Decays as Companies Quit," *Navy News and Undersea Technology*, May 22, 1989, p. 5; Jacques S. Gansler, "Needed: A U.S. Defense Industrial Strategy," *International Security*, Fall 1987, pp. 45–62; *Mobilizing U.S. Industry: A Vanishing Option for National Security?* ed. by John N. Ellison, Jeffry W. Frumpkin, and Timothy W. Stanley, Boulder, CO, Westview Press, 1988.

6. Pam McClintock and Laura Litvan, "Avtex Receiving Help From NSC," *Washington Times*, November 16, 1988, p. Cl; Malcolm Gladwell, "Avtex Gets $20 Million Bailout," *Washington Post*, November 19, 1988, p. D11; Malcolm Gladwell, "Just What's Behind the Avtex Closing?," *Washington Post*, November 21, 1988, p. 1.

7. John Noble Wilford, "Shortage of Rocket Fuel Creating New Crisis for U.S. Space Flights," *New York Times*, June 8, 1988, p. 1; Warren Strobel, "Lack of Rocket Fuel Forcing Drastic Shift in Space Program," *Washington Times*, June 9, 1988, p. 4.

8. Tim Carrington, "Military Dependence on Foreign Suppliers Causes Rising Concern," *Wall Street Journal*, March 24, 1988, p. 1; Ron Cowen "The Hidden Threat of Producing Electronic Components Overseas," *National Research Council News Report*, November 1986, p. 26; Richard Saltus, "G.A.—Its Future May Be Here," *Boston Globe*, November 24, 1986, p. Gl; Eliot Marshall, "Imported Chips: A Security Risk?" *Science*, April 4, 1986, p. 12; Michael Feibus, "U.S. Will No Longer Produce Silicon," *Philadelphia Inquirer*, November 28, 1988, p. C17.

9. *Report of the In Situ Resources Utilization Workshop*, ed. by Kyle Fairchild and Wendell W. Mendell, Houston, TX, NASA (Scientific and Technical Information Division), 1988; Gerard K. O'Neill, Gerald Driggers, and Brian O'Leary, "New Routes to Manufacturing in Space," *Astronautics and Aeronautics*, October 1980, pp. 46–51, with seven basic references; Carolyn Meinel, "Potential Bonanza for Ambitious Military Space Projects," *Defense Science*, February 1985, pp. 41–47; Ben Bova, "Moonbase Orientation Manual I: Transport and Manufacturing," *Analog*, June 1987, pp. 64–87; *Pioneering the Space Frontier: Report of the National Commission on Space*, New York, Bantam Books, 1986, pp. 71–92.

10. Hans Mark, "Warfare in Space," in *America Plans for Space*, Washington, National Defense University Press, 1986, p. 23.

11. Ibid.

12. *Military Space Operations: Shuttle and Satellite Computer Systems Do Not Meet Performance Objectives*, Washington, General Accounting Office, August 1988, pp. 2–5, 27–29.

13. Sam Fletcher, "Offshore Rigs Could Become Rocket Launchers," *Houston Post*, February 14, 1988, p. D10.

14. Bruce Blair, *Strategic Command and Control*, Washington, Brookings Institution, 1985, pp. 108–111, 138–139, 147–155; *Managing Nuclear Operations*, ed. by Ashton B. Carter, John D. Steinbruner, and Charles A. Zraket, Washington, Brookings Institution, 1987, pp. 323, 341, 501–502, 591–592.

15. Alain C. Enthoven and K. Wayne Smith, *How Much is Enough? Shaping the Defense Program, 1961–1969*, New York, Harper and Row, 1971, p. 197.

16. Richard M. Nixon, *U.S. Foreign Policy for the 1970s: Building for Peace*, Washington, U.S. GPO, February 25, 1971, p. 167.

17. U.S. Congress, House, *United States Defense Policies in 1960* (prepared by Charles H. Donnelly), 87th Cong., 1st Sess., Washington, U.S. GPO, May 26, 1961, p. 80; Harvey M. Sapolsky, *The Polaris System Development: Bureaucratic and Programmatic Success in Government*, Cambridge, MA, Harvard University Press, 1972, pp. 160–161.

18. U.S. ICBM and bomber force levels are contained in *The Development of Strategic Air Command, 1946–1986*, Offutt AFB, NE, Hq. Strategic Air Command, September 1, 1986. For Soviet air defense trends, see *Soviet Military Power*, Washington, U.S. GPO, 1988, pp. 80–82, and 1987, pp. 58–61; James T. Westwood, "Developments in Soviet Air Defense," *Armed Forces*, February 1988, pp. 64–67; Jim Bussert, "Soviet Air Defense Systems Show Increasing Sophistication," *Defense Electronics*, May 1984, pp. 75–76, 78, 80, 82, 84, 86.

19. *Report to Congress on the Strategic Defense System Architecture*, Washington, Strategic Defense Initative Organization, January 1988, p. 21.

20. Conversations with Jonathan E. Medalia and Steven A. Hildreth, Congressional Research Service, December 2, 1988.

21. Robert B. Giffen, *U.S. Space System Survivability: Strategic Alternatives for the 1990s*, Washington, National Defense University Press, 1982, pp. 20–21, 22–23.

22. For background about the hi-lo mix, see John S. Foster, Jr., *The Department of Defense Program of Research, Development, Test, and Evaluation, FY 1974*, Statement Before the Defense Subcommittee of the Senate Appropriations Committee, March 28, 1973, pp. 3-1 to 3-8; James R. Schlesinger, *Annual Defense Department Report on the FY 1975 Defense Budget*, Washington, Department of Defense, March 4, 1974, p. 223.

23. Kathy Sawyer, "Shuttle Atlantis Lifts Off After Racing the Clock," *Washington Post*, December 2, 1988, p. 1.

24. "Defense Budget Squeeze Puts Fate of B-2 Bomber in Doubt," *Aviation Week & Space Technology*, November 28, 1988, pp. 24–26; Mark Thompson, "Junk 'Stealth' Bomber, Scientists Say," *Philadelphia Inquirer*, November 18, 1988, p. 23; Jacob V. Lamar, "Will This Bird Fly?" *Time*, December 5, 1988, p. 20; Tom Morganthau, John Berry,

and Douglas Waller, "An $80 Billion Bust?" *Newsweek*, December 5, 1988, p.18.

25. One technique for comparing strengths and weaknesses of competitive options is contained in John M. Collins, *Strategic Nuclear Delivery Systems: How Many? What Combinations?* Washington, Congressional Research Service, October 7, 1974; Updated by *U.S. Strategic Nuclear Force Options: A Framework for Analysis*, Issue Brief IB 77046, archived January 24, 1984.

26. For background about total force concepts, see Melvin R. Laird, *Annual Defense Department Report on the Fiscal Year 1972–76 Defense Program and the 1972 Defense Budget*, Washington, Department of Defense, March 9, 1971, pp. 21–24.

27. Adapted from U.S. Congress, Senate, *United States/Soviet Military Balance: A Frame of Reference for Congress*, 94th Cong., 2d Sess., Washington, U.S. GPO, January 1976, pp. 21–26.

28. Klaus Knorr and Oscar Morgenstern, *Science and Defense: Some Critical Thoughts on Military Research and Development*, Princeton, NJ, Princeton University Press, 1965, pp. 19–27.

29. Theresa M. Foley, "SDI Moves Into Test Era With New Systems," *Aviation Week & Space Technology*, November 7, 1988, p. 36.

30. Requirements for a space cruiser are contained in Daniel O. Graham, *High Frontier: A New National Strategy*, Washington, High Frontier, Inc., 1982, pp. 68, 71–72, 129–134; G. Harry Stine, *Confrontation in Space*, Englewood Cliffs, NJ, Prentice-Hall, 1981, pp. 121–131; Stephen Korthals-Altes, "Assessing the Aerospace Plane," and "Will the Aerospace Plane Work?," *Technology Review*, January 1987, pp. 2, 43–51; Walter Froehlich, "The National Aero-Space Plane," *The World & I*, April 1987, pp. 162–167.

31. Requirements for preferential space-based homeland defense are contained in Sean K. Collins, "Preferential Boost-Phase Defense," *National Defense*, December 1985, pp. 30–36; Jack Swift, "Strategic Superiority Through SDI," *Defense & Foreign Affairs*, December 1985, pp. 17, 36; *Report to the Congress on the Strategic Defense System Architecture*, pp. 5–8, 12–13.

32. Requirements for special tools are contained in Stine, *Handbook for Space Colonists*, pp. 158–161.

33. Requirements for transfer vehicles, tethers, and military mass drivers are contained in *Pioneering the Space Frontier*, pp. 103–105, 122–127; Gerard K. O'Neill, *The High Frontier*, New York, Morrow, 1977, pp. 138–141.

34. Some specialized medical requirements are contained in Stine, *Handbook for Space Colonists*, p. 222.

35. David Fulghum, "New Satellites to Guide B-2 Crews, Civilians," *Air Force Times*, November 28, 1988, p. 21; George C. Wilson, "Curtailing of Stealth Bomber Urged," *Washington Post*, October 28, 1988, p. 5.

36. Cheryl Pellerin, "Eyes on the Future, Industry Puts AI to Work," *Washington Technology*, May 5–18, 1988, p. 16.

37. Tom Forester, "The Materials Revolution," *Futurist*, July–August 1988, p. 21.

38. For fundamental trends, see U.S. Congress, Office of Technology Assessment, *Advanced Materials by Design*, OTA-E-351, U.S. GPO, June 1988, and *New Structural Materials Technologies: Opportunities for the Use of Advanced Ceramics and Composites—a Technical Memorandum*, OTA-TM-E-32, September 1986; *Space Technology to Meet Future Needs*, Washington, D.C., National Academy Press, 1987, pp. 95–107.

39. John Holusha, "Withstanding 3,000-Degree Heat," *New York Times*, November 23, 1988, p. D7; Howard G. Maahs, "Carbon-Carbon Composites," *World & I*, June 1989, pp. 300–307.

40. Alan R. Wise, "High Performance Ceramics: The New Stone Age," *National Defense*, October 1987, p. 34; Forster, "The Materials Revolution," pp. 22–23.

41. Ward Worthy, "Wide Variety of Applications Spark Polymer Composites Growth," *Chemical & Engineering News*, March 16, 1987, p. 7; Marc S. Reisch, "High-Performance Fibers Find Expanding Military, Industrial Uses," *Chemical & Engineering News*, February 9, 1987, pp. 38–39, 41.

42. *Advanced Materials by Design*, pp. 9–10.

43. David J. Lynch, "SDIO Report Touts New Satellite As Answer to Soviet ASAT Threat," *Defense Week*, May 16, 1988, p. 8; Bill Sweetman, "Advanced Composites for Military Uses," *International Defense Review*, November 1986, pp. 1632, 1636; Holusha, "Withstanding 3,000-Degree Heat"; Gordon Graff, "Diamonds Find New Settings," *High Technology*, April 1987, p. 45; "New Materials Promise Low Radar Reflectance," *Aviation Week & Space Technology*, May 18, 1987, p. 22; Reich, "High Performance Fibers Find Expanding Military, Industrial Uses," p. 11.

44. Larry Lewis "Chemistry's New Workhorse," *High Technology*, July 1987, p. 21; Graff, "Diamonds Find New Settings," pp. 45, 46; Philip H. Efland, "Advances in Military Hermetic Connectors," *Electronic Engineering Times*, February 22, 1988, pp. 27–28; "Smart Skin for the ATF," *Defense Science*, March 1988, p. 12; George Leopold, "Developers Pursue Ability to See Enemy Without Being Seen," *Defense News*, August 15, 1988, p. 8.

45. U.S. Congress, Office of Technology Assessment, *Commercializing High-Temperature Superconductivity*, OTA-ITE-388, Washington, U.S. GPO, June 1988; Ron Dagani, "New Class of Superconductors Pushing Temperatures Higher," *Chemical and Engineering News*, May 16, 1988, pp. 24–29; Philip Campbell, "A Superconductivity Primer," *Nature*, November 5, 1987, pp. 21–24; Sharon Begley, "Superconductivity Heats Up," *Newsweek*, March 21, 1988, p. 77; Kristine Moe, "Superconductors Electrify Scientists," *San Diego Union*, March 28, 1987, p. 1.

46. James E. Mrazek, "Superconductivity: Super Opportunity," *U.S. Naval Institute Proceedings*, January 1988, pp. 112–115; Campbell, "A Superconductivity Primer," pp. 21–24; Robert Herzberg, "Superconductors," *International Combat Arms*, September 1987, pp. 20–21; David I. Lewin, "Temperature Rising," *Mechanical Engineering*, October 1987, p. 73.

47. Richard Saltus, "Gallium Arsenide—Its Future May Be Here," *Boston Globe*, November 24, 1986, p. G1; Jan S. Breemer, "Gallium Arsenide: Semiconductor of the Future," *National Defense*, April 1987, pp. 36–39.

48. J.M. Rowell, "Photonic Materials," *Scientific American*, October 1986, pp. 147–157; Trudy E. Bell, "Fiber Optics," *IEEE Spectrum* (25th Anniversary Issue), 1988, pp. 97–102; C. David Chaffee, *The Rewiring of America: The Fiber Optic Revolution*, New York, Academic Press, 1988.

49. Jan S. Breemer, "A Hair's Worth of Difference," *Sea Power*, August 1984, pp. 49–51, 53–54; Otis Port, "Now Optic Fibers Can Hear and Feel, Too," *Business Week*, December 5, 1988, p. 168A.

50. Mark Morrow, "Propulsion Key for 1990s," *Washington Technology*, November 3–16, 1988, p. 10; *Space Technology to Meet Future Needs*, pp. 60–61.

51. For propulsion theory, see Cochran, Gorman, and Dumoulin, *Space Handbook*, pp. 3-1 through 3-19, 3-48. Also *Pioneering the Space Frontier*, p. 113.

52. Cochran, Gorman, and Dumoulin, *Space Handbook*, pp. 3-19, 3-20, 3-21.

53. Ibid., pp. 3-19 through 3-22, 3-27; Alan Bond, "Propulsion for Economic Space Transportation Systems," *Aerospace*, August 1988, p. 11.

54. Cochran, Gorman, and Dumoulin, *Space Handbook*, pp. 3-28 and 3-29, 3-30, 3-31 to 3-33; Bond, "Propulsion for Economic Space Transportation Systems," pp. 9–10; Morrow, "Propulsion Key for 1990s," p. 11.

55. Kurt Stehling, "Solid-Fuel Rockets," *Air & Space*, October/November 1986, pp. 53, 57–58; Cochran, Gorman, and Dumoulin, *Space Handbook*, pp. 3-19, 3-27.

56. Cochran, Gorman, and Dumoulin, *Space Handbook*, pp. 3-24 through 3-27.

57. Ibid., pp. 3-29, 3-30, 3-31; Morrow, "Propulsion Key for 1990s," p. 11; Stehling, "Solid-Fuel Rockets," pp. 52–59.

58. Cochran, Gorman, and Dumoulin, *Space Handbook*, pp. 3-27, 3-34, 3-48.

59. Ibid., pp. 3-35, 3-38 through 3-42, 3-44, 3-46 through 3-48; "AF Looking at Antimatter Propulsion/Other Breakthroughs," *Defense Daily*, September 19, 1986, p. 102; "Revolutionary 21st Century Space Propulsion Concepts Sought," *Defense Daily*, October 31, 1986, p. 332; Neil McAleer, "The Light Stuff: Laser Propulsion," *Space World*, July 1987, pp. 9–11; Steven Aftergood, *Background on Space Nuclear Power*, Los Angeles, CA, Committee to Bridge the Gap, May 1988; *A Joint Proposal to Ban Nuclear Power in Earth Orbit* and *FAS Statement on the Joint Proposal of the Committee of the Soviet Scientists and FAS for a Ban on Nuclear Power in Earth Orbit*, Washington, Federation of American Scientists, May 13, 1988; David C. Morrison, "Space Nukes," *National Journal*, June 4, 1988, p. 1511; *Pioneering the Space Frontier*, p. 103.

60. Cochran, Gorman, and Dumoulin, *Space Handbook*, pp. 3-42, 3-44, 3-46.

61. *Pioneering the Space Frontier*, pp. 103–104.

62. Ibid., pp. 105, 124, 125–127; "Satellites on a String," *Flight International*, July 16, 1988, p. 34–36.

63. *Pioneering the Space Frontier*, pp. 112–113; Korthals-Altes, "Will The Aerospace Plane Work?," pp. 43–46; Bond, "Propulsion for Economic Space Transportation Systems," pp. 11–12; Froelich, "The National

Aero-Space Plane," pp. 164–165; William Welling, "Spaceplane!," *International Combat Arms*, January 1989, pp. 66–71.

64. Cochran, Gorman, and Dumoulin, *Space Handbook*, p. 4-1; *Space Technology to Meet Future Needs*, p. 86.

65. Cochran, Gorman, and Dumoulin, *Space Handbook*, p. 4-2; *Space Technology to Meet Future Needs*, p. 92.

66. Cochran, Gorman, and Dumoulin, *Space Handbook*, p. 4-14; *Space Technology to Meet Future Needs*, p. 90.

67. Cochran, Gorman, and Dumoulin, *Space Handbook*, pp. 4-1, 4-2.

68. Ibid., pp. 4-3, 4-6; *Electrochemical Storage and Conversion: Batteries and Fuel Cells*, Washington, U.S. Department of Energy, 1985; R. Rudney, J. Mullin, and D. Chaudoir, *The Evolution of Space Power Systems Technology*, Rockford, IL, Sunstrand Corp., 1987, pp. 1, 2.

69. Cochran, Gorman, and Dumoulin, *Space Handbook*, pp. 4-4, 4-5; Rudney, Mullin, and Chaudoir, *The Evolution of Space Power Systems Technology*, pp. 1, 2; *Electrochemical Storage and Conversion*, pp. 10–11.

70. Cochran, Gorman, and Dumoulin, *Space Handbook*, pp. 4-5, 4-6.

71. Ibid., pp. 4-6 through 4-8; William Broad, "Reactors in Space: U.S. Project Advances," *New York Times*, October 6, 1987, p. C1; *Space Technology to Meet Future Needs*, p. 93; Rudney, Mullin, and Chaudoir, *The Evolution of Space Power Systems Technology*, p. 2.

72. Rudney, Mullin, and Chaudoir, *The Evolution of Space Power Systems Technology*, pp. 3–4; Cochran, Gorman, and Dumoulin, *Space Handbook*, pp. 4-7, 4-8.

73. "Opening the Door for Utility Photovoltaics," *EPRI Journal*, January/ February 1987, pp. 5–15.

74. Cochran, Gorman, and Dumoulin, *Space Handbook*, pp. 4-9, 4-10, 4-11; Rudney, Mullin, and Chaudoir, *The Evolution of Space Power Systems Technology*, pp. 4, 5, 6; "Space Nuclear Power Crawls Along," *Military Space*, February 2, 1987, p. 7; *Space Technology to Meet Future Needs*, p. 86.

75. Figure 15 is adapted from Rudney, Mullin, and Chaudoir, *The Evolution of Space Power Systems Technology*, p. 6.

76. Ibid., pp. 4, 5, 6; Cochran, Gorman, and Dumoulin, *Space Handbook*, pp. 4-10 through 4-13, 4-14; *Space Technology to Meet Future Needs*, pp. 87, 88, 89, 91, 92; Broad, "Reactors in Space," p. C1; "Space Nuclear Power Crawls Along," p. 7.

77. Broad, "Reactors in Space," p. C1; *Space Technology to Meet Future Needs*, pp. 87–88; Cochran, Gorman, and Dumoulin, *Space Handbook*, p. 4-13.

78. *The National Challenge in Computer Science and Technology*, Washington, National Academy Press, 1988, pp. 41–43; Marcia Barinaga, "JPL Enthusastic Over New Slant to Parallel Computing," *Nature*, July 21, 1988, p. 186; Boyce Rensberger, "New Computer Works 1,000 Times Faster," *Washington Post*, March 14, 1988, p. 1; *Electronics*, Special Issue, March 3, 1988, pp. 53–77.

79. *Space Technology to Meet Future Needs*, p. 111; "Computing Remains Toughest SDI Challenge," *Military Space*, May 9, 1988, p. 1; U.S. Con-

gress, Office of Technology Assessment, *SDI: Technology, Survivability, and Software*, OTA-ISC-353, Washington, U.S. GPO, May 1988, pp. 199–217.

80. Office of Technology Assessment, *SDI: Technology, Survivablity and Software*, pp. 221–250, 259–269; *Space Technology to Meet Future Needs*, pp. 111–112; *The National Challenge in Computer Science and Technology*, pp. 46–49; James I. Baginski, "Military Computers Can't Talk to Each Other," *Armed Forces Journal*, June 1986, p. 55.

81. *The National Challenge in Computer Science and Technology*, pp. 44–46; Marshall Eliot, "The Scourge of Computer Viruses," *Science*, April 8, 1988, pp. 133–134; Fred Kaplan, "Pentagon Says Systems Are Secure . . .," *Boston Globe*, December 5, 1988, p. 1; Louise G. Becker, *Computer Security: An Overview of National Concerns and Challenges*, Washington, Congressional Research Service, February 3, 1983, pp. 45–49, 54–57, 114, 135; Peter Grant and Robert Riche, "The Eagle's Own Plume," *U.S. Naval Institute Proceedings*, July 1983, pp. 29–34.

82. *Space Technology to Meet Future Needs*, pp. 79–85, 113–114; *The National Challenge in Computer Science and Technology*, pp. 57–59; Robert L. North, "Neurocomputing: Its Impact on the Future of Defense Systems," *Defense Computing*, January/February 1988, pp. 20, 21.

83. *Artificial Intelligence and National Defense: Application to C³I and Beyond*, ed. by Stephen J. Andriole, Washington, AFCEA International Press, 1987; Kenneth H. Rose, "Why Artificial Intelligence Won't Work," *Military Review*, December 1986, pp. 57–58; Pollack, "New Generation of Tiny Motors Challenges Science to Find Uses," *New York Times*, p. C1.

84. *The National Challenge in Computer Science and Technology*, pp. 51–52.

85. Carl von Clausewitz, *On War*, ed. and trans. by Michael Howard and Peter Paret, Princeton, NJ, Princeton University Press, 1976, pp. 119–121.

86. Rose, "Why Artificial Intelligence Won't Work," pp. 59–60; *The National Challenge in Computer Science and Technology*, pp. 53–55; Janet Morton, "AI—Where It's Been, Where It's Going," *Defense Computing*, March/April 1988, pp. 39, 41.

87. *The National Challenge in Computer Science and Technology*, pp. 56–57; North, "Neurocomputing," pp. 18–22.

88. North, "Neurocomputing," p. 21; Rose, "Why Artificial Intelligence Won't Work," p. 61; Christine Gorman, "Putting Brainpower in a Box," *Time*, August 8, 1988, p. 59.

89. Cochran, Gorman, and Dumoulin, *Space Handbook*, Chapter 5; Latham, "C³I Aspects of Space Technology," in *America Plans for Space*, pp. 103–106.

90. Most EW material concerns army, navy, air force uses, but basic attributes apply to space. See, for example, Charles A. Fowler, "EW: At the Crossroads," *Journal of Electronic Defense*, February 1988, pp. 51–54; David C. Morrison, "The Electronic Warriors," *National Journal*, November 22, 1986, pp. 2832–2836; Herut Zemach, "Electronic Warfare 1985: Status, Tasks, and Prospects," *Defense Systems Review*, Vol. 3, No. 4, 1985, pp. 36–37; "Electronic Warfare: Principles, Tactics and

Products," *International Defense Review*, December 1985, pp. 3–78; Gerald Green, "Soviet Electronic Warfare," *National Defense*, April 1985, pp. 34–39, 42.

91. Office of Technology Assessment, *SDI: Technology Survivablity, and Software*, pp. 179–198.

92. Ibid., pp. 147–148; Latham, "C³I Aspects of Space Technology," in *America Plans for Space*, pp. 96, 97–98, 101–102.

93. Office of Technology Assessment, *SDI: Technology, Survivability, and Software*, p. 147; Latham, "C³I Aspects of Space Technology," in *America Plans for Space*, pp. 96, 98.

94. Graham Yost, *Spy-Tech*, New York, Facts on File Publications, 1985, pp. 99–100, 129, 134, 154; Office of Technology Assessment, *SDI: Technology, Survivability, and Software*, pp. 85, 87; Office of Technology Assessment, *Ballistic Missile Defense Technologies*, OTA-ISC-254, Washington, U.S. GPO, September 1985, pp. 159, 161, 162, 164.

95. William Broad, "New Space Challenge: Monitoring Weapons," *New York Times*, December 8, 1987, p. C1; M. Michael Waldrop, "The Mirror Maker," *Discover*, December 1987, pp. 78–82; Stephen P. Maran, "A New Generation of Giant Eyes Gets Ready to Probe The Universe," *Smithsonian*, June 1987, pp. 41–53; Steve Emond, "Orbiting Telescope to Open New Era in Astonomy," *Dallas Morning News*, September 19, 1988, p. D8; Office of Technology Assessment, *SDI: Technology, Survivability, and Software*, p. 89; Yost, *Spy-Tech*, pp. 94, 135–136; *Space Technology to Meet Future Needs*, pp. 118, 121.

96. Terence Dickinson, "Big Eye on The Sky," *Popular Mechanics*, September 1987, pp. 61–63; Yost, *Spy-Tech*, pp. 91, 92, 93, 99; Waldrop, "The Mirror Maker," p. 79; Maran, "A New Generation of Giant Eyes," p. 44; Linda M. Horton, "In Search of New Materials," *Mechanical Engineering*, September 1988, p. 47.

97. Office of Technology Assessment, *Ballistic Missile Defense Technologies*, pp. 159–166 and *SDI: Technology, Survivability, and Software*, pp. 85–87; Yost, *Spy-Tech*, pp. 93, 95, 129, 132–133; William J. Broad, "U.S. Designs Spy Satellites to be More Secret Than Ever," *New York Times*, November 3, 1987, pp. C1, C3; "Delta 181 Spotted Penetration Aids," *Military Space*, October 24, 1988, p. 3.

98. *Photonics: Maintaining Competitiveness in The Information Era*, Washington, National Academy Press, 1988, pp. 9–22.

99. Ibid., pp. 23–37; "Optical Computing: Beware of Overhype," *Advanced Military Computing*, April 27, 1987, p. 6.

100. *Photonics*, pp. 38–50; *Space Technology to Meet Future Needs*, p. 114.

101. *Soviet Military Power*, 7th ed., Washington, U.S. GPO, 1988, p. 65; Nicholas L. Johnson, *Soviet Military Strategy in Space*, London, Jane's Publishing Co., 1987, pp. 140–155; William H. Langenberg, "U.S. ASAT: Whither Now?," *Washington Quarterly*, Fall 1986, pp. 102–103, 104–105.

102. Langenberg, "U.S. ASAT: Whither Now?," pp. 101–102, 103–104; Paul B. Stares, *Space and National Security*, Washington, Brookings Institution, 1987, pp. 99–106.

103. Skeptical deployment dates are in Office of Technology Assessment, *SDI: Technology, Survivability, and Software*, pp. 153–155; Harold Brown, "Is SDI Feasible?" *Foreign Affairs* (America and the World, 1985) 1986, pp. 451–454.

104. John Bosma, *High Frontier: Supplemental Report*, Washington, High Frontier, Inc., 1983; Office of Technology Assessment, *SDI: Technology, Survivability, and Software*, pp. 106–110, 153–154.

105. Theresa M. Foley, "Brilliant Pebbles Testing Proceeds at Rapid Pace," *Aviation Week & Space Technology*, November 14, 1988, pp. 32–33; Office of Technology Assessment, *SDI: Technology, Survivability, and Software*, pp. 105, 106, 110–113, *Ballistic Missile Defense Technologies*, pp. 155–158, and *Antisatellite Weapons*, pp. 63–64; *SDI: A Technical Progress Report, Submitted to the Secretary of Defense*, Washington, Strategic Defense Initiative Organization, June 1985, p. 5; Warren Strobel, "Cheaper 'Pebbles' Offered as Stinger of 'Star Wars'," *Washington Times*, January 9, 1989, p. 1; "'Brilliant Pebbles' Seen as Promising SDI Interceptor," *Defense Daily*, September 2, 1988, p. 10; Lowell L. Wood, "'Brilliant Pebbles' Missile Defense Concept Advocated by Livermore Scientist," *Aviation Week & Technology*, June 13, 1988, p. 151; Warren Strobel, "The Last Line of Missile Defense," *Insight*, February 8, 1988, pp. 55–56.

106. Office of Technology Assessment, *Antisatellite Weapons, Countermeasures, and Control*, pp. 7, 63, 65–66; Carter, "Satellites and Anti-Satellites," pp. 84–87.

107. Ashton B. Carter, "Satellites and Anti-Satellites," *International Security*, Spring 1986, pp. 85–86.

108. Office of Technology Assessment, *SDI: Technology, Survivability, and Software*, pp. 119–123, 155, and *Ballistic Missile Defense Technologies*, pp. 156–157; Clarence A. Robinson, Jr., "Defense Department Developing Orbital Guns," *Aviation Week & Space Technology*, July 23, 1984, pp. 61, 63, 65, 67, 69; T.A. Heppenheimer, "Electromagnetic Guns," *Popular Science*, August 1987, pp. 54–57; William Bogle, "Rail Guns and Smart Rocks," *National Defense*, March 1986, p. 18.

109. Cosmo DiMaggio, *Directed Energy Weapons Research: Status and Outlook*, Washington, Congressional Research Service, August 30, 1985, pp. 5–8, 18–19, 22–23; Dietrich Schroeer, *Directed-Energy Weapons and Strategic Defense: A Primer*, Adelphi Papers 221, London, International Institute of Strategic Studies, Summer 1987, pp. 7, 12, 17, 60–61; Office of Technology Assessment, *SDI: Technology, Survivability, and Software*, pp. 105, 130, 136, *Ballistic Missile Defense Technologies*, pp. 147, 164, and *Anti-Satellite Weapons*, pp. 67, 68; James W. Canan, "Dangerous Waves in Electronic Combat," *Air Force*, July 1988, p. 25; "Flash-Blindness Protection," *Defense & Diplomacy*, Vol. 5, No. 4, 1987, p. 55; Cochran, Gorman, and Dumoulin, *Space Handbook*, pp. 9-1 through 9-16, 9-59,

110. Office of Technology Assessment, *SDI: Technology, Survivability, and Software*, pp. 132–134; DiMaggio, *Directed Energy Weapons Research*, pp. 6–7.

111. Office of Technology Assessment, *SDI: Technology, Survivability, and Software*, pp. 123–125, 126–128, 131–132, 134–136, 137–138, *Ballistic Missile Defense Technologies*, pp. 151–152, and *Anti-Satellite Weapons*, pp. 68, 69; DiMaggio, *Directed-Energy Weapons Research*, pp. 15–17, 27–28; Brown, "Is SDI Technically Feasible?" pp. 440–441; Schroeer, *Directed-Energy Weapons and Strategic Defense*, p. 15.

112. Office of Technology Assessment, *SDI: Technology, Survivability, and Software*, pp. 128–129, 132, and *Ballistic Missile Defense Technologies*, pp. 149–150, 150–151; DiMaggio, *Directed-Energy Weapons Research*, pp. 13–15, 26–27.

113. Office of Technology Assessment, *SDI: Technology, Survivability, and Software*, pp. 126, 128, 136, 138, 155, and *Ballistic Missile Defense Technologies*, pp. 148–149, 150, 151; DiMaggio, *Directed-Energy Weapons Research*, pp. 10–13, 24–26; Schroeer, *Directed-Energy Weapons and Strategic Defense*, pp. 13–14, 67.

114. Office of Technology Assessment, *SDI: Technology, Survivability, and Software*, pp. 129, 142, *Ballistic Missile Defense Technologies*, pp. 152–153, and *Anti-Satellite Weapons*, pp. 70–71; DiMaggio, *Directed-Energy Weapons Research*, pp. 17–18, 23, 28–29; Brown, "Is SDI Technically Feasible?" pp. 442, 450; Schroeer, *Directed-Energy Weapons and Strategic Defense*, pp. 20, 30–31.

115. Cochran, Gorman, and Dumoulin, *Space Handbook*, p. 9-51; DiMaggio, *Directed-Energy Weapons Research*, pp. 31, 34; Schroeer, *Directed-Energy Weapons and Strategic Defense*, pp. 10, 59; conversation with Michael Curtin, Booz-Allen Corp., January 1989.

116. Cochran, Gorman, and Dumoulin, *Space Handbook*, pp. 9-25 through 9-59; DiMaggio, *Directed-Energy Weapons Research*, pp. 31–33, 36; Schroeer, *Directed-Energy Weapons and Strategic Defense*, pp. 7, 8, 59; Office of Technology Assessment, *Ballistic Missile Defense Technologies*, p. 153.

117. Office of Technology Assessment, *SDI: Technology, Survivability, and Software*, pp. 129–130, 136, 138–142, 154N, *Ballistic Missile Defense Technologies*, pp. 153–155, and *Anti-Satellite Weapons*, pp. 71, 72, 74; Schroeer, *Directed-Energy Weapons and Strategic Defense*, pp. 9–10, 59, 66; Brown, "Is SDI Feasible?" p. 439; DiMaggio, *Directed-Energy Weapons Research*, pp. 33–34.

118. Jerry Gray, "Humans vs. Machines in Space Isn't Really The Issue," *Issues in Science and Technology*, Winter 1988, pp. 20–21; Rose, "Why Artificial Intelligence Won't Work," p. 63; Stine, *Confrontation in Space*, pp. 171–177; Donald C. Latham, "A Prescription for America's Galaxy of Problems in Space," *Armed Forces Journal*, September 1987, p. 43.

119. Whether Coventry was sacrificed deliberately is in dispute. See, for example, Anthony Cave Brown, *Bodyguard of Lies*, Vol. 1, New York, Harper and Row, 1975, pp. 36–49, and R.V. Jones, *The Wizard War: British Scientific Intelligence, 1939–1945*, New York, Coward, McCann, & Geoghegan, 1978, pp. 146–153.

120. G. Harry Stine, *Handbook for Space Colonists*, New York, Holt, Rinehart, and Winston, 1985, pp. 230, 237.

121. Ibid., pp. 181–182, 186–192, 238–242.

122. Ibid., pp. 231–232, 237–238.

123. Ibid., pp. 62, 154–155, 161–163, 217–218; *Space Technology to Meet Future Needs*, pp. 66, 67, 71; Christopher H. Dodge, in U.S. Congress, Senate, *Soviet Space Programs: 1976–1980* (with supplemental data through 1983), Part 2, Committee on Commerce, Science, and Transportation, 98th Cong., 2d Sess., Washington, U.S. GPO, October 1984, pp. 711–712.

124. *A Strategy for Space Biology and Medical Science: For the 1980s and 1990s*, Washington, National Academy Press, 1987; *Exploring the Universe: A Strategy for Space Life Sciences*, Washington, NASA, June 1988.

125. Peter H. Diamandis, "Providing Artificial Gravity: Physiologic Limitations to Rotating Habitats," paper presented in Brighton, UK, at the 38th Congress of the International Astronautical Federation, October 10–17, 1987; *Exploring the Universe*, pp. 101–111; *Space Technology to Meet Future Needs*, pp. 68–69; *A Strategy for Space Biology and Medical Science*, pp. 86–149.

126. Stine, *Handbook for Space Colonists*, pp. 113–131; *Space Technology to Meet Future Needs*, pp. 66, 67, 71; *Exploring the Living Universe*, pp. 53–66; Dodge, in *Soviet Space Programs: 1976–1980*, pp. 726–730.

127. *Exploring the Living Universe*, pp. 67–78; *A Strategy for Space Biology and Medical Science*, pp. 165–183.

128. *Exploring the Living Universe*, pp. 112–123.

129. *Space Technology to Meet Future Needs*, pp. 72, 73, 74.

130. Ibid., pp. 73, 74.

131. *A Strategy for Space Biology and Medical Science*, pp. 62–85; Dodge, in *Soviet Space Programs: 1976–80*, pp. 734–735.

Chapter 5.   U.S. and Soviet Military Space Postures

1. Few documents compare U.S. and Soviet military space postures. See, for example, Nicholas L. Johnson, *Soviet Military Strategy in Space*, London, Jane's Publishing Co., 1987, especially pp. 46–88, 191–219; Paul B. Stares, *Space and National Security*, Washington, Brookings Institution, 1987, especially pp. 8–44. See also Shirley Brooks Laseter, *Space—Military Aspects*, Special Bibliography Series, Maxwell AFB, AL, April 1986.

2. Fact Sheet, *Presidential Directive on National Space Policy*, Washington, The White House, Office of the Press Secretary, February 11, 1988, pp. 1–2.

3. Ibid., p. 3.

4. Frank C. Carlucci, *Report to the Congress on the FY1990/FY1991 Biennial Budget and FY1990–94 Defense Programs*, Washington, U.S. GPO, January 9, 1989, p. 211. For comparative purposes, see "Memorandum for Correspondents," *Department of Defense Space Policy*, Washington, Dept. of Defense, March 3, 1987, and *Air Force Manual (AFM) 1-6; Military Space Doctrine*, Washington, Dept. of the Air Force, October 15, 1982, pp. 1–6.

5. *Soviet Military Space Doctrine*, Washington, Defense Intelligence

Agency, August 1, 1984, pp. vii, 32; *Soviet Military Power*, 7th ed., Washington, U.S. GPO, 1988, pp. 62, 67.

6. Johnson, *Soviet Military Strategy in Space*, p. 200.

7. Steven A. Hildreth, *Arms Control: Negotiations to Limit Defense and Space Weapons*, Washington, Congressional Research Service, January 3, 1989; Fact Sheet, *Presidential Directive on National Space Policy*, p. 4; Gennadi Gerasimov, *Keep Space Weapon-Free*, Moscow, Novosti, Press Agency Publishing House, 1984; Marcia S. Smith, *U.S. and Soviet Positions on the Militarization of Space*, Washington, Congressional Research Service, April 3, 1985.

8. William E. Burrows, *Deep Black: Space Espionage and National Security*, New York, Random House, 1986, pp. 225–251, 328–346; Graham Yost, *Spy-Tech*, New York, Facts on File Publications, 1985, pp. 48–157; Johnson, *Soviet Military Strategy in Space*, pp. 89–124; and *Soviet Year in Space: 1987*, Colorado Springs, CO, Teledyne Brown Engineering, January 1988, pp. 22–81; Stares, *Space and National Security*, pp. 45–72.

9. Benjamin S. Lambeth and Kevin N. Lewis, *The Strategic Defense Initiative in Soviet Planning and Policy*, Santa Monica, CA, RAND, January 1988; *Soviet Military Power*, 1988, pp. 55–59; Carlucci, *Report to the Congress on the FY1990/FY1991 Biennial Budget*, p. 16; William J. Broad, "The Secrets of Soviet Star Wars," *New York Times*, June 28, 1987, p. 22.

10. Fact Sheet, *Presidential Directive on National Space Policy*; *Soviet Military Power*, 1988, pp. 62–63; Carlucci, *Report on the FY1990/1991 Biennial Budget*, pp. 17, 211; Caleb Baker, "Army Wins Battle With Navy Over Antisatellite System Testing," *Army Times*, January 30, 1989, p. 22; Cosmo DiMaggio and Marcia S. Smith, *Space Policy and Funding: Military Uses of Space*, Issue Brief 82117, Washington, Congressional Research Service, July 1, 1985; Cass Schichtle, *The National Space Program: From the Fifties into the Eighties*, Washington, National Defense University Press, 1983; comments on a draft of this study by Nicholas L. Johnson, February 20, 1989.

11. Fundamentally different programming philosophies permeate U.S. and Soviet systems. See references that accompany John M. Collins, *U.S.-Soviet Military Balance: Concepts and Capabilities, 1960–1980*, Washington, McGraw-Hill Publications, 1980, pp. 103–105.

12. John L. Piotrowski, "Muzzling the Bear," *Signal*, November 1987, p. 44; Johnson, *The Soviet Year in Space: 1987*, p. 6; Michael D. Lemonick, "Surging Ahead," *Time*, October 5, 1987, pp. 64, 65; U.S. Congress, Senate, *Soviet Space Programs: 1981–87*, p. 2.

13. James E. Oberg, "Tracking the Booster Gap," *Defense Electronics*, May 1988, pp. 85, 86, 87; Johnson, *The Soviet Year in Space: 1987*, pp. 1, 3; Piotrowski, "Muzzling the Bear," p. 44; Richard Jurmain, *Impact of National Aero-Space Plane (NASP) on National Competitive Strategies*, informal notes, St. Louis, MO, McDonnell Douglas Corp., July 14, 1988, p. 2; Hildreth, *The Strategic Defense Initiative*, pp. 8–9; U.S. Congress, Senate, *Soviet Space Programs: 1981–87*, p. 3; Robert B. Giffen, *U.S. Space System Survivability*, Washington, National Defense University Press, 1982, p. 22; Stares, *Space and National Security*, pp. 15, 43.

14. Oberg, "Tracking the Booster Gap," pp. 83, 86–87; Burrows, *Deep Black*, pp. 257, 258; Giffen, *U.S. Space System Survivability*, p. 22.

15. Stares, *Space and National Security*, pp. 13, 15; Burrows, *Deep Black*, p. 257; *Department of Defense Space Policy*, p. 4.

16. Nicholas L. Johnson, "Space Control and Soviet Military Strategy," *Defense Electronics*, May 1988, p. 75, and comments on a draft of this study, February 20, 1989.

17. "Soviets Investing in Survivability of Space Systems—Weinberger," *Defense Daily*, November 30, 1987, p. 163; "Soviets Seen Developing Covert, Mobile Launch Capability," *Aerospace Daily*, November 25, 1987, p. 8; *Soviet Military Power*, 1988, pp. 62, 65–67; John L. Piotrowski, Statement on Space Control, before the Subcommittee on Research and Development, House Committee on Armed Services, March 10, 1988, p. 15.

18. Carlucci, *Report on the FY1990/1991 Biennial Budget*, p. 212; Piotrowski, "Muzzling the Bear," p. 44; Latham, "A Prescription for America's Galaxy of Problems in Space," p. 27; William J. Broad, "Military Launches First New Rocket for Orbital Loads," *New York Times*, September 6, 1988, p. 1; *Pioneering the Space Frontier: Report of the National Commission on Space*, New York, Bantam Books, 1986, p. 109.

19. Carlucci, *Report on the FY1990/1991 Biennial Budget*, p. 17; Piotrowski, Statement on Space Control, pp. 15–16; Giffen, *U.S. Space System Survivability*, p. 22; U.S. Congress, Senate, *Soviet Space Programs: 1981–87*, p. 3.

20. Oberg, "Tracking The Booster Gap," p. 86; Ashton B. Carter, "Satellites and Anti-Satellites," *International Security*, Spring 1986, pp. 49–52, 55–62; Stares, *Space and National Security*, pp. 13–14; Yost, *Spy-Tech*, p. 58.

21. Burrows, *Deep Black*, pp. 276–283; Piotrowski, Statement on Space Control, pp. 14–15, 17–21, 28; *Soviet Military Power*, 1988, pp. 64–65; U.S. Congress, Office of Technology Assessment, *Anti-Satellite Weapons, Countermeasures, and Arms Control*, OTA-ISC-281, Washington, U.S. GPO, September 1985; Marcia S. Smith, *ASATS: Antisatellite Weapon Systems*, Washington, Congressional Research Service, January 14, 1987.

22. Marcia S. Smith, *Space Activities of the United States, Soviet Union and Other Launching Countries/Organizations: 1957–1987*, Washington, Congressional Research Service, February 29, 1988, pp. 15–39; *Department of Defense Space Policy*, pp. 2, 4.

23. Johnson, *The Soviet Year in Space: 1987*, pp. 82–101; Jeffrey M. Lenorovitz, "Long-Term Space Plan Will Lead to Soviet Orbital Infrastructure," *Aviation Week & Space Technology*, December 12, 1988, pp. 44–46; Cosmo DiMaggio and Marcia S. Smith, *Space Policy and Funding: Military Uses of Space*, p. 1–2; Michael Dobbs, "Cosmonauts Return to Earth After Record Year in Space," *Washington Post*, December 22, 1988, p. 1; "Space Hiatus Insignificant, Soviets Say," *Washington Post*, April 13, 1989, p. 42.

24. Johnson, "Space Control and Soviet Military Strategy," p. 74; Lemonick, "Surging Ahead," p. 67; Giffen, *U.S. Space System Survivability*, pp. 19–23; Office of Technology Assessment, *Anti-Satellite Weapons, Countermeasures, and Arms Control*, p. 5.

25. John L. Piotrowski, "A Soviet Space Strategy," *Strategic Review*, Fall 1987, pp. 60–62; Johnson, "Space Control and Soviet Military Strategy,"

pp. 76–77, 78, 80; Oberg, "Tracking the Booster Gap," pp. 83, 84, 88; Stares, *Space and National Security*, pp. 13, 44.

26. Caspar W. Weinberger, *Report of the Secretary of Defense to the Congress on the FY1988/FY1989 Budget and FY1988–92 Defense Programs*, Washington, Dept. of Defense, January 1, 1987, p. 289; Piotrowski, Statement on Space Control, p. 4; Giffen, *U.S. Space System Survivability*, p. 23.

27. Paul X. Kelley, "The Amphibious Warfare Strategy," *The Maritime Strategy*, Annapolis, MD, U.S. Naval Institute Press, January 1986, p. 28; Thomas C. Linn, "Over-The-Horizon Assault: The Future of the Corps," *Marine Corps Gazette*, December 1987, pp. 44–47; *Satellites for Arms Control and Crisis Monitoring*, ed. by Bhupendra Jasani and Toshibomi Sakata, New York, Oxford University Press, 1987; Ann M. Florini, "The Opening Skies," *International Security*, Fall 1988, pp. 91–123; Hugh de Santis, "Commercial Observation Satellites and their Military Implications: A Speculative Assessment," *Washington Quarterly*, Summer 1989, pp. 185–200; Michael Krepon, "Spying from Space," *Foreign Policy*, Summer 1989, pp. 92–108; George E. Brown, Jr., "The Future of Remote Sensing," and Jack E. Thomas, "Impact on the Military," *Technology in Society*, Vol. 11, No. 1, 1989, pp. 41–47 and 69–76.

28. Piotrowski, Statement on Space Control, p. 22; Collins, *U.S.-Soviet Military Balance, 1960–1980*, p. 136; Carlucci, *Report to the Congress on the FY 1990/1991 Biennial Budget*, pp. 211, 212.

29. *Presidential Directive on National Space Policy*, p. 1; *Soviet Military Power*, 1988, p. 62.

30. "Treaty on Outer Space," in U.S. Congress, *Legislation on Foreign Relations Through 1985*, Vol. III, Joint Committee Print, Senate Committee on Foreign Affairs, Washington, U.S. GPO, August 1986, p. 1065.

31. Alternative actions are contained in Albert Wohlstetter and Brian Chow, *Recommended Changes in U.S. Military Space Policies and Programs*, a paper by the Working Group on Technology, submitted to the Commission on Integrated Long-term Strategy, Washington, Dept. of Defense, October 1988.

32. Starting points for military space doctrine could include David E. Lupton, *On Space Warfare: A Space Power Doctrine*, Maxwell AFB, AL, Air University Press, 1988; Kenneth A. Myers, "Real Tenets of Military Space Doctrine," *Airpower Journal*, Winter 1988, pp. 54–68.

33. William J. Broad, "For Cheap, Versatile Spacecraft, Designers Discover Less Is More," *New York Times*, May 23, 1989, p. C1.

34. *Report of the Defense Science Board Task Force on the National Aerospace Plane (NASP)*, Washington, Office of the Under Secretary of Defense for Acquisition, September 1988; *National Aerospace Plane*, Washington, General Accounting Office, April 1988; Stephan W. Korthals-Altes, *The Aerospace Plane: Technological Feasibility and Policy Implications* (M.S. thesis, Massachusetts Institute of Technology), 1984.

35. Henry A. Kissinger, "News Conference at Moscow, July 3," *Department of State Bulletin*, July 3, 1974, p. 215.

36. Jack Swift, "Strategic Superiority Through SDI," *Defense & Foreign Affairs*, December 1985, p. 17.

Index

Index

Materials (*cont.*)
    stealth, 65
    types, prognosis, 97–101
Medicine. *See* Space medicine
Medium earth orbits (MEO), defined, described, 16, 17, 27, 109, 155
Mesosphere, defined, described, 9, 10, 155
Metal matrix, properties, 99
Meteorites described, 14N, 155
Meteoroids
    deception device, 60
    defined, described, 14, 14N, 22, 155
    hardening against, 36, 38, 125
Meteors, described, 14N, 155
Microgravity. *See* Artificial gravity; Gravity
Military doctrine
    purpose, 53
    U.S. problems, 140, 142
Military missions
    air, space compared, 1
    air superiority precedent, 53
    development, 1, 83
    influence separate service, 82
    U.S., Soviet, 130, 133–134
Military strategy
    interests, objectives underpin, 41
    new concepts needed, 41, 51, 140
    personal touch required, 123
    purposes, 51, 53
Military tactics, defined, described, 51, 123
Minimum energy transfers, depicted, described, 16, 18, 24, 155
Mir, Soviet space station, 134, 139
Mirrors
    laser weapons, 14, 57, 115, 120, 121
    telescopes, 113–114
Missions. *See* Military missions
Mobility, defensive measure, 63, 64, 66, 91, 155
Molniya orbits
    defined, 156
    Soviet uses,137, 138
Moon
    assumption, 52
    cause of war, 42
    colonization, exploitation predicted, 1, 23
    communication time, 6
    defensive measures, 15, 27, 63, 64, 66
    economic interests, 43
    gravity well, 24
    industrial potential, 43, 89
    infrastructure, 21, 23, 25, 36, 54, 68, 100
    key terrain, 23
    L4, L5 dominate, 25
    life-support systems, 36, 108, 124, 125
    maneuvers, 57–58, 66

    maps, 21, 25, 27
    materials, 15, 21, 25, 27, 43, 66, 89
    physical characteristics, 5, 19–21, 24, 26–27
    polar orbits, 24
    power supplies, 107, 108
    propulsion requirements, 101, 103
    radiation, 28, 38, 126
    R&D requirements, 96
    selenostationary orbits, 24, 160
    surge capabilities, 61
    targets, 54, 69
    telescopes, 113–114
    treaties, 42, 46, 141, 173–179
    waste disposal, 127
    weapons, 35, 36, 116
Moon Treaty, specifications, signatories, 42, 42N
Moratoriums, arms control, 46–47
Motion sickness, symptoms, 38

NASA, civil-military connections, 134, 156
National Aeronautical and Space Administration (NASA), civil-military connections, 134, 156
National Aerospace Plane (NASP)
    propulsion, 101, 104
    purpose, 142, 156
National security interests, identified, discussed, 41–44, 47, 141
National security objectives
    centers of gravity, 47, 48
    identified, discussed, 44–48, 92–93, 141
    military space priorities, 53
    related to interests, 41, 44, 47
    U.S., Soviet, 129, 130, 131, 132, 141
National will
    aids deterrence, 61
    center of gravity, 48
Navy
    ships as targets, 54
    U.S. space command, 75, 76
Neural networks, artificial intelligence, 112, 115
Neutral particle beams, defined, described, 34, 123, 156
Newton, Sir Isaac, Laws of Motion, 10N, 35
Nixon, Richard M., on sufficiency, 92
Nuclear power, types and prospects, 106, 108–109
Nuclear propulsion, types and prospects, 101, 103
Nuclear radiation. *See also* Electromagnetic pulse; Radiation
    defense against, 69
    degrades radios and radars, 29
    effects in vacuum, 28, 29, 57, 118

About The Author

John M. Collins, Senior Specialist in National Defense at the Library of Congress, Washington, D.C., is well qualified to write this seminal study of military space forces. He has 47 years of experience, much of it as a military strategist, contingency planner, and policy analyst. Senior national security officials and members of the media, industry, research institutes, and academic communities around the world respect his wide-ranging assessments.

An AFA/AEF Book

The Air Force Association (AFA), established on February 6, 1946, is an independent veterans' organization whose objective is to promote greater understanding of aerospace and national defense issues. On May 1, 1956, AFA established the Aerospace Education Foundation (AEF). The Foundation was established as a nonprofit organization in order to formulate and administer AFA's educational outreach programs.

With a membership of more than 240,000, AFA represents all elements of the Air Force family, military and civilian, active and retired, Reserve and National Guard, cadet and veteran, Civil Air Patrol, civil service, and aerospace workers.

Pergamon-Brassey's AFA Book Series is designed to assist AFA's Aerospace Education Foundation in fulfilling its mandate. AEF's goal is to inform AFA members—and indeed anyone involved in the national defense dialogue—about issues vital to the future of the U.S. Air Force in particular and air power in general. Forthcoming AFA Books may cover the topics of aerospace history, biography, technology, combat, strategy and tactics, personnel, management, leadership, and policy. Publication as an AFA Book does not indicate that the Air Force Association and the publisher agree with everything in the book, but does suggest that the AFA and the publisher believe this book will stimulate the thinking of AFA members and others concerned about important issues.

An AUSA Institute of Land Warfare Book

The Association of the United States Army, or AUSA, was founded in 1950 as a not-for-profit organization dedicated to education concerning the role of the U.S. Army, to providing material for military professional development, and to the promotion of proper recognition and appreciation of the profession of arms. Its constituencies include those who serve in the Army today, including Army National Guard, Army Reserve, and Army civilians, and the retirees and veterans who have served in the past, and all their families. A large number of public-minded citizens and business leaders are also an important constituency. The Association seeks to educate the public, elected and appointed officials, and leaders of defense industry on crucial issues involving the adequacy of our national defense, particularly those issues affecting land warfare.

In 1988 AUSA established within its existing organization a new entity known as the Institute of Land Warfare. Its purpose is to extend the educational work of AUSA by sponsoring scholarly publications, to include books, monographs, and essays on key defense issues, as well as workshops and symposia. Among the volumes chosen for designation as "An AUSA Institute of Land Warfare Book" are both new texts and reprints of titles of enduring value that are no longer in print. Topics include history, policy issues, strategy, and tactics. Publication as an AUSA Book does not indicate that the Association of the United States Army and the publisher agree with everything in the book, but does suggest that the AUSA and the publisher believe this book will stimulate the thinking of AUSA members and others concerned about important issues.